PRINCIPLES OF WOODWORKING

Mills and log storage at Bonner, Montana, near Lolo National Forest. (U. S. Forest Service Photo)

Principles of Woodworking

HERMAN HJORTH, M.S.

Instructor, Saunders Trades School, Yonkers, N. Y.

(Revised and Enlarged)

THE BRUCE PUBLISHING COMPANY
MILWAUKEE

BY THE SAME AUTHOR
Basic Woodworking Processes
Forty Pieces of Fine Furniture
Machine Woodworking
Operation of Common Woodworking Machines
Reproduction of Antique Furniture

(Fifteenth Printing — 1947)

PREFACE

During all ages wood has played an important and friendly part in the development of mankind. It enters, directly or indirectly, into the construction of more manufactured articles than any other material, and there is not an engineering project nor construction of any kind, in which wood is not used in some way.

A material, which enters so extensively into every phase of life, is of tremendous economic value to all civilized nations. The woodworking industries in this country, particularly the building and furniture industries, are among the most important, because they employ thousands of highly skilled workmen, designers, and artists, to produce useful as well as beautiful articles of wood. Other thousands are engaged in the distribution and selling of these products, and still other thousands in the manufacture of the numerous tools and machines used in woodworking.

This text is intended not only for the use of students in secondary and vocational schools, but also for adults who have taken up the study and practice of woodworking as a hobby.

Fundamental tool processes, common to all woodworking trades, have been compiled and arranged in family groups. With these as a basis, cabinetmaking has been emphasized throughout the book, because of its universal interest and appeal, and because this phase of woodworking is probably elected by most students.

All tool operations have been described and written in the form of instruction sheets. These have been further supplemented with related information about materials, tools, and machinery, and by a series of furniture projects, the construction of which has been carefully analyzed and described.

The teacher of woodworking will find the subject matter — both instruction sheets and related information — in convenient form for assignments.

Special attention is called to the method of planning and analyzing various tool operations involved in the construction of an object. By following this method, any cabinet job may be analyzed and reference made by number to topics describing the various tool operations. After the students have become acquainted with the book, they should do their own thinking and planning, and should formulate their own job sheets for approval by the teacher.

The review questions at the end of each chapter should be of value to the student in testing his knowledge of a given topic, and to the teacher in checking up on his class.

v

The teacher of general science will find much helpful material on forest conservation, seasoning of lumber, and the physiological processes of the tree.

The teacher of physics will find the chapter on machinery helpful in illustrating the principles and practical applications of simple machines and the transmission of power.

It is the sincere hope of the author that the increasing number of "home woodworkers" will find this book helpful and stimulating, and that it will contribute to their interest and pleasure in craftsmanship. May they experience that satisfaction and joy of achievement which comes with a piece of work well done.

Grateful acknowledgment is hereby given to the following: Miss S. E. Sievers of Saunders Trades School for valuable help in reading and preparing the manuscript; Mr. J. Macdonald and Mr. H. A. Carlberg of Saunders Trades School for suggestions and criticisms; Mr. Arthur Wakeling, Home Workshop Editor of *Popular Science Monthly,* for permission to use the material on Wood Turning and Inlaying which was published in a series of articles in that magazine, together with some of the illustrations in topics 281, 350, 356, 357, 360, and 363, which were used in these articles; *The Carpenter's Tool Chest* by Thos. Hibben, J. B. Lippincott Co., Philadelphia, Penn., for illustrations on pages 1, 2, 3, and 5; *Everday Life in the New Stone, Bronze, and Early Iron Ages* by Marjorie and C. H. B. Quennell, G. B. Putnam's Sons, New York, for Figure 597; the Forest Products Laboratory, Madison, Wis., and the National Lumber Manufacturers' Association for most of the illustrations appearing in the chapter on Wood; *The Handy Boy's Book* by John Barnard, Ward, Lock & Co., Ltd., London, for Figure 598; *Ancient Carpenter's Tools* by Henry C. Mercer, The Bucks County Historical Society, Doylestown, Penn., for Figure 599; the Metropolitan Museum of Art, New York City, for illustrations on page 4; Oliver Machinery Co., Grand Rapids, Mich., for Figures 123, 232, and 602; Walker-Turner Co., Inc., Plainfield, N. J., for Figure 170; Yates-American Machine Co., Beloit, Wis., for Figure 169; Wm. Zinsser Co., New York City, for Figures 736 to 740 incl.; and the Editor of the *Industrial Arts and Vocational Education* Magazine for permission to use material published in that periodical.

HERMAN HJORTH

Yonkers, N. Y.

CONTENTS

PREFACE v

1. HISTORY OF WOODWORKING TOOLS . . 1

2. HAND TOOLS 7
1. Bench. Measuring Tools: 2. Rule. 3. Measuring Tapes. 4. Try Squares. 5. Miter and Try Squares. 6. Sliding T Bevels. 7. Steel Square. 8. Brace Measure. 9. Octagon Measure. 10. Board Measure. 11. Rafter Table. 12. Marking Gauge. 13. Panel Gauge. 14. Slitting Gauge. 15. Mortising Gauge. 16. Butt Gauge 17. Dividers or Compasses. 18. Trammel Points. 19. Inside and Outside Calipers. 20. Plumb and Level. 21. Plumb Bob. 22. Summary. Saws: 23. Ripsaw. 24. Crosscut Saw. 25. Backsaw. 26. Dovetail Saw. 27. Compass Saw. 28. Keyhole Saw. 29. Turning Saw. 30. Coping Saw. 31. Miter Boxes. 32. Hack Saw. 33. Summary. Planes: 34. Wooden Plane. 35. Jack Plane. 36. Fore Plane. 37. Jointer. 38. Smooth Plane. 39. Circular Plane. 40. Block Plane. 41. Bullnose Rabbet Plane. 42. Rabbet and Fillister Plane. 43. Dado Plane. 44. Matching Plane. 45. Router Plane. 46. Universal Plane. 47. Plane Gauges. 48. Spokeshave. 49. Scrapers. 50. Summary. Chisels: 51. Firmer Chisel. 52. Paring Chisel. 53. Framing Chisel. 54. Butt Chisel. 55. Mortise Chisel. 56. Gouges. 57. Carving Tools. 58. Drawknife. 59. Summary. Boring Tools: 60. Auger Bits. 61. Dowel Bits. 62. Car Bits and Ship Augers. 63. Expansion Bits. 64. Foerstner Bits. 65. Gimlet or German Gimlet Bits. 66. Twist Bits. 67. Twist Drills. 68. Bradawl. 69. Countersink. 70. Plug Cutters and Washer Cutters. 71. Plain Brace. 72. Ratchet Brace. 73. Bit-Brace Extension. 74. Auger-Bit Gauges. 75. Automatic Drills and Reciprocating Drills. 76. Hand Drill. 77. Summary. Miscellaneous Tools: 78. Plain Screw Drivers. 79. Automatic Screw Drivers. 80. Screw-Driver Bits. 81. Claw Hammer. 82. Nail Sets. 83. Mallets. 84. Hatchets. 85. Ax and Adze. 86. Rasps and Files. 87. Steel Bar Clamps. 88. C Clamps. 89. Column Clamps. 90. Hand Screws. 91. Carpenter's Pincers. 92. Summary. Review Questions

3. MACHINE TOOLS 39
95. Circular Saw. 96. Directions for Setting Up Dado Head. 97. Safety Rules. 98. Band Saw. 99. Removing and Coiling Band-Saw Blade. 100. Safety Rules. 101. Jig Saw. 102. Jointer or Hand Planer. 103. Adjusting Outfeed Table. 104. Safety Rules. 105. Planer or Surfacer. 106. Swing Cutoff Saw. 107. Radial Saw. 108. Power Handsaw. 109. Mortising Machines. 110. Hollow-Chisel Mortiser. 111. Single-Spindle Borer. 112. Drill Press. 113. Shaper. 114. Safety Rules. 115. Router. 116. Sanding Machines. 117. Belt Sander. 118. Disk Sander. 119. Spindle Sander. 120. Drum Sanders. 121. Abrasives. 122. Wood Trimmer. 123. Compressed Air. 124. Sharpening Machines. 125. Automatic Knife Grinders. Review Questions

4. THE SHARPENING OF TOOLS 106
A. Hand Tools: 128. Sharpening a Saw. 129. To Sharpen a Plane Iron. 130. To Sharpen Gouges. 131. To Sharpen and Adjust a Cabinet Scraper. 132. To Sharpen a Hand Scraper. 133. To Sharpen an Auger Bit. Sharpening Turning Tools: 134. Gouge. 135. Square-Nose Chisel. 136. Skew Chisel. 137. Parting or Cutoff Tool. 138. Round-Nose Chisel. 139. Diamond-Point or Spear-Point Chisel. 140. Right or Left Skew Chisel or Turning Chisel. 141. To clean a Rasp

or File. B. Machine Tools: 142. Jointing Circular Saws. 143. Gumming a Circular Ripsaw. 144. Setting Circular Saws. 145. Filing a Circular Ripsaw. 146. Filing Circular Crosscut Saws. 147. Filing Circular Miter Saws. 148. To Braze Band Saws. 149. Setting Band Saws. 150. Filing Band Saws. 151. Grinding Jointer and Planer Knives. 152. Sharpening Shaper Knives and Router Bits. 153. Sharpening Hollow Chisels. Review Questions

5. PLANING AND SQUARING TO DIMENSIONS   .   137

156. To Square Small Boards to Dimensions. 157. To Joint Boards for Gluing. 158. To Square a Table Top. 159. To Make and Square a Table Top, Using Machine Tools. 160. To Square Legs for Tables and Cabinets. 161. To Square Table Legs, Using Machine Tools. 162. To Taper Square Legs for Tables and Cabinets. 163. To Taper Square Legs for Tables and Cabinets on the Circular Saw. 164. To Taper Table Legs on a Jointer. Review Questions

6. GROOVED JOINTS   153

167. To Make a Rabbet Joint. 168. To Make a Groove. 169. To Make a Dado Joint. 170. To Make a Gain or Stopped Dado Joint. 171. To Make a Dado-and-Rabbet Joint. 172. To Cut Grooved Joints With Machine Tools. Review Questions

7. DOWEL JOINTS   166

175. To Make a Doweled Butt Joint. 176. To Make a Draw-Bolt Joint. 177. To Dowel Boards Edge to Edge. 178. To Join Legs to a Turned Column With Dowels. 179. To Bore Dowel Holes With Machine Tools. Review Questions

8. LAP OR HALVING JOINTS   175

180. To Make an End-Lap Joint. 181. To Make an End-Lap Joint With Rabbet. 182. To Make a Cross-Lap Joint. 183. To Make a Dovetail-Lap Joint. 184. To Make Lap Joints on the Circular Saw. Review Questions

9. MORTISE-AND-TENON JOINTS   184

187. To Make a Blind Mortise-and-Tenon Joint. 188. To Make a Haunched Mortise-and-Tenon Joint. 189. To Make a Barefaced Mortise-and-Tenon Joint. 190. To Make a Through Mortise-and-Tenon Joint. 191. To Make a Slip Joint. 192. To Make a Keyed Mortise-and-Tenon Joint. 193. To Make a Mortise on a Mortising Machine. 194. To Cut Tenons on the Circular Saw. Review Questions

10. MITER JOINTS   200

197. To Cut a Miter Joint. 198. To Glue Mitered Frames. 199. Reinforcing Mitered Joints. 200. To Cope Moldings. Review Questions

11. DOVETAIL JOINTS   213

203. To Make a Through, Multiple, Dovetail Joint. 204. To Make a Half-Lap, Multiple, Dovetail Joint. Review Questions

12. MISCELLANEOUS CONSTRUCTIONS   217

207. To Make a Drawer. 208. To Make Drawer Rails and Guides. 209. To Make a Panel Structure. 210. To Make a Rule Joint. 211. To Make Supports for Table Leaves. Review Questions

13. GLUING AND CLAMPING   230

214. Properties and Uses of Glue. 215. General Directions for Gluing. 216. To Glue Two or More Boards Edge to Edge. 217. To Glue Bookshelves. 218. To Glue a Frame or Panel. 219. To Glue a Cabinet. 220. To Glue a Drawer. 221. To Glue a Chair. 222. To Glue Doweled Joints and Segments. Review Questions

14. METAL FASTENINGS 241

225. Nails. 226. Rules for Driving Nails. 227. Screws for Fastening Wood. 228. Rules for Driving Screws. 229. Bolts. 230. Hinges. 231. To Hinge a Door. 232. Cabinet Locks. 233. To Attach Locks. 234. Catches and Door Bolts. 235. To Attach Casters, Glides, Chair Tips, Drawer Pulls, and Knobs. 236. To Fasten a Table Top to a Frame. Review Questions

15. WOOD TURNING 261

239. History. 240. Wood-Turning Lathe. 241. Lathe Holding Tools. 242. Wood-Turning Tools. 243. Safety Rules. 244. Methods of Turning. Spindle Turning: 245. To Center and Clamp Stock in the Lathe. 246. To Turn a Plain Cylinder. 247. To Make Shoulder Cuts. 248. To Make Taper Cuts. 249. To Make Concave Cuts. 250. To Make Convex Cuts. 251. To Turn Legs With Square Parts. 252. To Turn Duplicate Parts. 253. To Do Split Turning. Faceplate Work: 254. To Fasten Stock to a Faceplate or Screw Chuck. 255. To Turn a Disk. 256. To Do Chuck Turning. 257. To Sand in the Lathe on a Spindle. 258. To Sand in the Lathe on a Disk. 259. To Finish and Polish Turned Work. Review Questions

16. SURFACE DECORATION 302

262. General Suggestions for Decorations. Inlaying: 263. To Inlay Lines or Bands. 264. To Inlay Insets. 265. To Cut Straight Reeds. 266. To Cut Spiral Reeds. 267. To Carve a Single Spiral on a Turned Cylinder. 268. To Carve a Double Spiral on a Turned Cylinder. 269. To Lay Out Tapered Spirals. Simple Carving: Tools. 270. To Cut Beads. 271. To Cut Chamfers and Hollows. 272. To Carve Borders. Moldings: 273. To Make Moldings. 274. To Shape the Edges of Table Tops. 275. To Do Simple Veneering. 276. To Decorate by Overlays, Frets, or Veining. Review Questions

17. UPHOLSTERY 335

279. History. 280. To Make a Plain Pad Seat. 281. To Make a Pad Seat With a Roll Edge. 282. To Upholster a Slip Seat. 283. To Weave a Fiber Seat. 284. To Weave a Cane Seat. 285. To Apply Cane Webbing. Review Questions

18. WOOD FINISHING 351

288. To Prepare the Surface. Stains: 289. Water Stains. 290. Spirit Stains. 291. Oil Stains. 292. Acid Stains or Stains Due to Chemical Action. 293. General Directions for Staining. 294. To Apply Wood Filler. 295. Production and Manufacture of Shellac. 296. To Apply Shellac. 297. To Apply Wax. 298. To Apply Linseed Oil. 299. To Apply Lacquer. 300. To Apply Varnish. To Paint Furniture and Interior Woodwork: 301. Preparation of the Surface. 302. Application of the Priming Coat. 303. Filling Holes and Other Imperfections in the Surface. 304. Applications of the Second and Third Undercoats. 305. Application of the Finishing Coats. 306. Summary. 307. Summary of Advantages and Disadvantages of the Finishing Coats Described. Review Questions

19. WOOD 368

310. Botanical Division of Trees. 311. Life Function of Trees. 312. Man's Dependence on Plants. 313. Conservation of Lumber. Structure of Wood: 314. Cell Formation. 315. Annual Rings. 316. Heartwood and Sapwood. 317. Cambium. 318. Bark. 319. Medullary Rays. 320. Porous Woods. 321. Weight of Wood. 322. Reproduction of Trees. 323. Logging Operations. 324. Sawing the Logs. 325. Plain- and Quarter-Sawing. 326. Seasoning of Wood. 327. Air Seasoning. 328. Kiln Seasoning. 329. Moisture Content. 330. Types of Kilns. 331. Shrinkage of Wood. 332. Drying Defects. Manufactured Lumber: 333. Standard Lengths and Thicknesses of Lumber. 334. Allowance for Planing. 335. Board Measure. 336. Matched, Grooved, and Beaded Boards. 337. Moldings. 338. Veneers. 339. Plywood. 340. Uses of Plywood. Selection and Uses of Lumber: 341. Lumber for Cabinetwork and Interior Woodwork. 342. Lumber for Building Purposes. Review Questions

20. APPLIED PROJECTS   391

347. Preliminary Steps in Construction. 348. Making Drawings and Blueprints. 349. To Read Working Drawings. 350. To Read the Drawing of the Serving Tray. 351. To Read the Drawing of the Bookcase. 352. To Read the Drawing of the Lamp Standard. 353. To Read the Drawing of the Step Ladder. 354. To Read the Drawing of the Cupboard. 355. To Read the Drawing of the Stool. 356. To Read the Drawing of the Mirror Frame. 357. To Read the Drawing of the Tilt-Top Table. 358. To Read the Drawing of the Magazine Holder. 359. To Read the Drawing of the Plain and Veneered Boxes. 360. To Read the Drawings of the Early English Gate-Leg Table. 361. To Read the Drawing of the End Table. 362. To Read the Drawing of the Sewing Table. 363. To Read the Drawing of the Chest

Chapter 1

HISTORY OF WOODWORKING TOOLS

The first woodworking tools were made of stone about 300,000 years ago. Stone axes, wedges, scrapers, saws, and drills, used at that early age, have been found all over the world. The oldest of these tools were very crude, but the ones made during the latter part of the stone age

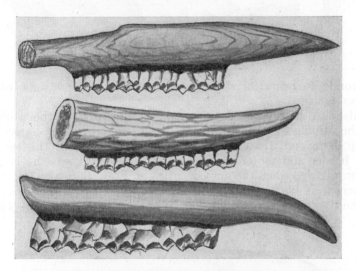

Stone saws with handles of wood or horn

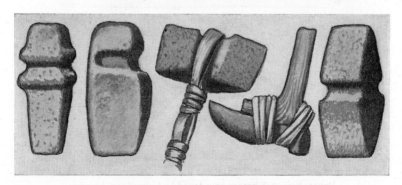

Axes from the ground stone age

1

Flaked flint tools from the new stone age

were ground to beautiful shapes, on other stones, and some of them were even polished.

Metals were first used by the people in that part of the world now called the Middle East. The first metal tools were made of copper. Then someone discovered that, by adding a small amount of tin, the metal became harder and therefore more serviceable. This was the beginning of the bronze age when the ancient cities of Troy, Babylon, Ur, Thebes, and others were built. The first bronze tools were cast in one-piece stone molds and were rather crude. The next step in the development was

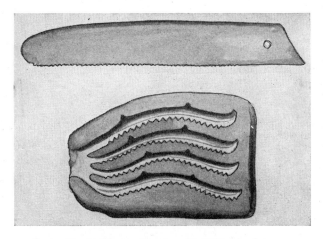

Upper: Nine-inch bronze saw found in Switzerland. Lower: Stone mold for casting bronze saws found in Sweden

Egyptian furniture makers. The carpenter on the left is using an Egyptian bow saw

the two-piece mold with both halves alike. Tools and utensils found during comparative recent excavations show that these ancient peoples — Sumerians, Assyrians, Egyptians, and others — possessed a high degree of manual and artistic skill and made a distinct contribution to the advancement of civilization. Written records and pictures describe how carpenters, smiths, and other artisans worked and what tools they used.

When the bronze age began is not definitely known, but a complete set of carpenters' tools, about 5000 years old, have been found on the island of Crete. Similar finds have been made at other points in this region. At the end of the bronze period — about 3000 years ago — when people first began to use iron, most of the carpenters' tools had been invented with exception of the plane and the brace.

Although much superior to bronze, iron tools at first were not well liked. The early Romans were allowed to use iron for farm implements only, and no workman was allowed to use iron tools in the building of Solomon's temple. Bronze tools, therefore, continued to be used together with iron tools for many years.

The ancient Romans were the first people to make saws with regular shaped and set teeth. They also invented the plane, made both tang and socket chisels, and developed the claw hammer. In fact, the carpenters' tools found in the ruins of Pompeii are a good deal like the ones used by present-day carpenters.

During the Middle Ages, the early iron tools, especially the saws, were improved in quality. Not until the fifteenth century, however, were the brace and boring bits invented.

In the Middle Ages workmen in the different trades grouped themselves and formed trade associations or guilds. There were three stages or grades in the guilds, the apprentice, the journeyman, and the master. An apprentice usually began to learn his trade at the early age of twelve. His parents made a contract with a master, to whom they paid a fee for which the master in return fed and clothed the boy and taught him the skills and knowledge of his trade. In the early days a master could have only one apprentice besides his own son or nephew.

Egyptian adze

Egyptian saw

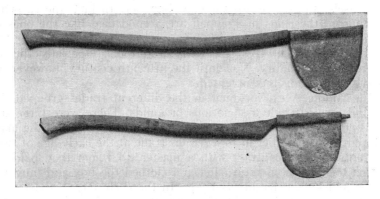

Egyptian ax

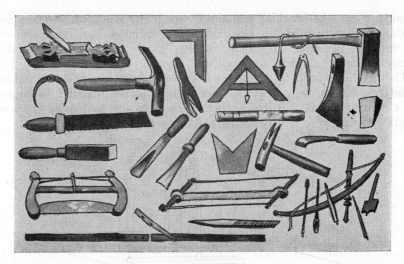

Roman tools

An apprenticeship lasted from one to twelve years, depending upon the necessary skills and knowledge to be acquired in a particular trade. At the end of the time of learning, the apprentice had to pass a stiff examination before he could become a journeyman and receive wages for his work. If a journeyman had sufficient ability and capital to set himself up as a master, he was required to work several years in one of the larger cities to gain experience. He then had to pass a very rigid test to demonstrate his skill, knowledge, and character, before he could proclaim himself a master.

The guilds were established for the protection and welfare of their members. These members were taken care of when sick and were given employment when out of work. On the other hand, the guilds had many stringent rules of conduct and workmanship which they enforced by frequent and careful inspections of the shops. Poor work and materials were destroyed and heavy fines imposed; a man might even be condemned to death for bad and dishonest workmanship. In this way, craftsmanship during the Middle Ages was kept up to a very high standard of excellence.

By the time machinery was invented, however, the guilds had fallen into disrepute and gradually disappeared. Masterships were sold by officers of the state without regard to ability, and shops were inherited from father to son. The master himself became more of a businessman, employing many people, and less of a craftsman working with his apprentices and journeymen.

The development of woodworking machinery began about 150 years ago. While some primitive sawing machines, driven by hand, water, or wind power, had been used in different localities during the Middle Ages, it was not until the end of the eighteenth century that the forerunners of our present woodworking machines were built. The greatest inventions in this field were made in England by Sir Samuel Bentham, who discovered the principle of *rotary cutting,* which is used in all modern planers, jointers, shapers, and molders.

The machines built by Bentham were very crude according to modern standards, having only heavy timber frames bolted together to support the cutting element and its bearings. Not until the middle of the nineteenth century were woodworking machines made entirely of metal.

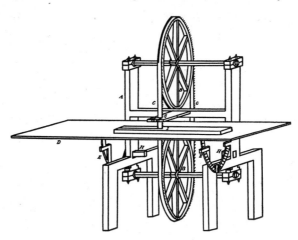

The first endless band saw patented by William Newberry
of London, England, in 1808

It is a curious fact that this crude machinery was first used in prisons where it enabled unskilled men to plane, saw, and bore as well and much faster than skilled woodworkers. The machines proved such a success that they were introduced in the shipyards where the work of building wooden ships was speeded up many times.

The first circular saw was invented in Holland, but was not successful, owing to the difficulty of making bearings and saw blades. The band saw was invented by Newberry and was patented in England in 1808.

REFERENCES:

The Carpenter's Tool Chest by Thomas Hibben (Philadelphia: J. B. Lippincott Co.)

Machine Woodworking by Herman Hjorth (Milwaukee: The Bruce Publishing Co.)

Chapter 2

HAND TOOLS

The woodworker uses a large variety of hand tools. Every workman should be familiar with the tools which he uses. He should know their proper names, the purpose for which each is used, and how they are sharpened and kept in good condition.

In this chapter a brief description is given of the most commonly used hand tools. In a later chapter the sharpening of tools is explained in detail.

1. **The bench** is a tool or appliance of the utmost importance to the woodworker. The best type of bench has a top that is constructed of narrow strips of hardwood, glued and bolted together. In this way warping is prevented. It usually has a recess or trough in which tools may be placed while working. The top is bolted to a frame consisting of four legs braced securely with crosspieces. This frame is often fitted with one or more drawers (Fig. 1).

The bench top is equipped with a side vise and sometimes also with a tail vise. These vises are made either of wood or iron. They have a central screw and parallel guide bars, one on each side of the screw (Fig. 2). Some iron vises are of the "continuous-screw" type and others of the "quick-acting" type. On some quick-acting vises a section of the

Fig. 1. Workbench

7

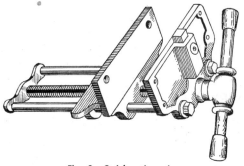

Fig. 2. Quick-acting vise

Fig. 3. Bench dog

screw thread is cut away throughout the entire length of the screw. This permits the movable vise jaw to be pulled in or out when the screw is in a certain position. A partial turn to the right tightens these quick-acting vises.

Some vises are equipped with an adjustable dog; i.e., a piece of iron which fits into a slot in the vise jaw. It can be set flush with the top of the vise jaw, or raised above it. A corresponding bench stop, or bench dog (Fig. 3), fits into holes bored in the bench top so that a piece of wood may be clamped firmly be-tween the bench stop and the vise jaw. A bench stop should not be confused with a bench hook, which is an all-wood device used for saw-ing and chiseling (Fig. 4).

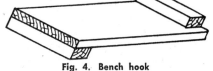

Fig. 4. Bench hook

A tail vise is a great convenience on a workbench, because it permits of clamping long pieces, such as table legs, for planing or mortising. Instead of a regular tail vise, a bench stop, which moves on a screw inserted in the bench top, often is used (Fig. 5).

Fig. 5. Bench stop used as tail vise

MEASURING TOOLS

2. A rule is generally the first tool used by the woodworker. Rules are made in different lengths and of different materials. Those used by the woodworker are usually of the folding type, and measure from 2 to 8 ft. in length (Fig. 6). Rules are generally marked off on both sides in inches and

Fig. 6. Folding rule

subdivisions of an inch, but they are also made with inch divisions on one side and metric divisions on the other.

3. Measuring tapes are used by carpenters, contractors, and architects. They are made of steel or cloth, and usually measure from 25 to 100 ft. in length (Fig. 7). Small steel tapes, 6 ft. long, often are used instead of folding rules. They are divided into inches and feet, or meters and centimeters.

4. Try squares are used for testing the squareness of lumber, and in checking the squareness of work being assembled, especially in places where the framing square would be too large. Try squares consist of

Fig. 7. Steel tape

two parts, the stock and the blade, which are firmly fastened together at right angles. The stock is thick and is made of wood or iron. The blade, which is thin, is made of steel and has an inch scale stamped on it (Fig. 8). Try squares are made in sizes of from 4 to 12 in., measured from the end of the blade to the stock.

5. Miter and try squares (Fig. 9) can be used at both 90 and 45 deg. Miter squares (Fig. 10) can only be used for angles of 45 deg.

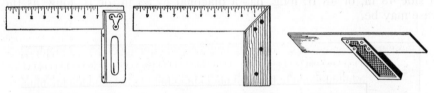

Fig. 8. Try square   **Fig. 9. Miter and try square**   **Fig. 10. Miter square**

6. Sliding T bevels (Fig. 11) are similar to try squares, but differ in that their blades are adjustable to any angle. They are used for laying out angles other than right angles, as, for instance, on corner braces, dovetails, or side rails for chairs.

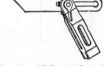

Fig. 11. Sliding T bevel

7. The steel square measures 16 by 24 in., or 18 by 24 in., and is of the same thickness, about ⅛ in., throughout. The 24-in. part is called the "blade" or "body," and is 2 in. wide. The 16- or 18-in. part is called the "tongue," and is 1½ in. wide. The "face" of the square is the side on which the manufacturer's name is stamped. The steel square is a very important tool, especially to the carpenter, who uses it in laying out the many different cuts employed in roof framing, stair building, oblique joints, etc. The cabinetmaker uses it mostly for testing the flatness of large surfaces (Art. 216) and for testing for squareness in gluing. The uses of the steel square are so numerous and varied that whole books have been written on this subject.

Fig. 12. Brace measure

Besides the divisions of the inch into eighths, tenths, twelfths, six-teenths, and thirty-seconds, which are marked on the inside and outside edges on both sides of the square, the following tables are marked on it: brace measure, octagon measure, board measure, rafter table, and the divisions of 1 in. into 100 parts.

8. **The brace measure** and octagon table are marked on opposite sides of the tongue. The brace measure consists of a series of three numbers. Two of the numbers are placed one above the other, and a third to the right of these as $\frac{48}{48}$ 67^{88} (Fig. 12). This means that a square having a side 48 in. or 48 ft. long, has a diagonal 67.88 in. or ft. long, as the case may be.

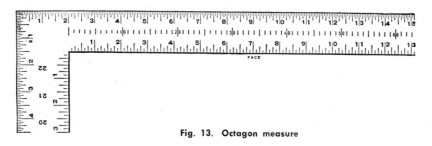

Fig. 13. Octagon measure

9. **The octagon measure** (Fig. 13) consists of a number of divisions marked along the center of the tongue. If an octagon is to be made from a square board having a side of 10 in., the octagonal shape is laid out as follows: Locate the center points on each of the four sides of the square. Set a pair of dividers equal to 10 of the spaces on the steel square, and lay off this distance on each side of the center divisions.

Connect all these points across the corners of the square board, and the octagon has been completed.

The following is a simple way to lay out an octagon from a square:

1. Draw the diagonals of the square.

2. With half the diagonal as a radius, and a corner of the square as a center, draw an arc from one side of the square to the other. Repeat the process from the remaining corners.

3. Connect the end points of the arcs across the corners of the square to complete the octagon (Fig. 14).

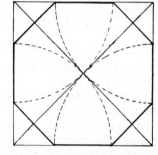

Fig. 14. To lay out an octagon from a square

10. **The board measure** is marked on the blade of the square, and enables one to read off the number of board feet a board or timber contains without making any calculations (Fig. 15). Under the 12-in. mark, on the outer edge of the steel square, is a column of figures which refers to the length of the boards to be calculated. The other numbers on the inch scale, to right and left of the 12-in. mark, refer to the width of the boards.

To use the scale, read off the length of the board to be calculated, follow this line to the number indicating its width, and the result is found in the column of figures under that number. For example, a board is 7 in. wide and 10 ft. long. Find 10 under 12 on the third line; follow to the left and stop under 7. The result, 5 ft. 10 in., is found on the third line under 7. For boards larger than 15 ft., divide the length into two smaller parts, find the board feet for each of these, and add the results. For example, to find the number of board feet in a board 10 in. wide and 17 ft. long, divide the length into 8 and 9, and follow these

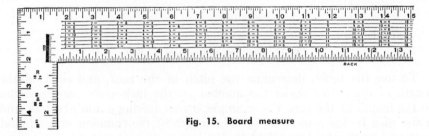

Fig. 15. Board measure

lines to the left until 10 is reached. An 8-ft. board contains 6 ft. 8 in. and a 9-ft. board 7 ft. 6 in. Adding these figures gives a total of 14 ft. 2 in. The scale is based on 1-in. boards. For 2-in. planks, multiply the results obtained by 2.

A board 12 ft. long contains as many board feet as it is inches wide. Similarly, a 6-ft. board contains half as many board feet as it is inches wide. For this reason the numbers 6 and 12 have been omitted from the column under the 12-in. mark.

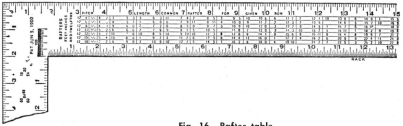

Fig. 16. Rafter table

11. The rafter table is not found on all squares, but when it is given it is stamped on the blade (Fig. 16). It can be used only for roofs having standard pitches.

Before explaining the rafter table, the terms "run," "rise," and "pitch" of a rafter must be understood. By the "run" is understood the level distance below any rafter, usually half the width of the building; by the "rise," the vertical height of the rafter over the top of the walls; and by the "pitch," the ratio between the rise and twice the run. The pitch is equal to the rise divided by twice the run (Fig. 17). A run of 12 ft. and a rise of 6 ft., therefore, give a pitch of 6/24 = ¼. A run of 18 ft. and a rise of 6 ft. give a pitch of 6/36 = ⅙, and so on.

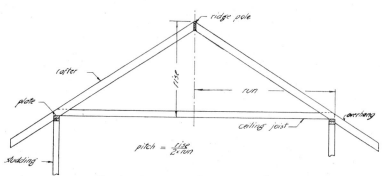

Fig. 17. Run, rise, and pitch of a rafter

To use the table, determine the pitch of the roof, and read off the length of the rafter under the number on the inch scale corresponding to the length of the run. For example, a roof having a run of 12 ft. and a rise of 8 ft. has a pitch of ⅓. The length of the common rafter found under 12 on the third line is 14 ft. 5½ in.

Some manufacturers of steel squares use a different form of rafter table, which shows the length of both common, hip, valley, and jack rafters. The length, however, is given per foot run only, which means that the number found on the steel square must be multiplied by the length of the run in order to obtain the total length of the rafter.

If the pitch is irregular, as 15-ft. run and 10-ft. 6-in. rise, the length of the rafter may be found by measuring across the square from 10½ on the tongue to 15 on the blade. If this measurement is made with an-

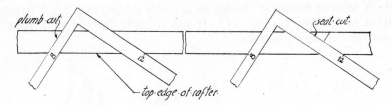

Fig. 18. Method of obtaining angles for cutting a
rafter or brace

other square, using the twelfth scale and counting each inch as a foot
and each twelfth of an inch as a full inch, the length is immediately obtained in feet and inches. This method is also very convenient for measuring the length of braces.

By placing the square on the side of the rafter or brace with the
numbers indicating rise and run in line with one edge, the proper angles
for cutting are obtained (Fig. 18).

12. **A marking gauge** is made of wood or steel. The
one most commonly used consists of a square,
wooden bar or beam, about 8 in. long, on which a
wooden block or head slides (Fig. 19). This block
can be fastened at any point of the bar by means of a brass setscrew
bearing against a brass shoe. The block, on the better grade of gauges,
is protected from wear by a piece of brass set flush with its surface. The
bar is graduated in inches and provided with a steel point or spur fastened
near the end with a screw. The spur must be filed to a fine point.

Fig. 19. Marking gauge

This tool is used for marking or gauging widths on narrow pieces of
wood, such as table legs, etc. When using it, move the gauge away from
you, and tip it slightly forward, keeping the block in contact with the
edge or face of the board at all times.

As the spur may be easily bent out of place, most workmen disregard
the graduations on the beam and measure the distance to be gauged from
the spur to the face of the block with an ordinary rule.

An attachment for marking along curved edges consists of a bent piece
of brass fastened to the block of the gauge.

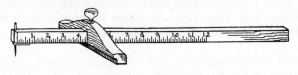

Fig. 20. Panel gauge

13. **A panel gauge** is similar to a marking gauge, but has a longer block
and a beam 17½ in. long (Fig. 20). It is used for gauging the width of
larger pieces, such as panels.

14. A slitting gauge is similar to a panel gauge, but has a handle in addition to the block (Fig. 21). It has a knife instead of a spur and is used for cutting thin stock.

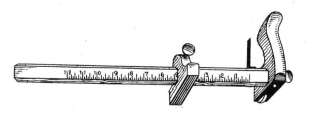

Fig. 21. Slitting gauge

15. A mortising gauge is a marking gauge with two spurs, which can be spaced at different distances and mark two parallel lines at the same time. One type is made of rosewood and has an adjusting screw in the end of the beam (Fig. 22), which moves one of the points up or down as desired. The other side of the beam is fitted with a single point as on the ordinary marking gauge. This gauge is used chiefly for laying out mortises and tenons. Other types are made entirely of metal and have two bars.

16. A butt gauge differs from a mortising gauge in that its spurs are at the extreme ends of the beams. It can, therefore, be used in internal corners such as on a door jamb when gauging for the width of hinges. It is made of steel and has three spurs (Fig. 24).

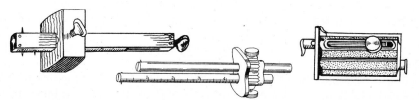

Fig. 22. Wooden mortising gauge   Fig. 24. Butt gauge

Fig. 23. Metal mortising gauge

17. Dividers or compasses consist of two slender steel bars or legs sharpened to a fine point and held together at one end either by a movable joint or a spring (Fig. 25). They are made in lengths from 6 to 10 in., and are used to scribe small circles. A pencil holder may be attached to one of the legs.

18. Trammel points consist of two steel points which can be fastened to a wooden stick or bar at any distance from each other (Fig. 26). They are used to scribe larger circles such as are needed for circular table tops. A pencil point can be fastened to one of the points. A finer tool for the same purpose, with bars made of steel, is used by draftsmen and is called a "beam compass." Trammel points may be improvised by driving two nails through a stick of wood.

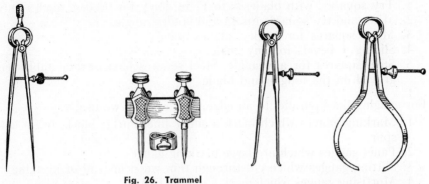

Fig. 25. Dividers

Fig. 26. Trammel
points

Fig. 27. Inside and outside calipers

19. Inside and outside calipers are similar in shape to dividers, but their legs are bent either inward or outward (Fig. 27). They are used chiefly in wood turning for measuring the inside or outside diameters of turned pieces.

Fig. 28. Plumb and level

20. The plumb and level is used principally by the carpenter. It consists of a piece of wood, often brass bound, about 1⅜ by 3 by 26 in., into which a spirit-level glass is fastened horizontally (Fig. 28). As the glass is not quite filled, a bubble always remains. When this bubble is in the center of the glass, indicated by lines marked on it, the structure on which the level rests is absolutely horizontal or level.

Most levels also have one or two glasses set vertically to the length of the level. These are called "plumb glasses," and serve to determine if a wall or timber is placed plumb or perpendicular to the horizontal. Levels are also made with an iron body. They vary greatly in length.

21. A plumb bob is a piece of metal shaped like a boy's top (Fig. 29). A cord is attached to the thick end of the bob. It is used in building construction, to test the perpendicularity or plumbness of any structure or part thereof. Plumb bobs are also used on leveling instruments to enable the surveyor to place the instrument accurately above any point.

Fig. 29.
Plumb bob

22. Summary.

For measuring length, we use the following tools:

1. Rules, steel or wood, straight or folding, from 2 to 8 ft. long.

2. Tapes, steel or canvas, from 25 to 100 ft. long.

For laying out angles, we use:

1. Try squares, with blades 4 to 12 in. long, for 90-deg. angles only.
2. Miter and try squares for 45 and 90-deg. angles.
3. Miter squares for 45-deg. angles only.
4. Sliding T bevels for any angle.
5. Steel squares for any angle. Steel squares have several tables engraved on the tongue and blade.

For gauging lines parallel to an edge, end, or side, we use:
1. Marking gauges which mark a single line. Parts: block, beam, and spur.
2. Panel gauges which are large marking gauges.
3. Slitting gauges which cut through thin wood instead of marking.
4. Mortising gauges which mark a double line.
5. Butt gauges which can be set to three dimensions and are of steel.

For marking arcs and circles, we use:
1. Dividers for small circles and for stepping off measurements.
2. Trammel points for marking large circles.

For measuring the diameters of turned work, we use:
1. Inside calipers.
2. Outside calipers.

For laying out and testing horizontal and vertical surfaces, we use:
1. The plumb and level.
2. The plumb bob.

SAWS

After measuring and laying out the portion of a board or plank wanted, the next step is to saw along the lines marked. Different types of saws are used for different sawing jobs. Some of the most common are as follows:

23. The ripsaw is used for ripping or cutting with the grain along a straight line. Blades of ripsaws vary in length from 20 to 28 in. They are always wider at the handle than at the end, in order to prevent them from bending or buckling when they are pushed through the wood (Fig. 30). The teeth of a ripsaw vary in size according to the fineness of the

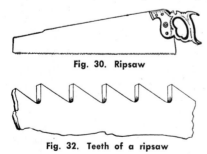

Fig. 30. Ripsaw

Fig. 32. Teeth of a ripsaw

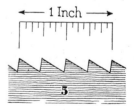

Fig. 31. Five points to the inch. Four complete teeth

work to be done. Their size is indicated by the number of "points" to the inch; i.e., the number of teeth occurring in 1 in. less one (Fig. 31). For example, a 7-point saw has 7 tooth points, but only 6 complete teeth in 1 in. The number of points a saw contains is stamped on the blade near the handle of the saw. The teeth of a ripsaw are shaped like chisel points, and their forward edges are at right angles to the length of the blade (Fig. 32).

Fig. 33. Teeth of a crosscut saw

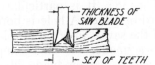

Fig. 35. Set of teeth showing clearance

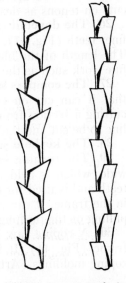

24. The crosscut saw is similar in shape and appearance to the ripsaw. The only difference lies in the shape of the teeth, which are filed to a point instead of square across as on a ripsaw (Fig. 33). The number of points to the inch varies from 8 to 12.

Fig. 34. Crosscut and rip-saw-teeth properly set. Bottom view of saws

The reason for this difference is that the wood fibers run lengthwise, and cannot be cut across smoothly except with a sharp knife point. A wider edge, like that of the teeth of a ripsaw, tears them apart and makes a rough and ragged cut. The wider-edged teeth, however, cut very smoothly in the same direction in which the fibers run, or with the grain. They also cut much faster than the teeth of a crosscut saw. This statement may be proved very easily and effectively by chiseling with and across the grain with a narrow chisel. A crosscut saw can be used to cut with the grain, but the work will proceed much slower than if a ripsaw is used.

All saws must be set. "Set" means to bend every other tooth to one side and the rest of the teeth to the opposite side. When the teeth are not set, the saw kerf, which is the slot the saw cuts in the wood, becomes too narrow for the saw blade to pass through without binding. Oiling or greasing the saw helps only momentarily. Setting the saw makes the saw kerf wider (Figs. 34 and 35). A saw set (Fig. 244) is used for setting hand saws.

The sharpening of saws is described in Article 128.

25. The backsaw is a crosscut saw with a thin blade and fine teeth (Fig. 36). A heavy piece of steel fitted over the back of the thin blade

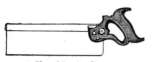

Fig. 36. Backsaw

Fig. 37. Dovetail saw

prevents it from buckling. The blades of backsaws are from 8 to 18 in. long. Backsaws are used for finer work such as the cheek and shoulder cuts on tenons as described in Article 187.

26. The dovetail saw is a backsaw with a thinner, narrower blade and finer teeth (Fig. 37). The handle of a dovetail saw is like a chisel handle. The length of the blade varies from 6 to 12 in. It is used for extremely fine work such as the cutting of dovetails, as described in Article 203.

27. The compass saw is shaped like a ripsaw, but its blade is so narrow that it can cut on curved lines (Fig. 38). It is particularly useful in cutting a section from within a board or panel. A hole is bored near the line to be cut and the pointed end of the saw is inserted in this hole.

28. The keyhole saw (Fig. 39) is a smaller and finer compass saw.

29. The turning saw consists of a very narrow blade, about 3/16 in. wide, which is held under tension in a frame (Fig. 40). It has ripsaw teeth and is used for cutting curves, as the blade usually can be revolved in the frame. It can also be set in the frame so that it cuts either on the pulling or the pushing stroke.

30. A coping saw is a very small turning saw usually having a metal frame (Fig. 41). It is used for sawing out fretwork patterns, and for coping moldings (Art. 200).

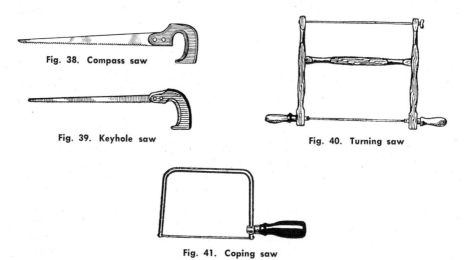

Fig. 38. Compass saw

Fig. 39. Keyhole saw

Fig. 40. Turning saw

Fig. 41. Coping saw

31. Miter boxes are made of either iron or wood. The iron miter box consists of a cast-iron frame fitted with a large backsaw, which is held perpendicular to the work by metal guides (Fig. 42). It can be adjusted to cut at any angle. It is used chiefly for mitering moldings and in picture-frame work. It is also very useful for cutting small pieces of wood at right angles.

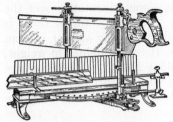

Fig. 42. Iron miter box

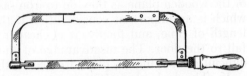

Fig. 43. Hack saw

32. A **hack saw** is not properly a woodworker's tool, but it is often a very convenient tool to have in the shop. It has a narrow blade set in a long, narrow metal frame, and is used for cutting metals (Fig. 43).

33. **Summary.** The fineness of a saw depends upon the number of *points to the inch. Set* means to bend the teeth to alternate sides to increase the width of the *saw kerf* and prevent binding. Common saws may be easily remembered when grouped in pairs.

1. **Ripsaw** is used for sawing along the grain. Teeth are like series of chisels.

1*a*. **Crosscut saw** is used for sawing across the grain. Teeth are like knife points.

2. **Backsaw** is a fine crosscut saw used in making joints.

2*a*. **Dovetail saw** is a smaller backsaw used for making dovetail joints.

2*b*. **Miter-box saw** is a large backsaw used in iron miter boxes.

3. **Compass saw** is a small pointed ripsaw used for interior cutting.

3*a*. **Keyhole saw** is a narrower compass saw used for interior cutting.

4. **Turning saw** has a narrower saw blade held in a wooden frame. It is used for cutting curves.

4*a*. **Coping saw** is a small turning saw held in a metal frame. It is used for cutting curves.

5. **Hack saw** is a machinist's tool used for metal only.

PLANES

After measuring and sawing a piece of lumber to rough dimensions, it is generally planed to finished dimensions.

Fig. 44. Wooden plane

Fig. 45. Jack plane

Planes, like saws, are made in many different forms for different planing jobs. Some of the most common types are as follows:

34. The wooden plane is the oldest type of plane (Fig. 44). It consists of a heavy cutting iron wedged in a block of hardwood. Although used very little in this country, it nevertheless has some advantages over the iron plane which are well worth noting. The most important of these is that shavings from resinous woods do not adhere to the sole or bottom of the wooden plane as they do to iron planes. It is also lighter in weight, which is an important consideration if the plane has to be used for any length of time, and finally, it is cheaper and will not break if it should fall to the floor. The disadvantage of the wooden plane, however, is the difficulty of setting the plane iron correctly.

35. The jack plane is the most useful, all-around plane in the woodworker's kit (Fig. 45). It is 14 or 15 in. long, and consists of an iron body to which the plane iron can be clamped. The bottom of the plane, which is either smooth or corrugated, is called the "sole." The front part of the sole is called the "toe," and its rear part, the "heel." A casting, called the "frog," is screwed to the iron body near its center. A wooden knob is screwed to the forward part of the body, and a handle to its rear part.

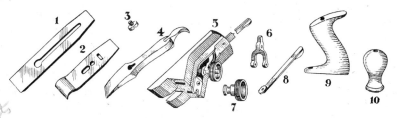

Fig. 46. Plane parts. 1, cutter iron; 2, plane-iron cap; 3, cap screw; 4, lever cap; 5, frog; 6, Y adjustment; 7, Y-adjustment screw; 8, lateral-adjustment lever; 9, handle; 10, knob

The plane iron, which in a jack plane is 2 in. or $2\frac{1}{4}$ in. wide, consists of two parts, the cutter and the cap. The latter is screwed to the back or flat side of the cutter, and is used to stiffen it and to break up the shavings. The plane iron is clamped to the frog by means of another iron, corresponding to the wedge in a wooden plane, called the "lever cap." The cap is fastened about 1/32 in. from the cutting edge of the blade. It must fit perfectly, otherwise shavings will be forced in between the two irons and "choke" the mouth of the plane. The plane iron can be adjusted to the depth of the cut by means of a brass screw engaging a wishbonelike casting. This is called the "Y adjustment." The plane iron can be adjusted laterally or level with the sole of the plane, by a lever riveted to the top of the frog (Fig. 46).

The sole of the plane keeps the thickness of the shaving uniform. If the board to be planed is uneven, it prevents the cutting iron from touching the hollow parts until all the high parts have been leveled off. Therefore, the longer the sole, the straighter the edge that is produced. The shavings enter through a narrow slit called the "throat" or "mouth." This slit is in the sole just forward of the cutting iron. The toe of the plane presses down on the wood in front of the shaving being taken, thus preventing it from splitting ahead. The width of the throat can be narrowed by moving the frog forward.

When planing an edge or a narrow board, the entire sole of the plane should be in contact with the wood to produce a straight edge. The tendency among beginners to hold the plane obliquely should be avoided and discouraged. Oblique cutting is a little easier, but it does not produce a flat surface, because only a small part of the sole is in contact with the wood.

Fig. 47. Fore plane

36. **The fore plane** (Fig. 47) is built exactly like a jack plane, but is 18 in. long and has a plane iron $2\frac{3}{8}$ in. wide.

37. **The jointer** is also like the jack plane, but is 22 to 24 in. long, and has a plane iron $2\frac{3}{8}$ or $2\frac{5}{8}$ in. wide (Fig. 48). The latter two planes are used for leveling larger surfaces and for jointing the edges of boards to be glued.

Fig. 48. Jointer

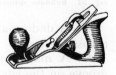

Fig. 49. Smooth plane

38. **The smooth plane** is of the same construction as the above-named planes, but it is shorter, being from $5\frac{1}{2}$ to 10 in. in length (Fig. 49). It also has narrower plane irons, from $1\frac{1}{4}$ to 2 in. It is used for planing smaller pieces and for very fine work.

Jack, smooth, fore planes, and jointers may be obtained either with smooth or corrugated bottoms.

39. **The circular plane** differs from the others in that it has a flexible bottom 10 in. long, which can be adjusted to either convex or concave curves (Fig. 50). It is used on curved work, such as round table tops and aprons.

40. **The block plane** is a small plane from 4 to 8 in. long (Fig 51). It has only a single plane iron, which is placed at a very low angle with the beveled side up. The lever cap is generally curved so that it fits smoothly

Fig. 50. Circular plane

Fig. 51. Block plane

within the hollow of the hand. This plane is used for planing end wood and in places where an ordinary plane could not be used.

41. The bullnose rabbet plane is about 4 in. long, and has the plane iron fastened to the extreme front of the body (Fig. 52). It is used for small and fine work.

42. The rabbet and fillister plane is an iron plane used for planing grooves or rabbets on the edges of a board (Art. 167). It has both a depth and a width gauge, as well as a spur, which scores the wood in advance of the plane iron, thereby preventing splitting (Fig. 53).

Fig. 52. Bullnose rabbet plane

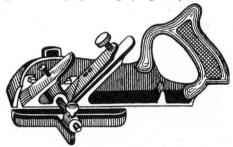

Fig. 53. Rabbet and fillister plane

43. A dado plane is similar to a rabbet plane, but is used for cutting across the grain.

44. A matching plane is used for matching boards; i.e., plowing a groove on the edge of one and a tongue on the edge of the other. It has two cutters, a plow and a tongue cutter (Fig. 54).

Fig. 54. Matching plane

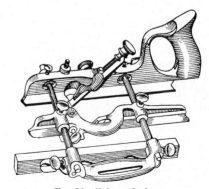

Fig. 56. Universal plane

Fig. 55. Router plane

45. The router plane (Fig. 55) is used for removing the wood between two sawed or chiseled edges such as dadoes (Art. 169) or grooves. The plane iron is lowered after each cut. It is furnished with a ¼-in., a ½-in., and a smoothing cutter.

46. The universal plane (Fig. 56) is used for planing a variety of different shaped moldings, beads, flutes, etc. Some planes have as many as 55 different and interchangeable cutters. The universal plane takes the place of as many wooden molding planes, because each molding plane can produce only one molding shape. The universal plane is rather complicated and difficult to set. With the many small and portable shapers available, the universal plane is not used so much at present.

47. Plane gauges are made both for iron and wooden planes. They can be attached to the sides of smooth, jack, fore, or jointer planes, and enable the operator to plane bevels or chamfers of any angle on the edge of a board without the continuous use of bevel or try square (Fig. 57).

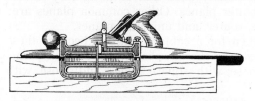

Fig. 57. Gauge attached to plane

Fig. 58. Iron
spokeshave

48. The spokeshave is like a plane with a very short bottom (Fig. 58). It is, therefore, suitable for smoothing curves that are too small for a circular plane. Spokeshaves are made in many patterns, generally with an iron body. One type, the *patternmaker's spokeshave*, is made of wood (Fig. 59).

The sharpening of plane irons is described in Article 129.

Fig. 59. Patternmaker's spokeshave

Fig. 60. Cabinet scraper

49. Scrapers are of two kinds; those sharpened like a plane iron and held in an iron frame or plane body (Fig. 60), and those that have square edges and are held in the hand only. The first class is called "cabinet scrapers" or "scraper planes," and the last type is called "hand scrapers" (Art. 132). Hand scrapers having curved edges are called "molding scrapers."

The action of a scraper can be likened to that of a piece of broken glass, whose sharp edges will cut fine shavings from a piece of wood. The scrapers are sharpened so that a fine, hooklike edge is formed which produces only very thin shavings.

Scrapers are used for smoothing a surface after it has been planed. Cross-grained and highly figured woods must always be scraped. As they usually can be planed only across the grain, the only tool that can be employed for smoothing them is a scraper. Veneers generally are not planed, but scraped.

All cutting and scraping should be finished before sanding. There is a good reason for this; for no matter how fine the sandpaper may be, tiny particles of quartz from the sandpaper become imbedded in the surface of the wood. This is not noticeable either to hand or eye; nevertheless these particles are sufficient to dull the edge of a sharp tool immediately.

The sharpening of cabinet and hand scrapers is explained in detail in Articles 131 and 132.

50. Summary. Advantages of a wooden plane are: resinous shavings do not stick to the bottom; it is lighter in weight, cheaper, and unbreakable.

Four iron planes constructed exactly alike and differing only in size are: smooth, jack, fore, and jointer planes. Other common planes are: circular, rabbet, bullnose, block, router, and universal planes.

A spokeshave is often mistaken for a cabinet scraper, because these tools look a good deal alike, but a spokeshave is in fact a small plane. Scrapers are of two kinds, those with square edges and those with beveled edges.

CHISELS

When a board has been planed to dimensions, the next operation usually is to join it to some other board or part of a structure. A chisel, in conjunction with other tools, is indispensable in the construction of most joints made by hand. It is indeed one of the most important and most used of woodworking tools.

According to their construction, chisels may be divided into two general classes: *tang chisels,* in which part of the chisel enters the handle, and *socket chisels,* in which the handle enters into a part of the chisel.

According to their use, chisels are divided into the following classes:

Fig. 61. Socket firmer chisel

51. The firmer chisel, which has a strong blade, may be used for both heavy and light work (Fig. 61).

52. The paring chisel, which has a slender blade, is used mainly for hand chiseling (Fig. 62). This type of chisel usually is beveled along the

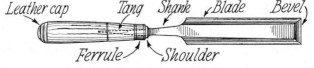

Fig. 62. Tang paring chisel

sides, so that fine work can be done, such as reeding (Art. 265) which requires an extra-thin blade.

53. **The framing chisel** has a very heavy and strong blade, and is used in rough carpentry work and shipbuilding. It often has an iron ring around the end of the handle instead of a leather cap.

54. **The butt chisel** (Fig. 63) differs from the others only in that it has a shorter blade and, therefore, can be used in more inaccessible places. It is commonly used in chiseling gains for hinges.

The above-named chisels are made in widths of from ⅛ to 2 in.

Fig. 63. Butt chisel

55. **The mortise chisel,** as its name implies, is used for chiseling mortises. It is, therefore, very thick just below the handle so that it will not break when it is used as a lever in forcing the shavings out of the mortise (Figs. 64 and 436).

Fig. 64. Socket mortise chisel

If the mortise is bored, it may be cleaned out and squared with an ordinary firmer chisel as described in Article 187.

The parts of a chisel are: the blade, on the end of which one bevel is ground; the shank, which is the upper narrow part of the blade; the socket, which is the end of the blade, shaped like a hollow cone, and in which the tapered end of the wooden handle fits. In tang chisels, the shank ends in a sharp point called the "tang," which is driven into the end of the handle. A projection on the shank, called a "shoulder," butts against the end of the handle and prevents the tang from entering further. A brass or iron ring, called the "ferrule," fits on the lower end of the handle and prevents it from splitting. Chisel handles are often leather tipped to protect them from the blows of the mallet.

56. **Gouges** are like chisels, except that their blades are bent lengthwise, so that in cross section they appear as a part of a circle. If the bevel is ground on the convex side, they are called "outside-bevel gouges" (Fig. 65), and if it is ground on the concave side, they are called "inside-bevel gouges." Some inside-bevel gouges have a bent shank, which is of advantage in giving room for the hand. This type of gouge is called "bent-shank gouge" (Fig. 66).

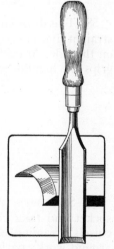

Fig. 65. Outside and inside-bevel gouges

Fig. 66. Bent-shank gouge

57. Carving tools (Fig. 67) are made in numerous different shapes. Many of these are gouges of different diameters and bend, others are chisels, but having two bevels; and still others have their blade bent lengthwise into a sharp angle, and are known as "veining tools." Veining tools are very useful, not only for wood carving, but also for two toning (Art. 276). The sharpening of chisels is described in Article 129. For description of turning chisels and how to sharpen them, see Article 134. Chisels with an oblique cutting edge are called *skew* chisels (Fig. 67).

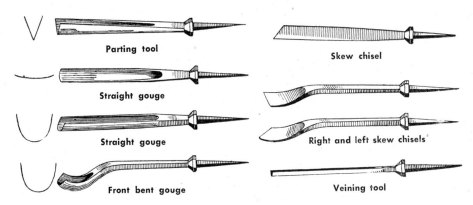

Parting tool

Skew chisel

Straight gouge

Straight gouge

Right and left skew chisels

Front bent gouge

Veining tool

Fig. 67. Carving tools

58. The drawknife is used for rough cutting, especially on edges, both straight and curved. It is a tool with a long blade whose cutting edge is on the side. At each end of the blade is a handle (Fig. 68). The operator grips the handles and draws the knife toward him.

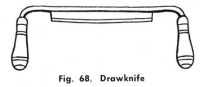

Fig. 68. Drawknife

59. Summary. According to their construction, chisels are divided into socket and tang chisels. According to their use, we have the following chisels: framing chisels for heavy, rough work; firmer chisels for all-around work; paring chisels for fine work; butt chisels for cutting gains for hinges, etc.; mortise chisels for cutting mortises.

Other types of chisels are: gouges, straight or bent shank with bevels ground either inside or outside; carving tools, woodturning chisels, and the drawknife.

BORING TOOLS

The woodworking and metal trades distinguish sharply between bits and drills and between boring and drilling.

Woodworkers never say that a hole is *drilled* in wood, but use the term *bored* instead.

The woodworker uses bits for boring holes for screws, dowels, and hardware, as an aid in mortising and in shaping curves and for many other purposes. As was the case with saws, planes, and chisels, bits vary in shape and structure with the type of work to be done. Some of the most common bits are the following:

Twist   *Shank*   *Tang*

Fig. 69. Auger bit

60. Auger bits are screw-shaped tools consisting of two main parts, the twist and the shank (Fig. 69). The twist ends in two sharp points, the nibs or spurs, which score the circle, and two cuttings edges, the lips, which remove the shavings from within the scored circle. A small screw point, in the center of the cutting end, centers the bit and draws it into the wood (Fig. 70). The threads of this screw are made in three different pitches — steep, medium, and fine. The steep pitch means quick boring and thick chips, and the fine or slight pitch means slow boring and fine chips. For end-wood boring, a steep- or medium-pitched screw should be used because end wood is likely to be forced in between the fine screw threads, and that prevents the screw from taking hold (Fig. 70).

The shank ends in a square-tapered tang, which is held by the chuck of the brace. The sizes of auger bits are indicated in sixteenths of an inch and are stamped on the tang. Number 10 means, therefore, 10/16 or ⅝ in.; 4 means 4/16 or ¼ in., and so on. Auger bits are made in sizes from 3/16 to 1 in. by sixteenths of an inch. The common woodworker's set ranges in size from ¼ to 1 in.

Fig. 70. End of auger bit
A, lips; B, nibs; C, screw medium pitch

Fig. 71. Fine-thread screw

61. Dowel bits are short auger bits 4½ in. long over-all. Ordinary auger bits up to 1 in. in diameter are from 7 to 9 in. long over-all.

62. Car bits and ship augers are auger bits from 18 to 24 in. in length.

63. Expansive bits have a movable cutter, which is adjustable to bore holes of different diameters (Fig. 72). Expansive bits are made in two

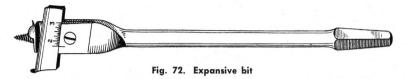

Fig. 72. Expansive bit

sizes. The largest size has three cutters, and bores holes up to 4 in. in diameter. On some expansive bits the cutter can be moved sidewise by means of a screw.

64. **Foerstner bits** have no twist and no screw. They cut with a sharp circular steel rim and two lips within this rim (Fig. 73). They bore very accurately, and are especially useful for boring thin wood and for end-

Fig. 73. Foerstner bit

wood boring. Moreover, when boring near the end of a piece of stock, a Foerstner bit is less likely to split the wood than an auger bit, the screw of which is wedge shaped. Their sizes are stamped on the tangs in sixteenths of an inch.

Fig. 74. Gimlet bit

65. **Gimlet or German gimlet bits** (Fig. 74) are used for boring holes of small diameters such as are needed when inserting screws in hardwood (see Art. 228). Their size, which varies from 1/16 to ⅜ in. by thirty-seconds, is stamped on the tang. Number 6 stamped on the tang therefore means 6/32 or 3/16 in. Their cutting edge is on the side and cannot be resharpened.

66. **Twist bits** are superior to gimlet bits. Their cutting edges are on the end and can be resharpened (Fig. 75). They range in size from 1/16 to ⅝ in. by thirty-seconds. The full fraction usually is stamped on the tang.

Fig. 75. Twist bit   Fig. 76. Twist drill

67. **Twist drills** are shaped like twist bits, but their cutting edges are not ground to as steep an angle. As the name implies, they are made for drilling in metal, but can also be used for wood. Twist drills used by machinists have only a round shank and can be held only in the chuck of a hand drill (Fig. 76). Twist drills used by woodworkers have a square shank like the other bits and are called bit-stock drills. They break more easily than twist bits. Twist drills are made in the same sizes as twist bits with the full fraction usually stamped on the round shank.

Fig. 77. Bradawl

Fig. 78. Rose countersink

68. The bradawl has the appearance of a small screw driver (Fig. 77). It is used for making holes into wood for screws and nails. The hole is produced by forcing the awl into the wood with a twisting motion. It should not be used in thin wood nor too near the edge. It forces the wood fibers apart, but does not cut any shavings.

69. The countersink is a small, cone-shaped tool used for widening the end of holes bored for flathead screws (Fig. 78). One type can be opened and sharpened on an oilstone (Fig. 79).

70. Plug cutters and washer cutters (Figs. 80 and 81) are used to cut circular disks from wood or leather. Such small disks are sometimes used to plug up holes in wood.

71. The plain brace is a tool used for holding a bit securely while boring a hole. At one end the brace has a chuck for clamping the bit. The chuck consists of two jaws and a sleeve which fits over the jaws and brings them together when turned to the right. At the other end is a knob which turns on ball bearings. The handle of the brace is shaped like a crank.

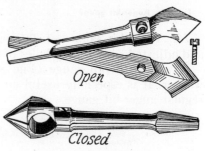

Open

Closed

Fig. 79. Countersink

72. The ratchet brace (Fig. 82) is fitted with an attachment which permits of boring in places where a complete turn cannot be made. The

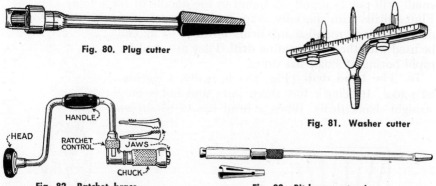

Fig. 80. Plug cutter

Fig. 81. Washer cutter

HANDLE

HEAD

RATCHET CONTROL

JAWS

CHUCK

Fig. 82. Ratchet brace

Fig. 83. Bit-brace extension

size of braces is given according to the *sweep;* i.e., the diameter of the circle that the handle makes in a complete revolution.

73. A bit-brace extension is a steel rod having a small chuck on one end and a square shank like a bit on the other (Fig. 83). A bit, ⅝ in.

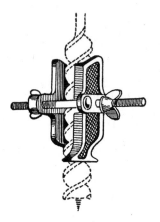

Fig. 84. Auger-bit gauge

or more in diameter, is inserted into the chuck of the extension, and this in turn into the chuck of the brace. The smallest hole that can be bored with this tool measures ⅝ in. Bit-brace extensions are made from 12 to 21 in. in length. The smallest hole that can be bored with the larger size measures ¾ in.

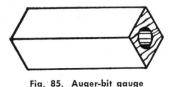

Fig. 85. Auger-bit gauge
made of wood

74. Auger-bit gauges of different types can be fastened to auger bits, and adjusted so that only holes of certain depths are bored (Fig. 84).

A wooden depth gauge (Fig. 85) can be easily made by any woodworker. It is especially useful on dowel bits which are too short for the regular auger-bit gauge.

Fig. 86. Reciprocating drill

75. Automatic drills and reciprocating drills. The automatic drill bores when it is pushed into the wood. The reciprocating drill bores both with the up and down strokes of the driver (Fig. 86). A magazine for small drill points usually is found in the handle of these tools (Fig. 87). Fluted drills with specially shaped top ends are used with the automatic drill. Ordinary round-shank drills up to 3/16 in. can be used with the reciprocating drill. They are used for rapid boring of small-size holes.

76. The hand drill (Fig. 88) is really a machinist's tool. Its chuck has three jaws and holds only straight-shank drills. When a brad has to be driven

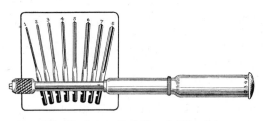

Fig. 87. Automatic drill and drill points

Fig. 88. Hand drill

into hardwood, a hole may be bored for it with a brad of the same size held in the chuck of the hand drill. The head of the brad is cut off before inserting it in the chuck. In this way, fine drills, which break easily, are saved for more important work.

77. Summary. The most important boring tool is the auger bit. It has the following parts: screw, which centers the bit and draws it into the wood; nibs, which score the circle; lips, which cut the shavings; shank, and square tang. The sizes 3/16 to 1 in., by sixteenths, are stamped on the tang.

Dowel bits are short auger bits; car bits are long auger bits. Screws of auger bits have fine, medium, and coarse threads.

Foerstner bits have no screw. They are useful for boring in end wood and thin stock. They are made in the same sizes as auger bits.

Expansive bits bore holes up to 3 or 4 in. in diameter.

Gimlet bits, twist bits, twist drills, and brad awls bore small holes for screws.

Countersinks enlarge the tops of screw holes for flathead screws.

Plug and washer cutters cut small disks of wood or leather.

Extension-bit holder is used for boring long holes ⅝ in. or more in diameter. The brace holds square-shank bits. Its parts are: chuck with sleeve and two jaws, ratchet, handle, and knob. "Sweep" means diameter of circle which the handle of the brace makes in boring.

Automatic drills and reciprocating drills are used for rapid boring of small holes. Fluted and straight-shank drills should be used. A hand drill is a machinist's tool.

Auger-bit gauges are used for boring holes to uniform depth.

MISCELLANEOUS TOOLS

78. Plain screw drivers are made with blades from 2 to 18 in. in length. The blades in the better grades are welded to a long steel ferrule, thereby preventing the possibility of turning in the handle (Fig. 89). A long screw driver is more powerful than a short one, because the long handle gives more leverage. The end of a screw driver should be flat and square and it should fit the slot in the screw to be driven. Screw drivers which are too thin for the slot or have rounded edges climb out of the slot and damage its edges.

Fig. 89. Screw driver   Fig. 90. Screw-driver bit

79. Automatic screw drivers are built on the same principle as automatic drills. A ratchet arrangement permits them to drive in one direction and release in the other. The best types can both drive and withdraw screws. They can also be locked so as to act as plain screw drivers.

80. Screw-driver bits are screw-driver blades, the upper ends of which have been forged to a square, tapered shank (Fig. 90). They are used with a brace. These bits are 5 in. long and from ¼ to ½ in. wide at the point.

81. **The claw hammer** is the type of hammer generally used by carpenters and woodworkers. It has two parts, the head and the handle. The end of the head, used for striking blows, is called the face; the other end is the peen. The peen of this hammer is bent and shaped so that it can be used for pulling nails (Fig. 91). Hammers used in other trades have peens of different shapes used for other purposes, as for example, the ball-peen hammer. The face of the hammer often is slightly convex, or bell-faced, so that it will not make a circular mark on the surface of the wood after striking the last blow on the head of a nail. It is important to keep the face of the hammer clean and free from grease or glue, so that it will not glance off the head of a nail and bend it. It can be cleaned by rubbing it over a piece of sandpaper. The size of the hammer is indicated by the weight of the head in pounds and ounces.

Fig. 91. Claw hammer

Fig. 92. Nail set

82. **Nail sets** are small steel bars about 4 to 5 in. long and ¼ in. in diameter (Fig. 92). They have a cup-shaped point, and are used to set nails below the surface. The size of the point varies with the size of the nail to be set.

83. **Mallets** are wooden hammers (Fig. 93). As wood is more elastic than iron or steel, a mallet should always be used when driving on wood. The blows of a steel hammer would soon splinter a chisel handle and mar a joint to be driven together beyond repair. A mallet with a head 3 in. in diameter and 5 in. long is a good size for woodworkers.

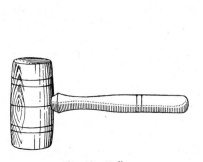

Fig. 93. Mallet

Fig. 94. Hatchet

84. **Hatchets** are used chiefly by carpenters in shingling and lathing. They have a short handle, a sharp edge for cutting shingles and laths to width and length, a hammer head for driving nails, and a slot for pulling them (Fig. 94).

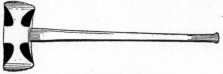

Fig. 95. Two-bitted ax

Fig. 96. Adze

85. The ax and the adze have long handles which are held with both hands. The ax is used for felling trees and splitting log sections. If it has two cutting edges, it is called a two-bitted ax (Fig. 95). The adze is used for squaring logs, in shipbuilding, etc. (Fig. 96).

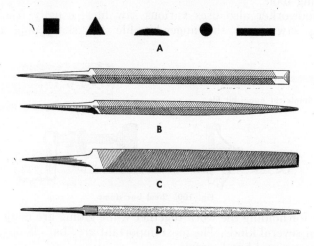

Fig. 97. Common files. A, Cross sections of common files;
B, single-cut triangular files, upper, blunt; lower, tapered;
C, double-cut flat file; D, open-cut round file

86. Rasps and files are used by the woodworker for reducing and smoothing edges that cannot be easily worked with a cutting tool. Saw files and auger-bit files also are used for sharpening saws, auger bits, and the point on marking gauges.

Files are made in more than three thousand different varieties. They have teeth or serrations of various degrees of fineness and pattern, cut diagonally across their surfaces. Rasps have triangular projections, and cut much faster than files.

To clean a rasp or file see Article 141.

Files are used in many different trades and for many different purposes. They are classified according to the shape of their cross section, as square, round, triangular, flat, half round, etc.; according to the manner in which the serrations or teeth are cut, as single cut (oblique parallel lines across the surface), double cut (two sets of parallel lines crossing each other obliquely), and open cut (oblique parallel lines, slightly broken); according to fineness of cut, as coarse, bastard, second cut, smooth, and dead smooth; according to length (not including the tang) usually from 3 to 14 in.; and according to outline, as blunt (having the same cross section throughout), and taper (Fig. 97).

Flat files having no teeth on one or both edges are said to have one or two safe edges as the case may be.

The surface of rasps is covered with rough, triangular points or projections, called "teeth" (Fig. 99). Rasps cut faster but rougher than files. They should, therefore, be used before files. When measuring the length of files and rasps, the tang should not be included.

The use of rasps or files on wood should be discouraged, except on special work as chairmaking or where it is impossible or impractical to use a cutting tool.

The woodworker also uses various saw files, usually triangular, for sharpening saws, and the auger-bit file for sharpening auger bits (Fig. 98).

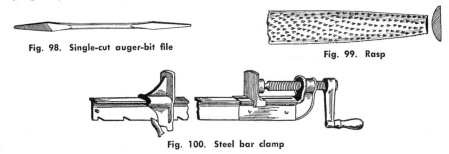

Fig. 98. Single-cut auger-bit file

Fig. 99. Rasp

Fig. 100. Steel bar clamp

Clamps for holding the work together while gluing are made in various sizes and of several kinds. The most important are: bar clamps, C clamps, column clamps, and hand screws.

87. Steel bar clamps consist of a steel beam or bar fitted with a screw and crank at one end, and a steel head which can be moved along the bar and fastened to it by means of slots cut into its lower edge or side at short intervals (Fig. 100). Another type has a smooth bar, to which the steel head is clamped by means of steel disks and a spring. Steel bar

Fig. 101. C clamp

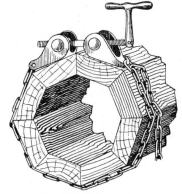

Fig. 102. Column clamp

clamps are made in lengths of 2, 2½, 3, 4, 5, 6, 7, and 8 ft. (Arts. 216, 217, 220, and 221).

88. **C clamps,** or screw clamps, sometimes called "carriage-maker's clamps," consist of a malleable-iron frame, bent in the shape of the letter C, and a steel screw with a swivel tip (Fig. 101). They are made in sizes which, when open, measure from 3 to 12 in.

89. **Column clamps** consist of a steel chain and a right and left screw (Fig. 102). They are very useful when gluing together polygons, shaped columns, and any circular work such as the apron for a round table.

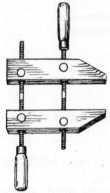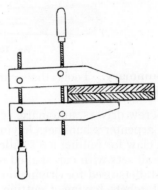

Fig. 103. Hand screw   Fig. 104. Tightening hand screw

90. **Hand screws** are most useful both in clamping up finished work and in holding work under construction (Arts. 157 and 198). They consist of two jaws made of hardwood and two steel spindles, the end and middle spindles (Fig. 103). They are opened or closed by grasping a handle in each hand and revolving the hand screw. The size of a hand screw is indicated by the length of the jaw in inches, the smallest being 6 in. and the largest 18 in.

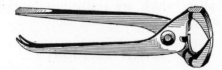

Fig. 105. Carpenter's pincers

Fig. 106. Monkey wrench

When tightening up hand screws on straight work, the middle spindle should first be tightened so that the jaws hold firmly at that point, but are a little open at the end (Fig. 104). When the end spindle is now tightened, the jaws will come together at the end and be parallel.

91. **Carpenter's pincers** (Fig. 105) are used for pulling nails. A monkey wrench (Fig. 106), tinner's snips (Fig. 107), cutting pliers

or nippers (Fig. 108), and gas pliers (Fig. 109), although not wood-workers' tools, will be found very convenient and useful in the wood-working shop.

Fig. 107. Tinner's snips

Fig. 108. Side-cutting pliers

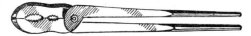

Fig. 109. Gas pliers

92. Summary. Tools that cannot readily be classified or grouped together are:

1. Screw drivers, automatic screw drivers and screw-driver bits.
2. Carpenter's hammers having a rounded face called "bell face" and a claw for pulling nails called the "peen."
3. Nail sets with cup-shaped ends for driving nails below the surface.
4. Mallets used for driving on chisel handles.
5. Hatchets having a cutting edge, a hammer head, and a slot for pulling nails.
6. Axes and adzes for felling trees and squaring logs.
7. Files which are classified according to shape of cross section, length, serrations, fineness, blunt or taper, and safe edge.
8. Rasps which are coarse files with triangular-shaped teeth.
9. Clamps for holding work while gluing: iron bar clamps, C-clamps, column clamps, and hand screws.
10. Carpenter's pincers for pulling nails, monkey wrench, tinner's snips, and pliers which are really metalworking tools, but convenient to have in a woodworking shop.

REVIEW QUESTIONS

Measuring Tools

1. A bench top is made of narrow pieces of wood, because ....
2. A bench hook is ....; a bench stop is ....
3. How does a try square differ from a steel square? Name the parts of each.
4. A 45-deg. angle may be marked with any of the following tools: (a) ....;
   (b) ....; (c) ....; (d) ....
5. Find the number of board feet in a plank 2 by 10 in. by 15 ft. 0 in. by using the board-measure scale. Check by calculation (Art. 335).
6. Find the pitch of a roof having a rise of 10 ft. and a run of 15 ft.
7. The principal parts of a marking gauge are: (a) ....; (b) ....;
   (c) ....
8. The mortising gauge differs from the marking gauge by having ....
9. The panel gauge differs from the marking gauge by being ....

10. The butt gauge is used for ....
11. The tools for measuring inside and outside diameters of turned work are called

....
12. What tools would you use for marking a circle 6 in. in diameter and another 36 in. in diameter?
13. How may a point on the floor be found that is directly below a point in the ceiling?
14. To test horizontal and vertical surfaces we use a ....
15. What could be substituted for a pair of trammel points?

Saws

16. The term "set" means ....
17. The teeth of a ripsaw are like a series of ....; the teeth of a crosscut saw are like a series of ....
18. By "points to the inch" is understood ....
19. What type of saw should be used for the following operations:
    a) Cutting four pieces 2 in. wide by 30 in. long from a plank 12 in. wide.
    b) Cutting a circular opening, 5 in. in diameter in a board ⅞ by 10 by 60 in.
    c) Cutting a circular table top 30 in. in diameter.
    d) Cutting a shoulder on a tenon.
    e) Cutting an intricate design in the center of a ¼-in. panel, 12 in. square.
20. The "saw kerf" is ....
21. The most common handsaws are .... (name 8).

Planes

22. What are the advantages and disadvantages of the wooden plane?
23. The casting screwed to the body of a jack plane is called the ....
    It is furnished with a screw and lever which ....
24. What is the proper plane to use for the following operations:
    a) Planing the ends of a piece of stock 2 in. wide.
    b) Planing faces, edges, and ends of a board ⅞ by 10 by 20 in.
    c) Planing the edges of two boards 4 ft. long that are to be glued.
    d) Removing the surplus wood from a dado whose edges have been sawed.
    e) Planing the edge of a circular table top, 36 in. in diameter.
    f) Planing a groove on the edge of a board.
    g) Planing a molding.
    h) Planing a rabbet on a picture-frame molding.
25. The spokeshave is often mistaken for a ....
26. Name four planes that are exactly alike except for size.
27. The hand scraper has .... edges; the cabinet scraper has one .... edge.
28. Why should all planing and scraping be done before sanding?

Chisels

29. According to their construction, the chisels are divided into .... chisels and .... chisels.
30. The most common chisels are ....
31. Make a sketch of a tang chisel and name its parts (6).
32. A gouge differs from a chisel by ....
33. A chisel having an oblique edge is called a ....

Boring Tools

34. Name the three cutting parts of an auger bit and explain the function of each.
35. How is the size of the following bits indicated: auger, Foerstner, gimlet, twist bit, twist drill?

36. A fine screw point on an auger bit should not be used when boring in end wood, because ....

37. What boring tools should be used for the following operations:
   - *a*) To bore for a ½-in. dowel.
   - *b*) To bore for a 1½ in. by 10 flathead screw.
   - *c*) To bore a hole 1¾ in. in diameter.
   - *d*) To bore in end wood.
   - *e*) To bore a hole ¾ in. in diameter and 16 in. long.
   - *f*) To bore for a ½ in. by 4 roundhead screw.
   - *g*) To bore a 7/16-in. hole near the edge in thin stock.
   - *h*) To bore a series of holes to uniform depth.
   - *i*) To cut a circular leather disk 2 in. in diameter.

38. The term "sweep" applied to a brace means ....

39. The brace has .... jaws, the hand drill has .... jaws.

40. How can a depth gauge for a dowel bit be made out of wood?

Miscellaneous Tools

41. To obtain the best results when driving a screw, the screw driver should have .... and ....

42. An automatic screw driver is built like ....

43. What do the terms "bell face" and "peen" mean?

44. A mallet should be used on a chisel handle, because ....

45. A hatchet is built so that it can: 1 ...., 2 ...., and 3 ....

46. Define the terms serrations, blunt, taper, safe edge, second cut.

47. A woodworker uses three kinds of iron tools for clamping work: 1 ....;
    2 ....; 3 ....

48. Make a sketch of a hand screw and name its parts.

49. Besides a claw hammer, a .... also is used for pulling nails.

50. The monkey wrench, tinner's snips. and cutting pliers are used for ....

Chapter 3

MACHINE TOOLS

During recent years there has been considerable progress in the field of woodworking machinery. Particular attention has been given to greater safety for the operator, and to convenience and ease in both the "setting up" and the operation of the machinery. Old types of production machines have been improved, and new types have been invented. Moreover, numerous types of bench and portable machines have been developed.

Since woodworking machinery is very dangerous to operate, improvements and inventions that will safeguard the operator are of the greatest importance. Some of the most notable advances have been cylindrical cutting heads on hand planers, safety switches, improved guarding devices, and the elimination of fast-moving belts through direct motor drives.

Developments within the field of production machinery have completely revolutionized the furniture industry, and have made cabinetmaking in its century-old form one of the disappearing trades. In large furniture factories, handwork has been reduced to a minimum, because machines have been invented which can be operated by semiskilled workers. Such machines perform practically all tool operations faster, better, and more uniformly than the skilled workman can by hand methods.

While a discussion of production machinery is interesting, both from a mechanical and a commercial point of view, it cannot be covered in this book, which deals mainly with handwork, hand tools, and the simpler and more commonly used woodworking machines and operations.

The development of the small bench and portable machines, on the other hand, is of interest to the manufacturer and the individual workman, as well as to students of woodworking, and the increasing number of amateurs, who find recreation, satisfaction, and joy in manual work. Large up-to-date factories have found it to their advantage to distribute a number of these small machines among their benchworkers, because they help to speed up production by eliminating practically all handsawing and planing.

For the same reasons, contractors and individual workmen use them in increasing numbers, not only for sawing and planing, but also for routing, shaping, boring, and sanding.

This type of machinery has also become very popular in schools, especially those of junior grade where the work done is usually limited to size.

A school shop equipped with woodworking machinery generally has a circular saw, a band saw or a jig saw, a jointer, one or more lathes, and a tool grinder. This equipment may be called basic, because these machines are the most useful in a general woodworking course and are in fact indispensable in any commercial shop. Trade, technical, and vocational schools may, in addition to these machines, have one or more of the following: a thickness planer, a cut-off saw, a mortiser, a boring machine, a shaper, a router, various types of sanding machines, and a wood trimmer.

95. **The circular saw** is, no doubt, the most useful and indispensable of woodworking machines. Besides the regular ripping and cross-cutting operations, for which this machine is especially built, many other operations such as cutting of grooves, rabbets, dadoes, tenons, miters, tapers, etc., may be performed on the circular saw. On smaller machines even edge planing and shaping of straight moldings may be done.

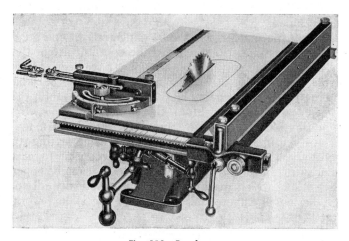

Fig. 112. Bench saw

Circular saws are made in many sizes from the large production machines to the small bench saws, which are fastened to heavy wooden tables or iron stands in order to bring the saw table up to the proper working height, which is about 36 in. (Fig. 112). The most common saws are the *universal* saw and the *variety* saw (Figs. 113 and 114).

A circular saw consists of a heavy casting to which an iron table with a smooth, level surface is fastened. The universal circular saw, Figure 113, has two saw arbors supported on a saw-arbor yoke, which can be revolved by means of a handwheel, both when the machine is stationary and in motion. Two saws, therefore, can be used on this machine at the same time, and either one brought into action when desired. Each saw can be adjusted and clamped at different heights above the table.

The variety saw has only one saw arbor. It is generally a smaller machine than the universal saw, but is similar in construction. Some

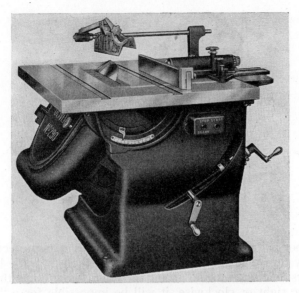

Fig. 113. Double-arbor universal saw — motor-on-arbor
type with tilting saws, but horizontal stationary table.

variety saws are equipped with a mortising and boring attachment
(Fig. 114).

The older circular saws were belt driven (Fig. 117), but the newer
ones have what is termed "a motor on arbor drive," which means that

Fig. 114. Variety saw with mortising attachment

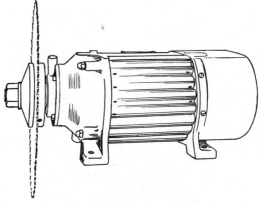

Fig. 115. Saw arbor as rotor of a motor

the saw arbor is the rotor of the motor (Fig. 115). Its projecting end has a *left* screw thread for the nut which clamps the saw blade between two large collars, one fixed to the arbor, the other loose. Since the saw arbor turns to the right or clockwise, it will be impossible for a "left" nut to work loose.

The table consists of two parts. The larger one to the right of the saw blade is stationary and the smaller one to the left is movable both lengthwise and crosswise. The lengthwise movement past the saw is for the purpose of crosscutting wide boards; the crosswise movement is

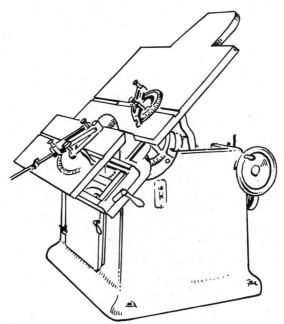

Fig. 116. Two-section tilting saw table

simply for the purpose of changing saws and for making room for thick grooving saws and dado heads. The table is mounted on roller bearings for the lengthwise movement.

Some tables are made in one solid piece and are, therefore, provided with throat plates which can be removed when changing saws. A throat plate is a soft metal casting which fits into an opening cut for it in the iron table (Fig. 113). Each throat plate has a slot through which the saw blade projects. Several throat plates with slots of different widths are furnished.

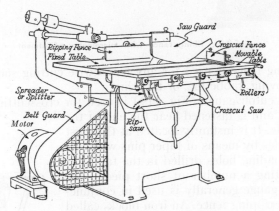

Fig. 117. Belt-driven circular saw

On older circular saws the table can be tilted toward the left to an angle of 45 deg. (Fig. 116). On the latest types the saw blade and, therefore, the whole motor is tilted while the table is fixed in a horizontal position. On the universal saw, the whole yoke carrying the two motors is tilted (Fig. 113). While the current is on, only the motor carrying the saw above the table rotates; the other is automatically cut off. Circular saws with tilting saw blades are safer to operate than the ones with tilting tables, because the operator need not stand in an awkward position to hold the stock on the table. Another good safety device on modern saws is a brake which automatically stops the saw when the current is cut off.

A circular saw is equipped with three types of fences or gauges for ripping, crosscutting, and mitering.

The ripping fence is a rectangular casting, which may be fastened to the saw table on either side of the saw. It is used mostly on the stationary part or right side of the table. It is fastened parallel to the line of the saw for ordinary ripping, and may be tilted to any angle between 45 and 90 deg. It may be easily and quickly adjusted to rip any width up to 26 in., depending upon the size of the machine. The ripping fence usually can be set according to a scale engraved in the table. It is generally fitted with a very accurate micrometer adjustment (Fig. 118).

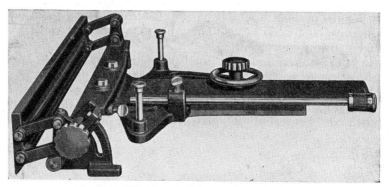

Fig. 118. Tilting fence with micrometer adjustment

The ripping fence is used for any lengthwise cutting such as ordinary ripping, grooving, rabbeting, or tapering.

The miter cutoff gauge (Fig. 119) is used for crosscutting or mitering wide boards, and is fastened near the end of the movable table. It is instantly located at the most common angles by means of taper pins which fit into corresponding holes drilled in the table.

Fig. 119. Cutoff gauge

When cutting a number of short pieces, the miter cutoff gauge generally is used in conjunction with the ripping fence. An iron block, called a clearance block, is screwed to the end of the ripping fence which is then fastened at the correct distance to the right of the saw. The piece to be cut is held with an edge against the cutoff gauge and the end butting against the iron block.

When the table is pushed past the saw, the piece is cut off and left lying

Fig. 120. Cutting short pieces to length on circular saw. The guard has been removed in order to make the operation more clear. Sawing should never be done without the guard in place

on the stationary part of the saw table, there being sufficient clearance between the saw and the ripping fence to prevent it from binding and being thrown backward by the saw (Fig. 120).

When longer pieces are to be cut, a square steel rod is clamped in a corresponding groove in the face of the gauge. It projects beyond the saw table to the left of the operator, and is furnished with an iron stop, which is set at the required distance to the left of the saw (Fig. 121). In

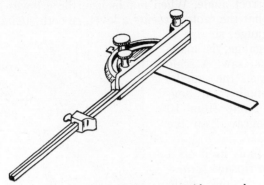

Fig. 121. Universal or miter gauge with stop rod
and block

this "setup," the ripping fence should be pushed out of the way so that the table around the saw is clear. The pieces cut off fall to the left of the saw and usually are removed by an assistant. Clearance blocks and stop rods also may be made of wood as shown in Figure 122.

The miter cutoff gauge can be set to any angle from 30 to 135 deg. by means of a graduated scale marked on the table.

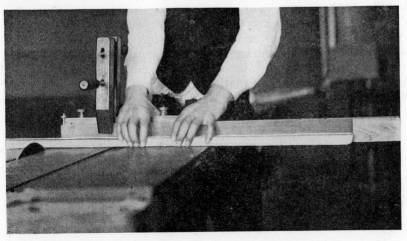

Fig. 122. Cutting long pieces to length on circular saw. The guard has been removed
in order to make the operation more clear. Sawing should never be
done without the guard in place

The universal gauge is a smaller cutoff gauge which runs in shallow grooves cut in the face of the table (Fig. 121). Two of these gauges, which can be set to any angle between 30 and 135 deg., are generally furnished with the saw. They can be used on either side of the saw for mitering or crosscutting. They can also be yoked together as shown in Figure 114 for crosscutting large pieces. Compound miters are cut by using these gauges while at the same time tilting the saw blade or the table to the correct angle. When not in use, the grooves are filled with steel strips so that the table presents a level, smooth surface.

A segment gauge, similar to the universal gauge, is made for the universal saw. A scale for determining the angle, length, and number of segments in any circle from 10 to 80 in. is engraved on the table (Fig. 123).

The cutting tools used on a circular saw are ripsaws, crosscut saws, miter saws, dado heads, straight and shaped molding cutters.

The teeth of circular ripsaws

Fig. 123. Segment-gauge drawing

and crosscut saws are shaped very much like those of the corresponding handsaws. The miter saw has a series of about half a dozen crosscut teeth alternating with a ripsaw tooth all around its circumference. It makes a very fine, clean cut. When ordering any one of these saws, the following specifications should be given: kind of saw, as rip, crosscut, etc., diameter of saw, number of teeth, gauge or thickness, and diameter of arbor hole (Fig. 124).

Grooving saws are thick saws designed to cut grooves in wood.

A dado head consists of two saws or outside cutters, and a number of inside cutters of various thicknesses which may be placed between these. Grooves of from ¼ to 2 in. in width can be cut with a dado head. The outside cutters have a combination of rip and crosscut teeth, and cut equally well with or across the grain (Fig. 125). A dado sleeve and collars are furnished with the dado head.

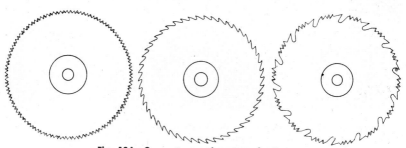

Fig. 124. Crosscut saw, ripsaw, and miter saw

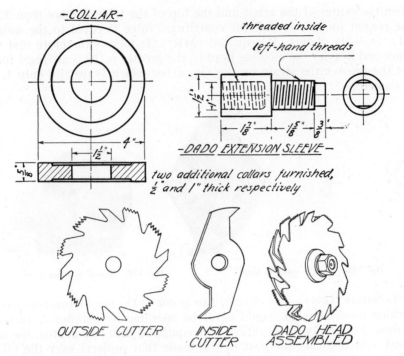

Fig. 125. Dado head

96. Directions for setting up a dado head. In setting up a dado head, proceed as follows: Screw the dado sleeve to the saw arbor, and slip on one of the outside cutters or saws. Note that the arbor holes in the cutters and collars are larger than on the regular saw and collar. Select the inside cutters which, together with the two saws, will make up the desired thickness (for example, to cut a groove ¾ in. wide). Space these inside cutters so that their teeth are about the same distance apart. Slip on the other saw or outside cutter, press the whole together with the hand, and check thickness measurement. The collars are now placed on the sleeve. Be sure that the last collar projects beyond the shoulder of the dado sleeve. Put on the regular collar and nut, place a throat plate in position, or slide the movable saw table in place, and fasten it. Turn the dado head by hand to see that it is clear. Adjust it to height above the table, turn on the power, and make a trial cut. If it is necessary to readjust for width, this can often be done by inserting a small cardboard washer between the cutters. Narrow dadoes may be cut without the dado sleeve extension. The cutters have the regular size arbor hole and are used directly on the saw mandrel.

A molding head is a solid casting, to which may be fastened straight knives for edge planing, or curved ones for molding work (Fig. 126). Molding heads also are circular in shape (Fig. 127). Molding heads should not be used on the larger circular saws where the distance between the center of the arbor and the top of the table is more than 3 in. The reason for this is that the centrifugal force is equal to the weight (M) times the radius (R) squared (MR^2). It follows therefore that the larger and heavier the molding head is, the greater is the centrifugal force and the greater the strain on the saw arbor which is usually only 1 in. in diameter.

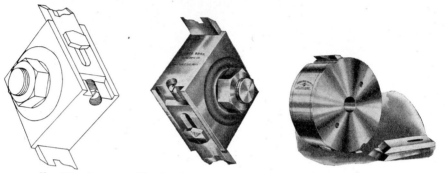

Fig. 126. **Square molding head** Fig. 127. **Round molding head**

97. Safety Rules. The circular saw is one of the most dangerous wood-working machines and should never be operated by nervous or careless persons. For safety in operation, it is equipped with two guards, the saw guard, which covers the part of the blade that projects over the table, and the splitter guard, which looks like a curved sword and is bolted to the frame behind the saw blade. Its back is a little thicker than the saw blade and serves to keep the saw kerf open so that the wood being sawed does not pinch the saw and cause a dangerous "kickback." The saw guard is made of metal, wire mesh, or wood. Sometimes the two guards are combined in one (Fig. 128).

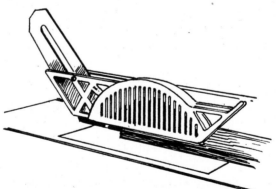

Fig. 128. **Saw and splitter guard combined**

A real foolproof guard that can be used under all conditions has unfortunately not yet been invented. It is often in the way and must be removed for measuring and for certain sawing operations. Therefore,

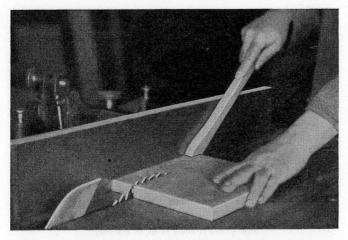

Fig. 129. Ripping stock to narrow widths. Note splitter and push
stick. Saw guard removed while taking photo

many operators, unless compelled to use the guard, get into the habit
of using the saw without it.

When stock which is being sawed is thrown backward with great force
and speed, it is called a kickback. This is one of the greatest dangers in
operating the circular saw. It may occur when the saw has too little set,
when the splitter guard is not used, when the clearance block is not used
in crosscutting, when badly warped stock is sawed, or when small pieces
of wood fall on an unguarded saw or are picked up by the back teeth.
Observe the following safety rules:

1. Keep the machine in perfect working order and the saw blades
sharp and properly set. It is dangerous to work with dull blades.

2. Keep the floor around the machine clean and in good repair so as
to avoid slipping or stumbling.

3. Keep your mind and eyes on the job and don't talk to anyone while
operating the saw.

4. Use all guards and other safety devices whenever possible.

5. Use a push stick when ripping narrow pieces (Figs. 129 and 130),
or saw halfway through from one side and then reverse the piece and saw
the other half (Fig. 131).

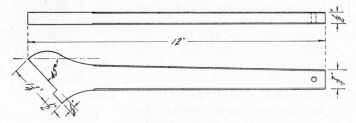

Fig. 130. Push stick

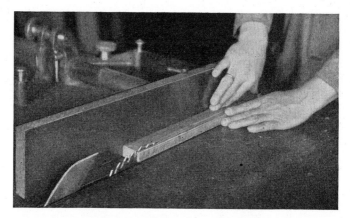

Fig. 131. Ripping narrow stock by cutting halfway from each end. Saw guard is likely to be in the way

6. Stand to the left of the saw to avoid being hurt by pieces that may be thrown back by the saw.

7. Adjust the saw so that it projects only ⅛ in. above the stock being sawed.

8. Never reach over the saw to pick up pieces that have been sawed.

9. Stock must lie flat on the saw table and have one straight edge to be held firmly against a fence or guide. Never saw "freehand."

10. Make no adjustments while the machine is in motion.

11. Roll up your sleeves above the elbows or wear tight-fitting ones. Tuck your necktie inside your shirt, or better, do not wear any. Don't under any circumstances wear gloves.

98. The band saw, like the circular saw, is one of the oldest and most indispensable woodworking machines. It is made in many sizes, from the large band mill with wheels 7 ft. or more in diameter to the little bench saw with 10-in. wheels. Band saws used mainly for sawing curves are called *scroll saws* (Figs. 132 and 133).

The most important parts of a band saw are the endless, flexible-steel saw blade from which it derives its name, two wheels on which this saw blade revolves, a heavy cast-iron frame, and a steel table. The wheels are fastened to shafts, which are mounted in roller bearings on the frame.

Fig. 132. Ten-inch bench band saw

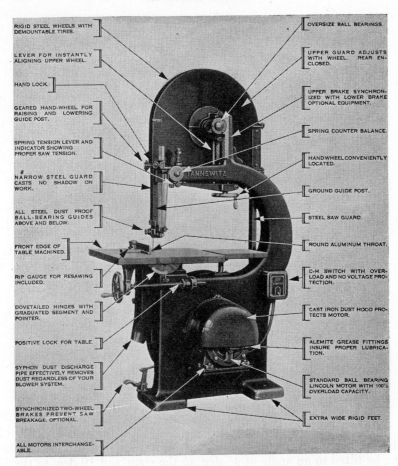

RIGID STEEL WHEELS WITH DEMOUNTABLE TIRES.

LEVER FOR INSTANTLY ALIGNING UPPER WHEEL.

HAND LOCK.

GEARED HAND-WHEEL FOR RAISING AND LOWERING GUIDE POST.

SPRING TENSION LEVER AND INDICATOR SHOWING PROPER SAW TENSION.

NARROW STEEL GUARD CASTS NO SHADOW ON WORK.

ALL STEEL DUST PROOF BALL-BEARING GUIDES ABOVE AND BELOW.

FRONT EDGE OF TABLE MACHINED.

RIP GAUGE FOR RESAWING INCLUDED.

DOVETAILED HINGES WITH GRADUATED SEGMENT AND POINTER.

POSITIVE LOCK FOR TABLE.

SYPHON DUST DISCHARGE PIPE EFFECTIVELY REMOVES DUST REGARDLESS OF YOUR BLOWER SYSTEM.

SYNCHRONIZED TWO-WHEEL BRAKES PREVENT SAW BREAKAGE. OPTIONAL.

ALL MOTORS INTERCHANGE-ABLE.

OVERSIZE BALL BEARINGS.

UPPER GUARD ADJUSTS WITH WHEEL. REAR EN-CLOSED.

UPPER BRAKE SYNCHRON-IZED WITH LOWER BRAKE OPTIONAL EQUIPMENT.

SPRING COUNTER BALANCE.

HAND WHEEL CONVENIENTLY LOCATED.

GROUND GUIDE POST.

STEEL SAW GUARD.

ROUND ALUMINUM THROAT.

C-H SWITCH WITH OVER-LOAD AND NO VOLTAGE PRO-TECTION.

CAST IRON DUST HOOD PRO-TECTS MOTOR.

ALEMITE GREASE FITTINGS INSURE PROPER LUBRICA-TION.

STANDARD BALL BEARING LINCOLN MOTOR WITH 100% OVERLOAD CAPACITY.

EXTRA WIDE RIGID FEET.

Fig. 133. High-speed band saw

These wheels are of the same size, and one is directly above the other. The upper one is supported on a curved arm of the casting called the "gooseneck." It can be moved up or down for the purpose of giving tension to the saw and to accommodate saw blades which have become shorter through breakage and resoldering. It can also be tilted forward or backward so that the saw can be made to run on any part of the rim. This is called "tracking." The lower wheel is not adjustable.

The wheels usually are made of cast iron, and their rims are covered with rubber bands or tires which protect the teeth, cushion the saw, and prevent it from slipping. A tire made of a perforated metal band imbedded in vulcanized rubber is used on the newer high-speed band saws having a special disk wheel with a demountable rim (Fig. 134). It need not be cemented or shellacked in place like the ordinary soft rubber tires; it wears much longer and is safer to use, because it cannot break or be thrown from the wheels (Fig. 134).

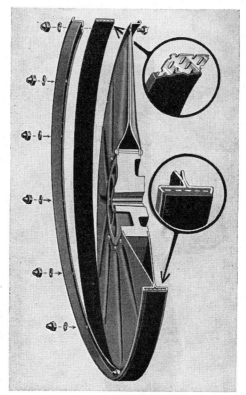

Fig. 134. High-speed band-saw tire and
demountable rim

The table is fastened to the casting directly above the lower wheel. It can be tilted to an angle of 45 deg. to the right and 10 deg. to the left. It is slotted for the saw from the center to one edge and is furnished with a soft-metal or wood throat plate. A ripping fence is furnished with most band saws. Those of smaller size very often are grooved for a miter and crosscutting gauge (Fig. 135). The larger band saws have a two-piece table, the smaller or left part of which is fixed.

In order to keep the saw blade running straight and true and prevent it from being pushed off the wheels when sawing, two guides are used, one above the table and one below. A *guide* consists of two hardened steel jaws between which the blade runs, and a guide wheel which spins around when the back of the saw is forced against it (Figs. 136 and 137). The upper guide is fastened to the *guide post,* which is a steel bar that can be moved up or down as the

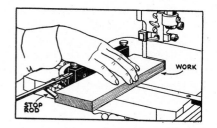

Fig. 135. Squaring longer pieces, using miter gauge and stop rod

Fig. 136. Upper band-saw guide fastened to guide post

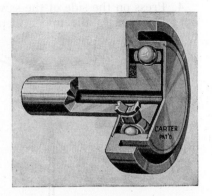

Fig. 137. Ball-bearing guide wheel

thickness of the stock being sawed demands. It has a spring counter-balance, which makes it easier to push up and which prevents it from slipping down by its own weight.

The *guards* on a band saw are two metal doors enclosing the wheels, and a channel-shaped piece of steel which is fastened to the guide post and slides up and down with it so that only the cutting part of the saw is exposed. A fixed guard covers the left part of the saw between the wheels.

Band saws are driven by individual motors connected by chains, gears, or couplings to the lower wheel shaft, or by the newer motor-on-arbor drive in which the lower shaft is the rotor of the motor. The speed of band saws varies considerably and is dependent upon the size of the wheels and the use for which the saw has been designed. The cutting speed in feet per minute may vary from 4000 to 11,000 or more for machines used in production work. To calculate the speed in feet per minute, find the circumference of the wheel in feet (π x D) and multiply that by the revolutions per minute of the motor (r.p.m.).

Example: A 36-in. band saw makes 700 r.p.m. What is its cutting speed in feet per minute?

Solution: π x D x r.p.m.   22/7 x 36/12 x 700 = 6600 f.p.m.

99. Removing and coiling a band-saw blade. When a band-saw blade needs to be sharpened or is too narrow or too wide for the work to be done, it must be removed from the wheels and another one put in its place. Proceed as follows:

1. Pull out the little round pin from the slot in the table, open both the doors guarding the wheels, and lower the upper wheel by loosening the vertical adjustment screw.

2. The saw blade can now be slipped off the wheels and should then be coiled into three loops.

3. Hold the saw blade in the same position as it occupies on the wheels, but with the teeth pointing away from you. Place your hands in about the middle of the blade so that the loop above them is of the same size as the loop below them (Fig. 138).

4. Press on the side of the saw with the thumbs so that the teeth turn out. This causes the upper loop to bend down toward the lower one (Fig. 139).

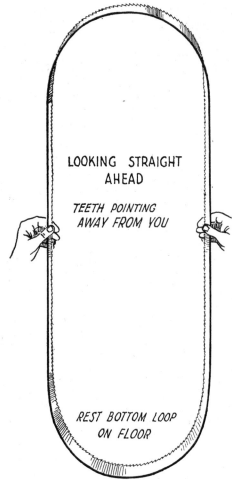

LOOKING STRAIGHT
AHEAD

*TEETH POINTING
AWAY FROM YOU*

*REST BOTTOM LOOP
ON FLOOR*

Fig. 138. Holding band saw ready for
coiling, teeth pointing away from body

5. Place the upper loop inside the lower one and move both hands together until one crosses the other (Fig. 140). Then let go of the saw and it will coil up on the floor in three loops (Fig. 141).

6. When putting the new blade on the wheels, see that the teeth on the right side of the saw point downward. If they should point up, remove the saw from the wheels and turn it inside out. When you replace it on the wheels, you will find that the teeth point down.

7. Push the guides back and tighten the vertical adjustment screw. Rotate the wheels by hand and note on which part of the wheels the saw

runs. If it does not run in the center of both wheels, tilt the upper wheel until it does. This is called "tracking the saw." It is important that the rear edge of the saw is plumb or perpendicular to the table (Fig. 142). If the rubber tires are worn in the center, tilt the upper wheel so that the saw blade runs either on the front or the rear part of the rims. Good band sawyers watch the wear on the tires and adjust the position of the blade back and forth so that this will be even.

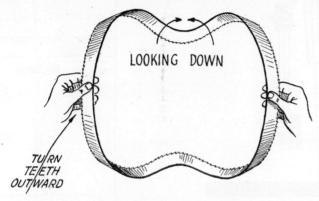

Fig. 139. Teeth bent out, upper loop of saw pointing toward floor

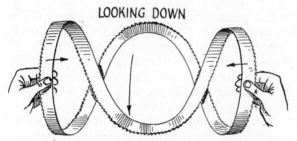

Fig. 140. Placing upper loop of saw inside the lower one

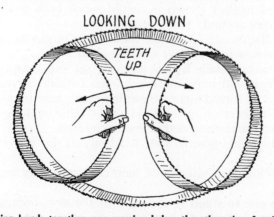

Fig. 141. Moving hands together, one crossing below the other, thus forming three loops

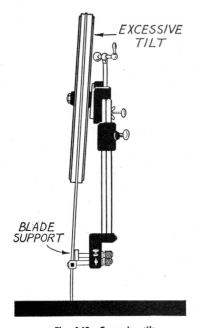

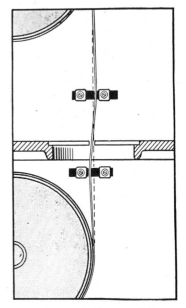

Fig. 142. Excessive tilt   Fig. 143. Guides out of line

8. Move the two guides forward until the two jaws of each are in line with the gullets of the teeth. The points of the teeth must be outside the jaws, because they are set or bent to alternate sides.

9. Bring the jaws as close together as possible while still allowing the blade to run between them without friction. To do this accurately, place a piece of paper on each side of the saw blade while bringing the jaws together. Be sure the guides are in line (Fig. 143).

10. Finally, move the guide wheels forward until they are about 1/32 in. from the rear edge of the saw. When the saw runs without doing any work it should not touch the guide wheels, but when it is cutting, the stock is pressed against it and it should touch both guide wheels and cause them to spin around.

100. Safety Rules. 1. Check the adjustment of guides and saw blade, and see that the saw is in perfect working order.

2. Use only a saw blade that is properly set and sharpened. If it has not enough set, it will burn the wood when cutting curves; if it is not sharp, the stock is forced against it which may cause breakage.

3. Leave no tools or scraps of wood on the table, and see that the floor around the machine is clean and in good condition.

4. Adjust the guide post so that it is only ¼ in. above the stock to be cut.

5. Avoid backing the saw out of long cuts as it may be easily pulled off the wheels.

6. Allow no one to stand to the right of the saw, because they might be injured if the blade should break.

7. Replace a worn throat plate, because chips may fall through it and be caught between the blade and the lower wheel, causing the blade to snap.

8. Roll up your sleeves or wear tight-fitting ones. Never wear gloves or ragged clothing.

101. The jig saw is a small scroll saw which is used for lighter and finer work than the band saw. Like most other machines, jig saws are made both in large and small sizes. The bench saw is the most common (Fig. 144).

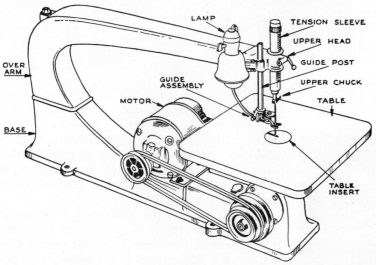

Fig. 144. Jig saw

The jig saw resembles the band saw in having a table which is fastened to the base, and an arm which extends over the table. It differs from the band saw in that the saw blade moves up and down in short strokes and that pierced work or interior cutting can be done on it.

The driving mechanism of the jig saw is the so-called pitman movement, which converts a rotary motion into a reciprocating one, or vice versa, as for example in the steam locomotive and the mowing machine (Fig. 145). The pitman movement consists of a driving wheel with a crankpin off center, over which a bar or connecting rod fits. The other end of this bar, called the "crosshead," slides up and down between parallel guides called "gibs." The saw blade is held in a chuck on the other end of the crosshead (Fig. 146).

The upper chuck is fastened to the end of a bar which moves up or down inside a tube. This tube, called the "tension sleeve," is clamped to the arm above the table. It can be moved up or down so that saws of different lengths can be used. It also contains a tension spring which keeps the saw blades from buckling.

A guide post is clamped to the end of the arm next to the tension sleeve. On its lower end it has a guide plate with slots of different widths and

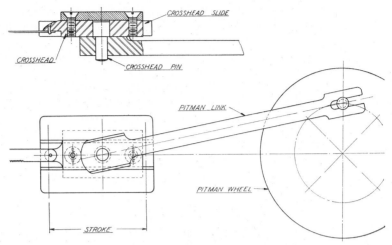

Fig. 145. Pitman mechanism

Fig. 146. Guides, saw, table milled for throat plate, quadrant, and saw clamp

depths and a steel roller corresponding to the guide wheel on a band saw. In order to prevent the work from being lifted off the table on the upward stroke of the saw, a hold-down foot is fastened below the guide plate (Fig. 147).

Also fastened to the guide post is a tube which blows a steady stream of air to clear away the sawdust obscuring the lines. The table can be tilted 45 deg. to each side and has a soft-metal throat plate.

The speed of the jig saw can be varied from 650 to 1750 r.p.m. by means of two cone pulleys, one of them fastened directly to the rotor of the motor and the other to the pitman wheel.

Fig. 147. Upper jaw, sleeve, hold-down foot, and air tube of jig saw

The size of a jig saw is determined by the distance between the inside curve of the arm and the saw blade. On a 24-in. jig saw it is possible to handle work 48 in. wide, because the saw will cut 24 in. to center.

Fig. 148. Jig-saw blades

Jig-saw blades vary a great deal in size and fineness of the teeth (Fig. 148). For softwoods use saws with fairly large teeth (about 10 to the inch); for hardwoods use saws with fine teeth. Saber blades are short, thick, and wide. They are fastened only in the lower chuck and are used for ripping and for sawing thicker stock. A special guide below the table is needed for saber saws. If a fence is clamped to the table, straight cuts

Fig. 149. Jig-saw files

may be made. As saber blades are not fastened to the upper chuck, the arm, extending over the table, may be removed to accommodate wider stock (Fig. 146).

Besides sawing, the jig saw also may be used for filing and sanding (Figs. 149 and 150). For sanding, run the saw at slow speed.

102. The joiner or hand planer.
(Figs. 151 and 152) is, next to the circular saw, the most necessary and useful machine in the woodworking shop. It takes the place of the hand plane and is particularly useful in straightening the surfaces of warped boards or planks, jointing edges of boards to be glued, rabbeting, squaring surfaces, and all straight planing in general.

The main parts of the joiner are a heavy cast-iron bed supported on two columns, two tables, a fence, and a cutterhead mounted on the bed. The cylindrical shape of the modern cutterhead is a great improvement in smoothness and safety of operation over the old, square cutterhead. On modern machines it runs in ball bearings bolted to the bed near its center. It has either two, three, four, or six thin steel knives. The size of the machine is given according to the length of the knives. These run from 4 in. on the small bench joiner (Fig. 152) to 36 in. on the large production machine.

Fig. 150. Sanding attachment

Instead of cutting long, narrow shavings like a hand plane, the joiner cuts wide and extremely short shavings. As each knife strikes the wood, it makes a small hollow across the entire width of the surface. As the wood is pushed along, a series of small ridges are therefore formed between these hollows. This is called "rotary cutting," the principle discovered by Samuel Bentham in 1791.

To minimize the ridges and hollows, the cutterhead must be perfectly balanced and the knives set so that they all project the same distance.

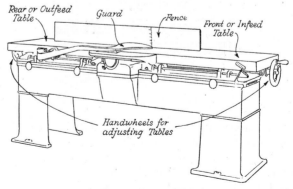

Fig. 151. Large jointer

Other factors are: greater speed, more knives in the cutterhead, and slower feeding of the stock.

With a motor-on-arbor drive, the cutterhead ordinarily revolves at a speed of 3600 r.p.m. For production work, however, this speed may be

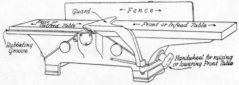

Fig. 152. Bench jointer

increased or even doubled by the use of a frequency changer, or simply by a belt drive. A frequency changer is an electrical device which increases the alternating-current impulses from the usual 60 cycles to 120 or more. Doubling the number of cycles doubles the speed of the motor.

Fig. 153. Tables pulled away from cutterhead showing throat plates

The tables are from 1 to 2 in. wider than the knives, and can be lowered or raised on inclined ways by means of handwheels. For all ordinary work, the rear or outfeed table should be level with the knives at their highest point of revolution. Both tables have steel lips or throat plates next to the cutterhead. These lips are bolted to the table and may be renewed in case they become nicked or worn (Fig. 153). Some jointer tables have a recess on their outer edges for rabbeting (Fig. 154); others have a rabbeting arm bolted to the infeed table (Fig. 155). The tables may be pulled away from the cylinder for the purpose of changing or sharpening the knives. A knife-grinding and setting attachment (Fig. 156) consists of a small motor-driven emery wheel, which can be moved back and forth over the knives. It is bolted to the table and, therefore, eliminates the work of removing knives from the cutterhead every time they need sharpening (Art. 151).

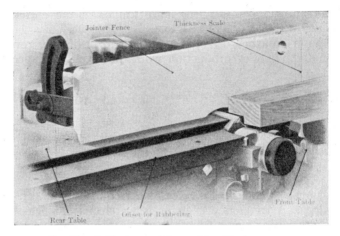

Fig. 154. Rabbeting on jointer with rabbeting groove

A fence, somewhat similar to the ripping fence of a circular saw, is clamped to the outfeed table and may be moved across its entire width. It may also be tilted to any angle between 45 and 90 deg.

Several types of guards are being used for covering the part of the knives not in contact with the wood being planed. The most common one is made of aluminum and is held against the fence with a spring. When a piece of stock is planed, it pushes the guard outward, but the spring holds it against the stock so that it covers the part of the knives in front of the operator. As the stock leaves the infeed table, the guard slips back against the fence (Fig. 157).

103. Adjusting the outfeed table. (1) The outfeed or rear table must be at exactly the same height as the edge of the knives at their highest point of revolution. The distance the infeed or front table is below the outfeed table equals the depth of the cut made when planing a piece of wood. Most jointers have a graduated scale indicating depth of cut.

2. If the outfeed table is too high, more is planed off at the beginning of the cut and little or nothing at the end (Fig. 158). The experienced

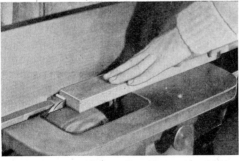

Fig. 155. Rabbeting on jointer with square-edged tables. Note rabbeting arm

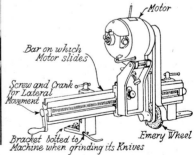

Fig. 156. Knife-grinding attachment

Fig. 157. Planing face of board using pusher

operator will also notice that the front end of the wood bumps against the lip of the outfeed table.

3. If the outfeed table is too low, the wood will drop down as it leaves the infeed table and the knives will cut deeper on the last inch or two (Fig. 159). This depression can be felt very plainly when running the hand over the planed surface.

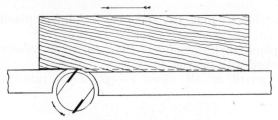

Fig. 158. Outfeed table too high

4. The table can be set to the correct height as follows: Start the machine and run the edge of a piece of wood over the cutterhead until it projects a few inches over the outfeed table. Then stop the machine. If the table is too low, there will be a space between the table and the wood. If it is too high, lower it until there is a space between the table and the stock (Fig. 160). Then bring the table up slowly until it just touches the wood. Check the adjustment by planing the edge of a piece of stock.

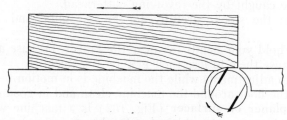

Fig. 159. Outfeed table too low

5. Once the table has been adjusted, it may be a good plan to remove the handwheel.

104. Safety Rules. (1) The gap or distance between the lips of the tables should be as small as possible. Bring them as close together as you can without touching the cutterhead. See that it revolves freely before turning on the power.

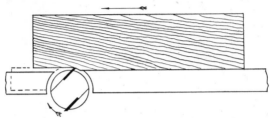

Fig. 160. Adjusting outfeed table to height. Stock part way over outfeed table

2. See that the knives are sharp. It is always dangerous to work with dull tools. Do not take too heavy cuts, because that, or dull knives, may cause a kickback; that is, the wood under your hands will be thrown back. Should your hands drop down on the knives, it will cause a serious injury.

3. Use a push block (Figs. 157 and 161) for all face planing, especially on short pieces of stock.

4. Do not plane anything shorter than 10 in. or thinner than ½ in. unless it is backed with heavier stock.

5. Use the guard at all times except when rabbeting and stop chamfering.

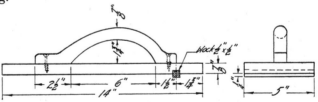

Fig. 161. Pusher for jointer

6. Wear no loose or ragged clothing and never any gloves. Be particularly careful of your necktie that it does not hang loose, because it may easily be caught by the revolving cutterhead.

7. Examine the stock carefully for knots, splits, and nails before planing it.

8. Do not hold your hands too near the knives, because a sudden jar may easily cause them to lose their grip on the stock.

9. Make no adjustments while the machine is in motion.

10. Keep the floor around the machine clean and in good condition.

105. The planer or surfacer (Fig. 162) is a machine which planes boards or planks to an even thickness. Double surfacers have two cutter-

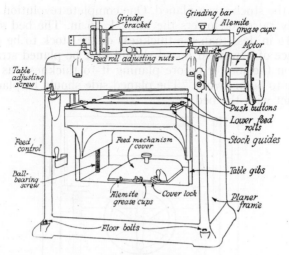

Fig. 162. Planer

heads, and plane both surfaces of a board at the same time, while single surfacers have only one cutterhead and can plane only one surface at a time. Planers are made in widths from 15 to 20 in., and usually can take stock from 6 to 8 in. in thickness.

A single surfacer consists of the following main parts: a casting, between the sides of which a heavy table or bed can be raised or lowered, a cutterhead mounted over the table, four feed rolls driven by gears, belts, or chains, a chip breaker, and a pressure bar.

Fig. 163. Frame of planer showing wedges

Briefly, the action of a planer is as follows:

1. The table is moved up or down, either by two pairs of wedges which slide upon one another (Fig. 163) or by two heavy screws which move in unison (Fig. 164). The wedge action is the better and more accurate and is used mainly on big production machines. On smaller planers the lifting mechanism is activated by a handwheel; on larger ones by a special motor hoist. A graduated scale on the front of the frame indicates the

thickness of the stock when planed. One complete revolution of the hand-wheel usually raises or lowers the table 1/16 in. The bed should be set to about 1/16 in. less than the thickness of the stock to be planed.

One surface of a warped board should first be planed straight, or out of "wind," on the jointer before planing it to thickness, as it otherwise will continue to be in "wind." The planed side should be placed "down"; i.e., in contact with the bed.

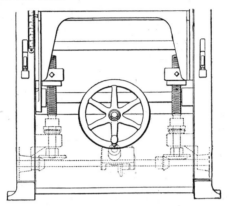

Fig. 164. Raising screws for planer table

When planing a rough board, always place the smoothest side down, run it through the planer, and then reverse the surfaces.

2. Start the machine, set the feed to the speed desired, ordinarily from 20 to 130 ft. per minute, and then start the feed rolls. Some planers have a separate motor which drives the feeding mechanism, others have a belt drive from the cutterhead shaft. When belt-driven, a lever usually

Fig. 165. Gear-driven feed rolls

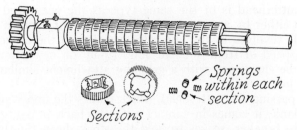

Fig. 166. Sectional feed roll

tightens or loosens the belt, thereby starting or stopping the feed. When motor driven, the feeding mechanism is also started or stopped independently of the cutterhead. On newer machines, a safety device stops the feed rolls automatically when too heavy a cut is taken. The four feed rolls are usually connected by gears, which are completely enclosed (Fig. 165).

3. Push the board or plank into the machine. It is first gripped by the sectional feed roll on its upper side and a smooth steel roll mounted on the bed directly below this.

The sectional feed roll (Fig. 166) consists of a cylinder, on which a series of wheels with corrugated edges are mounted. They yield as much as ⅜ in. independently of each other. This is to allow for unevenness in the thickness of the stock being planed. This sectional feed roll is held down on the stock by means of heavy weights or springs. On older or smaller machines the upper front feed roll is one solid corrugated cylinder.

4. The feed rolls now carry the stock along without further pushing. It next comes in contact with the chip breaker, which is a heavy sectional bar, also held down on the stock by means of an adjustable weight. It is placed immediately before the cutterhead, and can be swung out of the way without coming in contact with the knives. It holds the stock firmly to the bed and prevents chips from tearing its surface (Fig. 167).

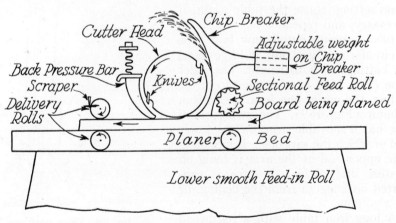

Fig. 167. Sectional view of planer

5. The cutterhead is of the same type as the ones used on jointers. It is driven either by a motor on arbor, or a motor coupled or belted to the shaft. It revolves in the opposite direction to the movement of the stock at a speed of from 3600 to 5000 r.p.m. on newer machines. The knives can be sharpened with a grinding attachment similar to that described for jointer knives.

6. After passing the cutterhead, which planes the upper surface of the board or plank, it comes in contact with the back pressure bar, which, like the chip breaker, serves to hold the stock down tightly to the bed so as to prevent chattering. This bar is held down by a spring, the pressure of which can be regulated by two screws (Fig. 167).

7. Directly behind the back pressure bar are the delivery rolls, which are smooth steel rolls carrying the stock away from the cylinder. One is mounted in the bed below the stock and the other one above the stock. The upper one sometimes has a scraper which keeps it free from shavings (Fig. 167).

The person operating a planer should stand a little to one side to avoid the danger of being hurt by chips, which occasionally may be thrown back with great violence. For the same reason, pieces shorter than the distance between the feed and delivery rolls should not be planed on the surfacer.

It is often necessary to run stock several times through the machine to reduce it to the desired thickness. When several pieces are to be planed to the same thickness, run the thickest ones through first, then raise the table, and run them all through with the same setting. Raise the table again, if necessary, and repeat.

106. A swing cutoff saw is a type of circular saw used only in large shops for cutting stock to length. The older type (Fig. 168) is suspended from the ceiling, the newer one from a cast-iron column (Fig. 169). The swing cutoff saw has a movable arm, on the lower end of which the saw blade is mounted. The upper end of the arm is hung on a steel shaft, which in turn is supported on hangers from the ceiling, or on a column.

A long iron table with a hardwood

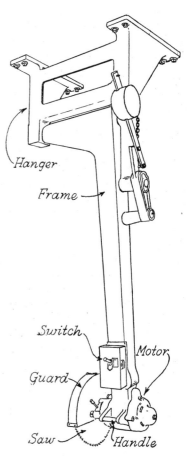

Fig. 168. Swing cutoff saw

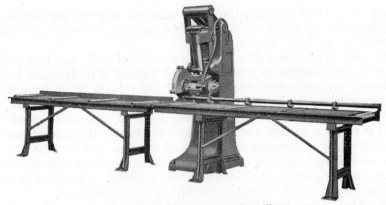

Fig. 169. Compact, self-contained cutoff saw

or steel top is placed below the saw. The stock to be cut to length is placed on the table and is held against a fence while the swinging arm is pulled toward the operator and across the stock. The saw blade, which revolves counterclockwise, cuts just below the surface of the table. As

Fig. 170. Radial saw

soon as the cut is completed and the operator releases the handle, the arm automatically swings back to its first position, because it is counterbalanced by weights or springs.

The table is equipped with rollers, a graduated scale, and iron stops to facilitate the handling of the lumber and cutting it to accurate lengths.

Modern machines, both the suspended and column types, have motor-on-arbor drives. Dadoing may also be done on the swing cutoff saw.

107. **The radial saw** (Fig. 170) may be used as a swing cutoff saw, but it is really a variety saw, because of the many adjustments possible. The cutting unit, mounted on the end of the arm, can be turned to any angle so that ripping, crosscutting, plain and compound mitering, grooving, and dadoing can be performed on this machine. In addition, a special attachment permits the use of router bits of various sizes.

108. **The power handsaw** is a portable circular saw with which all ordinary sawing operations can be performed. It is especially useful in carpentry work and other building construction, because it is portable.

One type (Fig. 171) has a flat base which rests firmly on the work, so that ripping, beveling, and crosscutting can be done accurately with guides. This saw may also be converted into a radial saw, because a radial arm and saw table may be obtained for it. Special saw blades for cutting brick, tile, or sheet metal also can be had.

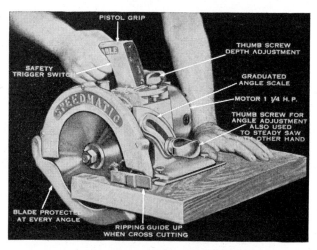

Fig. 171. Power handsaw

109. **Mortising machines** are made in three types, each operating on a different mechanical principle. The most common of these is the hollow-chisel mortiser; the others are the chain-saw mortiser and the oscillating-bit mortiser.

The hollow-chisel mortiser has an auger bit which revolves inside a square hollow chisel. It is used for all-round work and makes a mortise with square sides, ends, and bottom. The chain-saw mortiser has an endless chain with saw-shaped teeth, which revolves around an oblong guide bar (Fig. 172). It is the fastest mortising machine and is used principally for door- and window-sash work. It makes a mortise with a rounded bottom (Fig. 173). The oscillating-bit mortiser cuts mortises with a

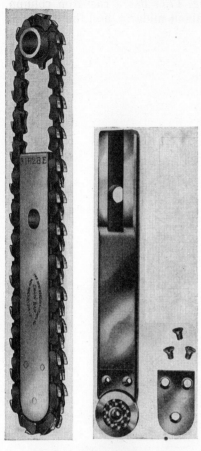

Fig. 172. Chain, chain bar, and sprocket wheel

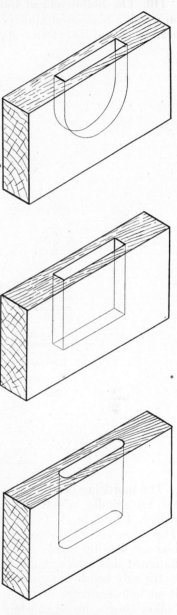

Fig. 173. Shape of mortises produced by mortising machines. Upper: chain-saw mortiser; center: hollow chisel mortiser; lower: oscillating-bit mortiser

Fig. 174. Router bit and mortise

router bit (Fig. 233). Because it makes relatively small and shallow mortises, it is used principally for chair making and other curved work. It makes a mortise with rounded sides (Fig. 174).

110. The hollow-chisel mortiser (Fig. 175) has a cast-iron column, on which a horizontal table is mounted about midway, and the mortising head or ram at its extreme upper end.

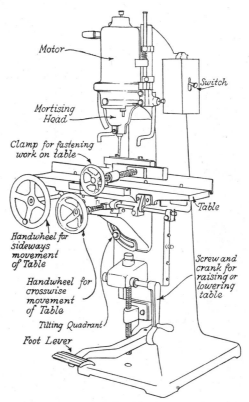

Motor

Switch

Mortising Head

Clamp for fastening work on table

Table

Handwheel for sideways movement of Table

Screw and crank for raising or lowering table

Handwheel for crosswise movement of Table

Tilting Quadrant

Foot Lever

Fig. 175. Hollow-chisel mortiser

The mortising head or ram in belt-driven machines (Fig. 176) carries the bit spindle, which is mounted in two self-oiling bearings. A long pulley, 4 by 8 in., is fastened to this spindle between the two bearings. The lower end of the spindle carries a chuck, in which the ends of the bits are held by means of a setscrew. The bits and the bushings have a flattened side, which should butt up against the end of the screw.

Directly below this chuck is a similar chuck mounted on the mortising head independently of the spindle. This lower chuck holds the square hollow chisels, inside of which the bits revolve. When putting a bit in the machine, fasten the hollow chisel first, and then insert the bit from below and fasten it in the spindle chuck. A little clearance should be allowed at the end of the chisel so that the bit revolves freely, without overheating.

In a newer type, the mortising head consists of a ball-bearing self-contained motor (Fig. 175). The end of the armature carries the bit chuck, while the chuck for the hollow chisels is held in the motor casting.

The mortising head is moved downward by means of a foot lever. When this is released, a spring causes it to return to its first position. Some mortising machines are equipped with an adjustable power feed to give from 15 to 50 strokes per minute. The length of the stroke is also adjustable. A blower keeps the work free from shavings and cools the chisel and bit.

The table can be moved up or down on the column to allow for work of different dimensions. It has a crosswise movement for centering the stock to be mortised directly under the chisel, and a clamp for holding it firmly in place. It also has a sidewise movement for making successive cuts to complete a mortise. For example, if a ½-in. mortise 3 in. long has to be made, the mortising head must be moved down 7 or 8 times, while the table is moved a little sideways between each cut or stroke.

When a number of pieces have to be mortised alike, the sidewise movement of the table may be controlled by iron rods and stops. The table is

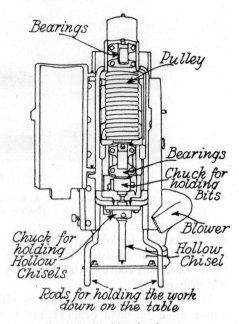

Fig. 176. Mortising head or ram of a belt-driven machine

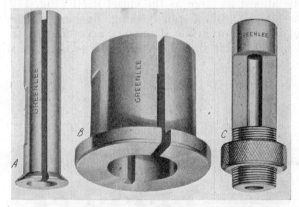

Fig. 177. Hollow chisel and bit bushings. A, Split bit bushing; B, split chisel bushing; C, adjustable bit bushing

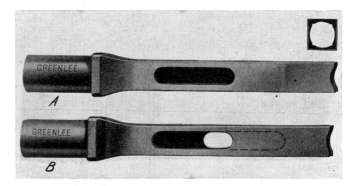

Fig. 178. Hollow chisels. A, Regular hollow chisel; B, hard-wear
hollow chisel

also adjustable for oblique mortising. Two bent iron bars fastened to the column can be adjusted so that they hold the work firmly against the table, thus preventing the tendency to climb up when the chisel is withdrawn.

Mortising machines are driven either by belts or by an individual motor mounted on a bracket and belted to the spindle pulley, or by a ball-bearing motor on arbor. This latter type eliminates all pulleys and belts. The speed of the spindle should be about 3600 r.p.m.

The hollow chisel is generally square and is made in sizes from ¼ to 2½ in. For ordinary work, though, ¾ in. is the largest size used. The length of the chisel varies with its size. Its lower end is reamed out and sharpened; its upper end is round and held in a split bushing having one flat side for the setscrew (Fig. 177). One or two oblong holes are made in the sides of the chisel, through which the shavings drop (Fig. 178).

Hollow-chisel bits are similar to auger bits, but have no screw in the center. The nibs are wider than the diameter of the bit, so that the hole bored will be almost as large as the chisel itself (Fig. 179). The round shank of the bit is held in a split bushing. Bushings for both chisel and bits vary in the size of inside diameters according to the size of the chisels and bits. The bit should be adjusted so that the wide nibs just

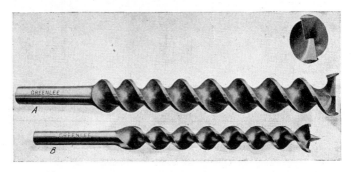

Fig. 179. A, Regular hollow-chisel bit; B, hard-wear hollow-chisel bit

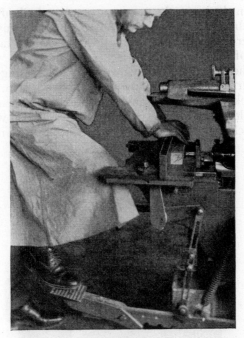

Fig. 180. Operating a horizontal mortiser on
a circular saw

clear the cutting edges of the chisel, as any friction will otherwise tend
to overheat both chisel and bit, causing them to turn blue and lose their
temper.

When a circular saw has a mortising attachment, the chisel is in a
horizontal position. The opposite end of the saw arbor carries a chuck
for the bit, and the motor casting has a chuck for the hollow chisel. A
table is adjustable vertically and slides in machined ways on the side of
the saw base. A fence is bolted to two T slots and can be moved crosswise.
The stock is held by the hands only against this fence. The table is moved
against the chisel, which is stationary, by means of a foot lever. A spring
returns it to its original position in the same manner as on the vertical
foot-power machines (Fig. 180).

Hollow-chisel mortisers can be used as boring machines by using
machine boring bits.

Boring machines are used a great deal in woodworking shops, especially those in which furniture and radio cabinets are manufactured.
Boring machines may have either vertical or horizontal spindles, and may
have either one or several spindles.

111. The single-spindle borer looks very much like a hollow-chisel
mortiser (Fig. 181). It has a cast-iron column, a table, and a boring head,
which in the modern machine is an electric motor. The table is wider than
that on the mortiser. It is adjustable vertically but not horizontally and

sideways. It can, however, be swung around and tilted to any angle. It has a movable back fence which can be clamped in any position on the table. A number of holes and slots are drilled in the table for fastening stops and jigs of various kinds.

The boring head is moved downward by depressing a foot pedal. A coil spring returns it automatically to its first position. Hold-down bars prevent the stock from climbing up while boring. The length of the stroke is also adjustable. Large boring machines are equipped with a power-feed mechanism which can deliver 16, 25, or 37 strokes per minute.

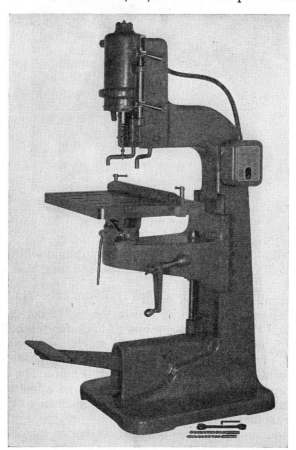

Fig. 181. Electric single-spindle mortiser

Various types of machine boring bits are shown in Figure 182. The first three are auger bits; 4 is a center bit used for boring shallow holes of large diameter; 5 is a twist bit, and 6 is a spur bit, which is especially useful for boring in cross-grained woods. Both 7 and 8 are router bits; 9 is a counterboring bit for enlarging holes, and 10, 11, and 12 are countersink bits, which bore and countersink a hole in the same operation. Number 13 is a plug cutter.

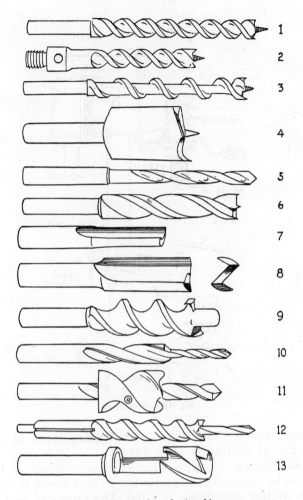

1
2
3
4
5
6
7
8
9
10
11
12
13

Fig. 182. Machine boring bits

112. The drill press formerly was used only for drilling holes in metal. A new type, however, is made which is suitable for the small woodworking shop, because it is such a versatile tool (Fig. 183). Besides drilling in metal, the following woodworking operations can be performed on it: boring, mortising, routing, shaping, planing, sanding, and grinding.

The principal parts of this type of drill press are a polished steel column, which is screwed into a cast-iron base, a table, which can be clamped to the column at any point, and a motor-driven head.

The head contains a boring spindle which revolves inside a sleeve called the "quill." The upper end of the spindle has a cone pulley, which is driven by a V-shaped belt from a corresponding pulley on a motor bolted to the rear side of the head casting. The cone pulleys give the drill press

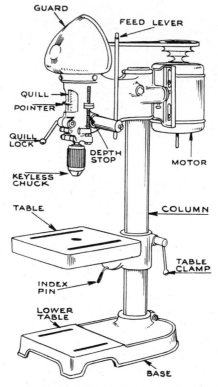

Fig. 183. Drill press

a speed range from 600 to 5000 r.p.m. Various types of spindles are furnished with the drill press (Fig. 184).

The table is of cast iron with a planed upper surface. It is slotted so that work can be clamped to it, and it has a central hole in which a pivot pin, used in routing operations, is fitted. The table can be tilted to any angle, and it can be swung all around the column.

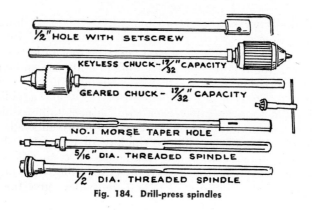

Fig. 184. Drill-press spindles

The base also is slotted, and its upper surface is planed, so that it can be used as a table when long stock has to be bored.

The size of a drill press is given as twice the distance from the center of the table to the column. If this distance is 10 in., you have a 20-in. drill press; or, in other words, stock 20 in. wide can be bored through the center.

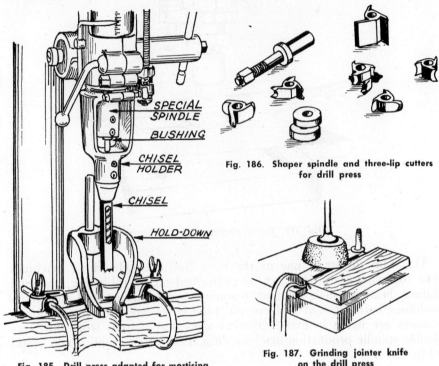

SPECIAL SPINDLE

BUSHING

CHISEL HOLDER

CHISEL

HOLD-DOWN

Fig. 186. Shaper spindle and three-lip cutters for drill press

Fig. 185. Drill press adapted for mortising

Fig. 187. Grinding jointer knife on the drill press

For mortising, a special fitting, which holds the hollow chisel, is screwed onto the quill, while the bit is held in the spindle chuck. A special fence and hold-down bars are also provided (Fig. 185).

For shaping, a special shaper spindle is clamped in a ½-in. chuck. Three-lip shaper cutters fit over the end of this spindle (Fig. 186).

Knife grinding can be done with a cup-shaped wheel as shown in Figure 187, and edge sanding can be done with spindles up to 3 in. in diameter (Fig. 188).

Planing may even be done with a device consisting of a steel disk fastened to a ½-in. arbor. Three cutters, projecting from the lower face of the disk, plane the stock placed on the table smooth and to an even thickness (Figs. 189 and 190).

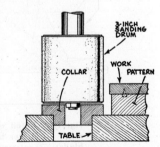

3-INCH SANDING DRUM

COLLAR

WORK PATTERN

TABLE

Fig. 188. Sanding after pattern

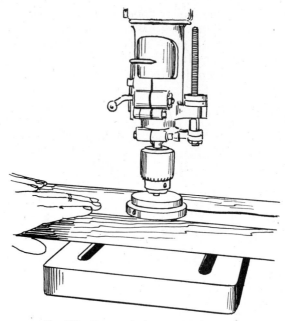

Fig. 189. Rotary planing on the drill press

113. The shaper is one of the most useful woodworking machines. The following operations can be performed on it: rabbeting, grooving, fluting, beading, sash sticking, tenoning, panel raising, and shaping of moldings both straight and curved. Like other woodworking machines, shapers are made in many different sizes and shapes, from the large, double-spindle production machine (Fig. 191) to the small bench shaper (Fig. 192).

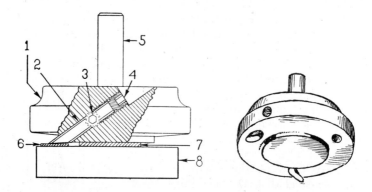

Fig. 190. Detail and sectional view of rotary planing attachment. (1) Cutter body, dia. 3⅛ in.; (2) high-speed steel cutter blades; (3) setscrew for holding blades; (4) setscrew for adjusting blades; (5) half-inch arbor; (6) .010 feeler gauge; (7) .012 feeler gauge; (8) true block

Fig. 191. Shaping after template. Stock clamped to
template

The principal parts of a shaper are a cast-iron base and a table through which the vertical shaper spindle projects. On the larger machines the table is stationary, and the spindle, which is mounted in a casting called a "yoke," can be moved up or down by means of a handwheel (Fig. 193). On some of the smaller bench machines the table can be moved vertically while the spindle remains at a fixed height.

The spindle is a steel forging and revolves in two roller bearings. On modern machines it is run at a speed of from 5000 to 10,000 r.p.m. and is, therefore, in most cases belt-driven from a motor bolted directly to the base. On account of its high speed, the bearings on larger machines are oiled by a force pump.

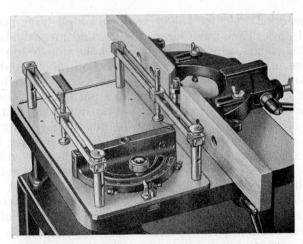

Fig. 192. Sliding jig for end-grain shaping from right side
of machine, showing stop and pointer on miter-gauge head

The spindle top is a turned steel bar which is screwed to the threaded upper end of the spindle. Spindle tops vary both in length and diameter according to the work to be done and the size of the machine used.

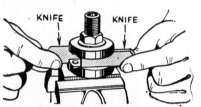

Fig. 194. Flat or open-face knives inserted between collars

Fig. 193. Yoke with belt-driven spindle

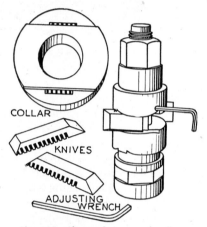

Fig. 195. Shaper knives and collars with screws. Right: assembly of collars and cutters on spindle top

Two identical flat shaper knives are used on all large machines and many small ones. They have beveled edges and are held between two round, slotted collars, which are slipped over the spindle top (Fig. 194). One or more plain, round collars are used both above and below the slotted collars, and a nut tightens up the whole assembly. While tightening the nut, the spindle is held stationary with a pin which passes through it or it can be fastened with a clamp. It is very important that the knives are exactly of the same width and that the nut is tight, otherwise one of them might work loose and injure someone. To prevent this, knives with corrugated edges and collars with corresponding screws may be used (Fig. 195). The safest type of shaper cutter is the three-lip or wing cutter which slips over the spindle top and cannot get loose (Fig. 186).

Smaller shapers usually have a fence that can be clamped to the table, as well as a sliding fence resembling the universal gauge of a circular saw. The fence clamped to the table is used for shaping straight edges and the sliding fence for shaping end wood (Figs. 192 and 196). Curved work is held against a shaper collar of the right diameter. No other fence

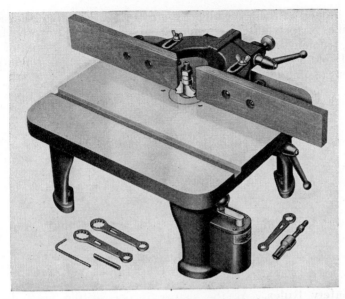

Fig. 196. Bench shaper with adjustable fence

or guide except a starting pin is used. Two rings fit in the central hole in the table around the spindle, one inside the other. Some rings have a raised edge against which curved work may be guided. Frictionless shaper collars prevent the burning of the edge of the wood, because they do not revolve (Fig. 197). Although the outside edge of shaper collars is highly polished, considerable friction is generated. Note that the spindle always revolves against the wood being cut.

Shaper cutters, either plain or milled, may also be fastened to square or round cutterheads, which can be slipped over the spindle (Figs. 198 and 199). Only a flat bevel needs to be ground on milled cutters. If this

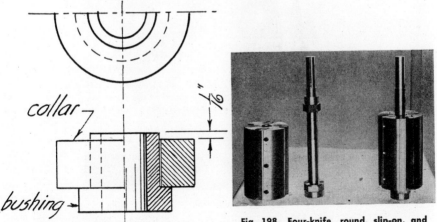

Fig. 197. Frictionless shaper collar

Fig. 198. Four-knife, round, slip-on, and screw-on cutterheads

bevel is ground at the same angle, the cutters will always be shaped exactly alike. Shaper cutters resembling grooving saws are used for door sticking, tenoning, and panel raising (Fig. 200). Various types of guards, jigs, and hold-down springs are made for the shaper and should be used whenever possible (Figs. 201 and 202).

Fig. 199. Shaper head with milled
knives

114. Safety Rules. As the shaper is one of the most dangerous machines to operate, it is important to observe the following safety rules:

1. Remove all tools and materials from the shaper table before starting the machine.

2. Be sure that the knives are of exactly the same width and weight, and that all bolts, screws, and clamps are tightened.

3. See that the spindle is free before turning on the power.

4. Use guards and hold-down bars or springs when possible.

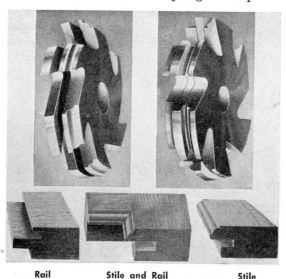

Rail   Stile and Rail   Stile

Fig. 200. Solid shaper cutters for door and window sash,
and work turned out on shaper

Fig. 201. Hold-down springs

5. Never "back up" any work, because it may be torn out of your hands. Stop the machine and start over again.

6. Roll up your sleeves, tuck in your necktie, and do not wear any loose or ragged clothing.

7. Do not take your attention off the work for one instant.

8. Check the machine every time before using it.

For portable shapers see the following Article.

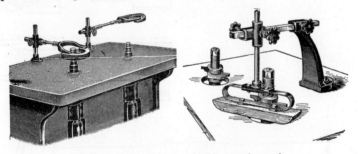

Fig. 202. Combination hold-down and guard

115. The router is one of the newest and most indispensable machines in the furniture industry, because so many operations can be performed on it. The router is used for making fine lines and grooves for veining and inlaying; it may be used for light shaping cuts, for shallow boring and mortising, and for dovetailing, fluting, grooving, etc. For pierced work it completely eliminates the jig saw, because it produces finished, shaped edges at one cut. Furthermore, rope moldings, spiral turnings, rosettes, and other decorative work can be produced on the larger machines.

The production router has a substantial cast-iron frame, whose upper part is an arm extending over the table. On some machines the router is moved down to the table, on others the table is moved up to the router. The raising or lowering is done by a treadle, and the length of the stroke is adjustable. The table can be tilted and is equipped with a fence and a steel guide pin, which is directly below the spindle.

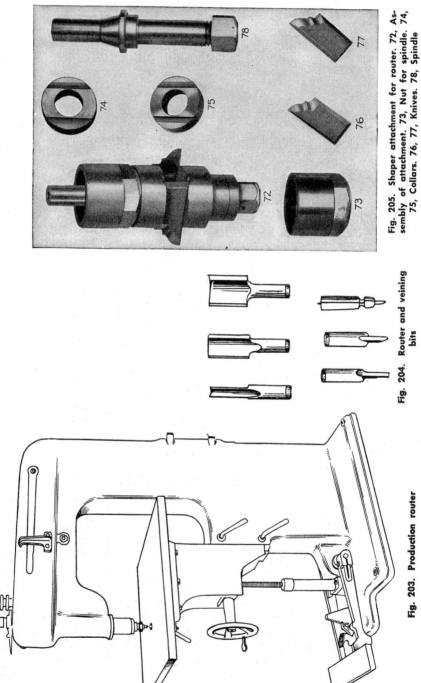

Fig. 205. Shaper attachment for router. 72, Assembly of attachment. 73, Nut for spindle. 74, 75, Collars. 76, 77, Knives. 78, Spindle

Fig. 204. Router and veining bits

Fig. 203. Production router

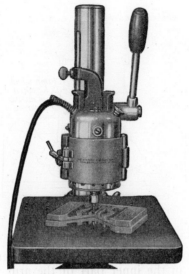

Fig. 206. Routing after pattern,
using guide pin in table

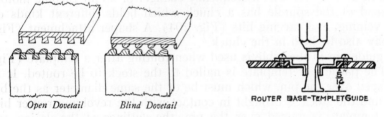

Open Dovetail   Blind Dovetail   ROUTER BASE-TEMPLETGUIDE

Fig. 207. Special bit and guides for cutting dovetails

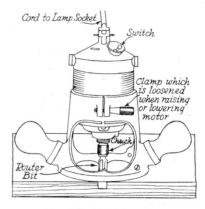

Fig. 208. Portable router

The spindle in Figure 203 is mounted in the outer end of the arm and is belted to a motor in the inner part of the arm, which drives it at a speed of from 10,000 to 20,000 r.p.m. Other router motors obtain their high speed directly through a frequency changer or an air-turbine motor.

The end of the spindle has a chuck which holds different kinds of router, veining, and carving bits (Fig. 204). A shaper attachment (Fig. 205) may also be held in the chuck.

The guide pin in the table is used when routing after a template (Fig. 206). The pattern or template is nailed to the stock to be routed. It is then placed over the pin, which must be of the same diameter as the bit in use, and the stock is brought in contact with the revolving router bit. As the template is moved over the pin, the outlines of the design are followed and reproduced exactly in the stock.

Special bits and guides are used for dovetailing (Fig. 207).

Fig. 209. Vein-line routing on flat work

Fig. 210. Guide for router and veining bits

A portable router (Fig. 208) is simply a high-speed motor, which is held in the hand while it cuts. The motor screws into an aluminum base which is equipped with guides for routing or veining along straight and curved edges. When veining lines along an irregular template, as shown in Figure 209, a follower must be used over the bit. If such a follower, or guide, is not used, there is a possibility of cutting into the template, thus ruining the entire job. A guide for this work is shown in Figure 210. Portable routers and shapers can usually be mounted on a table or arm and can be tilted to various angles (Fig. 211). Some portable routers can be used either for shaping or routing. Those with turbine motors, driven by air pressure, make as much as 50,000 r.p.m. (Fig. 212).

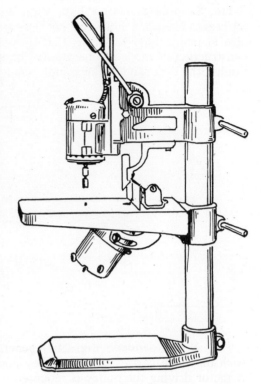

Fig. 211. Portable router and shaper attached to table

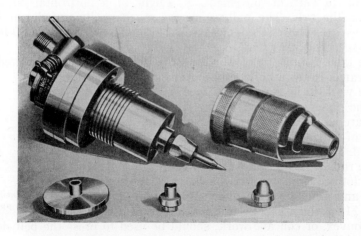

Fig. 212. Portable air-turbine router. Upper left, motor; upper right, hand router; lower illustrations, three types of pattern followers

116. Sanding machines have been developed during the past 50 or 60 years. These machines are not only made in many different sizes, but also in many different forms that do not resemble each other either in construction or mode of operation. The most common types are the belt sander, the disk sander, the spindle sander, and the drum sander.

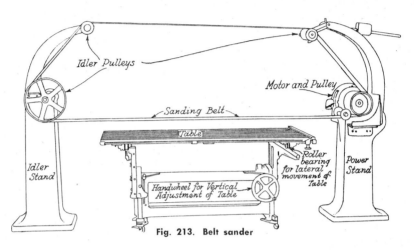

Fig. 213. Belt sander

117. A belt sander (Fig. 213) generally has two cast-iron columns, each of which carries a large pulley and a table placed between these. A motor driving the pulley is mounted on one of the posts. This post is, therefore, called the "power stand." The other post is called the "idler stand." On some machines the two pulleys, including the motor, are adjustable vertically as much as 48 in., and are moved in unison by means of a screw, bevel gears, connecting shaft, and handwheel. On others the table has a vertical movement. A weight or a horizontal adjustment tightens the belt. The pulleys on the machine illustrated run in ball bearings, are rubber faced, measure 24 in. in diameter, have a 10-in. face, and a speed of 600 r.p.m.

The table is built up of wooden strips set 1 in. apart and bolted to an iron frame. It has a horizontal movement of 36 in.

The work to be sanded is placed on the table, and the pulleys carrying the sanding belt or the table are adjusted to the right height. The belt is made of canvas to which the abrasive has been applied. It is known as garnet cloth and is sold by the roll.

Fig. 214. Pneumatic sanding pad

A cloth-covered wooden block with rounded edges and a handle, or a pneumatic sanding pad (Fig. 214) which can be inflated to conform to flat, convex, or concave work, should be used to press the belt down to the work being sanded.

Other belt sanders, called automatic-stroke sanders have a motor-

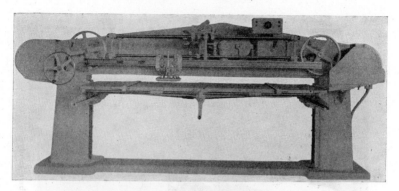

Fig. 215. Automatic-stroke sander

driven sanding block which slides back and forth on a steel bar and exerts a uniform pressure on the work being sanded (Fig. 215).

The hand-lever-stroke belt sander also has a sanding block which slides on a metal bar, but it is pushed back and forth and pressed against the sanding belt by hand.

Fig. 216. Variety sander in vertical position

Fig. 219. Portable belt sander

Fig. 217. Variety sander in horizontal position

Fig. 218. Bench belt sander

Smaller belt sanders are called *variety sanders* (Fig. 216). They have a table with a back plate between the pulleys. The machine illustrated can be operated either in a vertical or a horizontal position and it can be used both for flat and curved work (Fig. 217).

Belt sanders are also made in bench and portable types (Figs. 218 and 219). They are similar in construction to the variety sander having

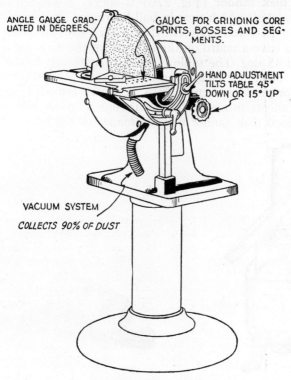

ANGLE GAUGE GRAD-
UATED IN DEGREES

GAUGE FOR GRINDING CORE
PRINTS, BOSSES AND SEG-
MENTS.

HAND ADJUSTMENT
TILTS TABLE 45°
DOWN OR 15° UP

VACUUM SYSTEM
COLLECTS 90% OF DUST

Fig. 220. Disk sander

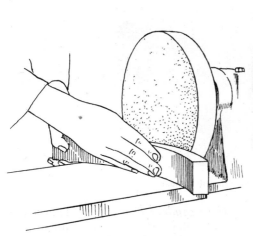

Fig. 221. Lathe disk sander, wooden table   Fig. 222. Sanding on a band saw

a flat shoe, corresponding to the table, between the pulleys. They are used mostly for sanding flat work.

118. The disk sander (Fig. 220) is simply a wooden or metal disk mounted on a shaft which runs in ball bearings. The larger machines are fastened to a cast-iron column; the smaller ones are bench machines. Disk sanders have a guard on the left side of the disk and a table which can be tilted 45 deg. The table is slotted lengthwise for an angle gauge resembling a universal gauge on a circular saw. Most machines also have a metal jig for sanding circular disks. A special cement is used for gluing the sanding sheets to metal disks, although a casein glue may be used.

A fairly good disk sander may be made for the lathe by fastening a

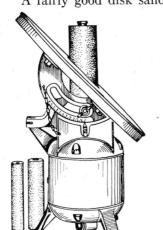

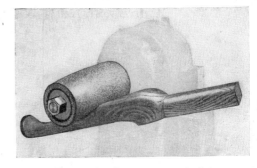

Fig. 223. Spindle sander   Fig. 224. Sanding on pneumatic drum

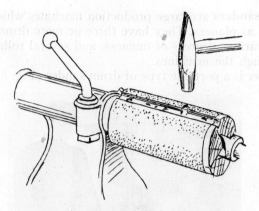

Fig. 225. Fastening sandpaper to spindle
with staples

piece of 1¾-in. stock to a faceplate, and turning it to as large a diameter as the lathe will swing. An auxiliary table may be made of wood and can be clamped to the lathe bed (Fig. 221). See also Article 258.

A small band saw may be used as a belt sander when the saw blade is replaced with a narrow sanding belt. The guides should be removed and a backing, made of wood or metal, clamped to the saw table behind the belt (Fig. 222).

119. The spindle sander is composed of a vertical spindle projecting through a horizontal table, which is supported on a cast-iron column. Steel rolls of different diameters can be fastened to the end of the spindle, which revolves at a speed of about 1700 r.p.m. and has an oscillating up-and-down movement. The table may be tilted to various angles. It may be driven by belts or by a self-contained ball-bearing motor (Fig. 223). Some spindle sanders are horizontal and have pneumatic spindles or spindles made of soft rubber. They are used for sanding irregular-shaped pieces such as chair parts (Fig. 224).

Horizontal spindles may also be turned on the lathe and covered with sandpaper. The sandpaper may be fastened with staples in a groove about ¼ in. wide and ⅛ in. deep, cut lengthwise in the cylinder (Fig. 225). Another way to fasten the sandpaper is to turn the cylinder in two halves, fold a piece of sandpaper around each half, and then screw them together (Fig. 226). See also Article 257.

Fig. 226. Split sanding spindle

120. Drum sanders are large production machines which work on the same principle as planers. They have three or more drums covered with sandpaper of various degrees of fineness, and several rollers which carry the work through the machines.

A floor sander is a portable type of drum sander (Fig. 227).

Fig. 227. Drum-type floor sander

121. Abrasives are materials for rubbing down or polishing other materials as metals, plastics, and wood. Therefore, emery wheels, grindstones, oilstones, and sandpaper are all abrasives.

In the old days, sand and a piece of wet hemp rope were used for smoothing wood and metals. Later on glass was crushed and glued to paper, hence the names of sandpaper and glass paper. Sand is broken pieces of rock, but when seen under a microscope it will be found that most of its edges are rounded by the continuous grinding against each other (Fig. 228). Other abrasives now used by the woodworker are flint, garnet, silicon carbide, and aluminum oxide.

Flint or *quartz* is the least durable and is used only on the cheaper grades of sandpaper. It is yellow in color and is found in most of the states in this country.

Garnet is a reddish-colored crystal found imbedded in rock in the

Adirondack Mountains in New York State. It is used a great deal in the woodworking industry.

Silicon carbide is produced by baking clay, sand, and coke in an electric oven. It is shiny black in color and is used for machine sanding both in the woodworking and shoe industries.

Aluminum oxide is another artificial abrasive which is also produced under extremely high temperatures in an electric oven. It is made from bauxite ore, from which aluminum is made, and other chemicals. It has a brownish color and is used both by woodworkers and metalworkers. These artificial abrasives are very hard and durable and, therefore, are used mostly for machine sanding.

All abrasives are first crushed and then graded by sifting. Some abrasive papers have only 150 particles to a square inch, while others have as many as 35,000,000, depending upon the fineness of the sandpaper. The coarsest paper is No. 3½ and the finest No. 8/0.

The abrasive particles are glued to ordinary paper or cloth. On waterproof sandpaper, used for wood finishing, the particles are fastened to the paper with varnish, which does not dissolve readily in water or oil (see Wood Finishing, pp. 357, 362, and 363).

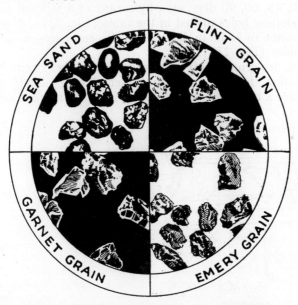

Fig. 228. Photomicrographs of the three natural abrasive grains compared with common sea sand, showing outstanding differences in shape and structure

The backing of cloth or paper, the abrasive, and the glue are all brought together in one machine. As the abrasive particles are dropped on the backing, a strong electric current is passed through them making them all stand on end (Fig. 229). Since each particle is about three times as long as it is thick, the tendency would be for the majority of the particles to lie flat if merely dropped on the backing. When the sharpest edges of the particles all stand up, the abrasive naturally cuts better. Sandpaper is made in rolls from 24 to 48 in. wide and in lengths from one to five miles.

Fig. 229. Abrasive particles standing on end after electrostatic treatment

122. The wood trimmer, although not power driven, is essentially a machine tool. It is particularly useful in the pattern and cabinet shop for cutting all kinds of angles, mitering moldings, and for segment work.

It is composed of the following main parts: a table mounted on a cast-iron column, and two knives which are moved from side to side by a pilot wheel geared to a rack (Fig. 230). Two gauges, which can be adjusted to any angle between 30 and 135 deg., are fastened to each end of the table. They can be set instantly and accurately to the principal angles as 30, 45, 60, 90 deg., etc., by means of a tapered pin which fits into corresponding holes drilled in the table (Fig. 231). A segment scale for circles from 6 to 72 in. in diameter is also engraved on the table of the larger machines (Fig. 232).

The knives are ground only on one side, and it is extremely important, when regrinding them, to keep the other side absolutely flat, as they otherwise have a tendency to work away from the stock. They are bolted

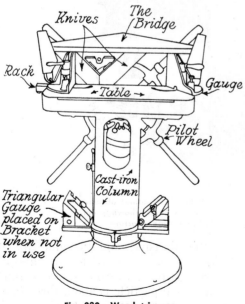

Fig. 230. Wood trimmer

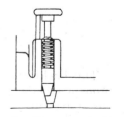

Fig. 231. Tapered pin fitting into table

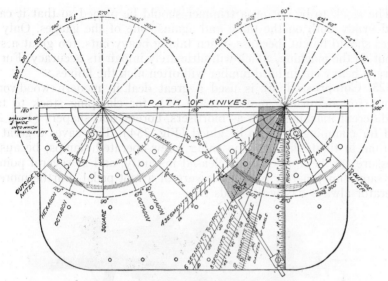

Fig. 232. Graduation of wood-trimmer table

to a carriage which slides in a groove milled at the rear edge of the table. A corresponding groove is milled in a casting called the "bridge" which supports the upper end of the carriage. A pinion on the pilot wheel engages a rack and moves the carriage from side to side. Smaller size trimmers are operated by a lever instead of a pilot wheel.

A triangular gauge, placed against one of the other gauges, is useful in trimming the shoulders of mortises and half-lap joints. Metal guards at each end of the machine cover the knives.

Fig. 233. Oscillating-bit mortiser with pneumatic clamps

The stock to be cut on a trimmer should be planed so that it can be held firmly both on the table and against one of the gauges. Only *thin* slices should be cut, because, when taking heavy cuts, too great a strain is put on the machine, which will ultimately impair its accuracy. Furthermore, a heavy cut in hard lumber will often nick the knives.

123. Compressed air is used a great deal in modern woodworking plants for air-turbine motors (page 89), for clamping stock to tables of different machines such as mortisers, borers, and shapers (Fig. 233), and for clamping stock to be glued (Fig. 234). This saves a great deal of time in tightening and loosening screw-operated clamps, because air pressure can be applied and released instantly, and at several points at the same time, merely by the pressure of a foot pedal. Furthermore, the operator always has both hands free.

Fig. 234. Pneumatic-clamp table

124. Sharpening machines are saw-filing machines, saw-setting machines, grindstones, emery grinders, and automatic knife grinders.

Of these, the first two are discussed in connection with the directions given for sharpening saws in Chapter 4.

The old-fashioned grindstone is a natural sandstone wheel, which is mounted on a troughlike iron frame. It may be driven either by belt or by coupled motor drive. The arbor of the motor has a worm gear which engages a cogwheel on the shaft of the grindstone.

Water should drip continually on the stone while it is in use. When its surface becomes glazed or filled with small particles of steel, a truing device, consisting of a corrugated roller, can be clamped to the iron frame and forced against the revolving stone, making its cutting surface as sharp as ever. For grinding chisels and plane irons the grindstone is an excellent machine tool (Fig. 235).

Emery grinders vary in design and construction all the way from the single hand-driven emery wheel to the ball-bearing, motor-driven, oilstone grinder shown in Figure 236. A machine of this type usually has two emery wheels, one coarse for rapid grinding and one fine for whetting.

The wheels are often cup-shaped, being about 8 in. in diameter and having a 2-in. face. The oil drips on the inside of the cup wheels, saturating them, and a wiper prevents the oil from being thrown off the wheels. These wheels run at a speed of 300 r.p.m.

Besides these wheels the machine illustrated carries a dry emery wheel, an emery cone for grinding gouges, and a leather stropping wheel.

The latter three wheels run at a speed of 1800 r.p.m.

The machine has a table which can be tilted to different angles, and a tool

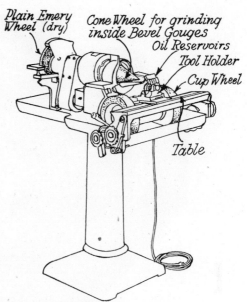

Fig. 236. Oilstone grinder

holder for chisels, plane irons, and similar cutting tools (Fig. 237). The tool holder which slides in a groove in the table has a screw-feed mechanism. Gears and wheels are fully guarded.

125. Automatic knife grinders are similar to oilstone grinders, but have a table which automatically slides back and forth at right angles to the cutting wheels (Fig. 238). With the new knife-grinding attachments on jointers and planers, these machines are not so indispensable for ordinary woodworking machinery.

The lathe is described in Chapter 13 on Wood Turning.

For further information on woodworking m a c h i n e s and

Fig. 237. Grinding a plane iron on an oilstone grinder. Kerosene drops on inside of cup wheel and filters through to the surface

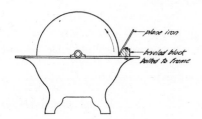

Fig. 235. Old-fashioned grindstone

Fig. 238. Knife grinder

machine operations consult the author's books *Machine Woodworking* and *Operation of Common Woodworking Machines,* both published by The Bruce Publishing Company, Milwaukee, Wisconsin.

REVIEW QUESTIONS

The Circular Saw

1. In the motor-on-arbor drive, the arbor is ....
2. How does a universal saw differ from a variety saw?
3. A circular saw with a tilting saw is superior to one with a tilting table, because ....
4. When the left part of a saw table has a lengthwise movement, ... stock .... on it.
5. The clearance block is fastened to ...., and should always be used ....
6. When ripping use the ....; when crosscutting use the .... or the ....

7. The micrometer adjustment is a part of the ....
8. A throat plate is made of ...., and is used on saws ....
9. The splitter guard is fastened ...., and is used for ....
10. A stop rod is used with .... or with ....
11. Give five reasons why a "kickback" may occur.
12. Make a sketch of a push stick, and explain its use.
13. Name and describe three types of saw blades commonly used on the circular saw.
14. The parts of a dado head are: (a) ....; (b) ....; (c) ....;
    (d) ....
15. The saw arbor has a left screw thread, because ....
16. The saw blade should project only .... above the stock being sawed.

The Band Saw

17. The gooseneck is ....
18. The rubber tires are fitted on the wheels for the purpose of (a) ....;
    (b) ....; (c) ....
19. Tracking the saw means ....
20. The guide post is clamped to .... When the clamp has been loosened a .... prevents it from sliding down.
21. A band saw has .... guides located .... Each guide has the following parts: ....
22. How is a band saw guarded?
23. Find the speed per minute of a band saw making 600 r.p.m. and having wheels 14 in. in diameter.
24. A worn throat plate should be replaced, because ....
25. How should the guides of a band saw be adjusted with reference to the saw blade?

The Jig Saw

26. The pitman movement has three principal parts: (a) ....; (b) ....;
    (c) ....
27. How is a jig saw kept under tension?
28. Describe a jig-saw guide.
29. Saber blades are used for: (a) ....; (b) ....; (c) ....

The Jointer

30. A hand plane cuts .... shavings; a jointer cuts .... shavings.
31. The speed of the cutterhead may be increased by (a) ....; (b) ....
32. The table from which the work is started is called ....; the other table is called ....
33. For rabbeting, the tables have either .... or ....
34. If the outfeed table is too low, the operator will notice that ....
35. If the outfeed table is too high, the operator will notice that ....
36. Knives of unequal weight will cause ....
37. A kickback may be caused by .... or by ....

The Planer

38. A single surfacer has .... sectional feed roll and .... smooth feed rolls.
39. The table is raised either by .... action or by ....
40. The chip breaker is located .... and prevents ....
41. The pressure bar is located .... and prevents ....
42. The feed rolls are driven by .... or by ....

43. Why is the pressure bar not sectional like the chip breaker?
44. The shortest stock that will feed through a planer is equal in length to ....
45. Boards "in wind" are first planed ...., because ....

The Swing Cutoff Saw

46. The swing cutoff saw is used principally for .... and ....
47. The swinging arm carries the .... and is suspended from ....
    or ....
48. The table under the saw is equipped with .... and ....
49. The radial saw can be used for the following operations: (a) ....;
    (b) ....; (c) ....; (d) ....; (e) ....;
    (f) ....
50. The power handsaw is used principally for ....

The Mortiser

51. Types of mortising machines are: (a) ....; (b) ....; (c) ....
52. The ram on the hollow-chisel mortiser carries .... and ....
53. The table has the following adjustments: (a) ....; (b) ....;
    (c) ....; (d) ....
54. Bushings are used on .... and ....
55. On a variety saw with mortising attachment, the bit is fastened ....
56. The hollow-chised bit differs from the regular auger bit by ....
    and ....

The Drill Press

57. Name six woodworking operations which can be performed on a drill press.
58. The quill is located .... and contains ....
59. The table is .... and .... for clamping work to it.
60. The size of a drill press is given according to ....

The Shaper

61. The yoke on a shaper holds ....
62. Flat shaper knives are held ....
63. A wing shaper cutter has .... cutting edges and ....
    in the center for ....
64. The advantage of milled cutters over flat knives is ....
65. Work with straight edges is held against ....; work with curved edges
    is held against .... or ....
66. The shaper cutter revolves .... the stock being cut.

The Router

67. List eight operations which can be done on a router.
68. The guide pin in the table is used for ....
69. A turbine motor is used for ...., and runs at .... r.p.m.
70. A portable router consists of .... and a ....
71. A follower is used over .... when ....

The Sander

72. The common types of sanding machines are: (a) ....; (b) ....;
    (c) ....; (d) ....
73. A power stand is part of ....
74. The best portable sanders are .... sanders.

75. Name six belt sanders.
76. Explain how a disk sander and a spindle sander may be made for use in a lathe.
77. Four types of abrasive papers are used by woodworkers. They are:

(*a*) .... color .... made from ....
(*b*) .... color .... made from ....
(*c*) .... color .... made from ....
(*d*) .... color .... made from ....

The Wood Trimmer

78. The knife carriage is moved by a .... or a ....
79. The "bridge" is ....
80. Too heavy cuts are likely to .... and ....

Chapter 4

THE SHARPENING OF TOOLS

The ability to sharpen tools properly is the first requisite of anyone aspiring to become a woodworker. It always pays *to take the time to sharpen tools, both from the standpoint of performance, as well as actual time saved in the execution of the work.*

A. HAND TOOLS

128. Sharpening a Saw. The process of sharpening a saw may be divided into three operations: (1) jointing and shaping the teeth, (2) setting, and (3) filing. *Jointing* is necessary only when the teeth of a saw have been worn uneven by hard use, or damaged through carelessness or accident.

1. To joint a saw, clamp it in a saw vise, and run a flat file over the teeth until every tooth is touched by the file (Fig. 242). The points of some of the teeth will now be quite flat, while others will barely be touched by the file. The best results are obtained if the file is fastened in a holder made especially for the purpose.

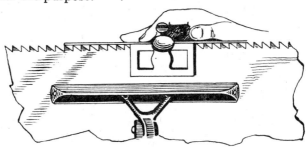

Fig. 242. Jointing a saw

2. When the teeth are of uniform height, they are filed until they are of the same size and shape. Use a 6 or 7-in. slim-taper, triangular file, and begin in the gullet next to the handle. File down into the blade, until the tooth to the right is up to a point, and half of the flat point of the tooth to the left has been removed. Start the file in the next gullet to the left, and continue until all the teeth have been filed. The file is held level and at right angles to the blade of the saw, whether the saw is of the rip or crosscut type. Make no attempt to bevel the teeth of a crosscut saw at this stage. As shaping the teeth requires experience and skill, the learner should practice on an old saw with a new one as a model in front of him.

Setting a Saw. When the teeth of a saw are all even as in a new saw,

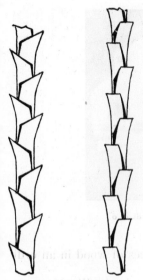

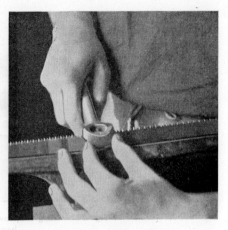

Fig. 245. Setting a saw

Fig. 243. Crosscut and ripsaw teeth properly set. Bottom view of saws

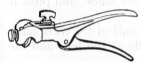

Fig. 244. Saw set

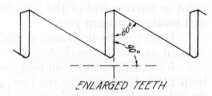

ENLARGED TEETH

Fig. 246. Enlarged ripsaw teeth

they must be bent slightly outward (Fig. 243) so that the saw kerf will be wide enough to prevent the saw from binding in the wood. This operation is called "setting," and requires a special tool called a "saw set" (Fig. 244). All saws need to be set.

3. The saw set is adjusted so that the amount of set given the teeth corresponds to the number stamped on the lower edge of the saw blade near the handle or to the number of points per inch (p. 16). Some saw sets have a metal disk or anvil varying in thickness on the edge of which several numbers indicating points to the inch are stamped. When the disk is turned until the desired number is opposite the plunger pin the teeth will be bent to the correct angle.

4. Fasten the saw in the vise, and, starting at one end, bend every other tooth in the same direction it was bent before. The teeth should be bent about two thirds from the point to the gullet. Reverse the saw, and set the other half of the teeth in the same way (Fig. 245). A saw usually can be filed several times between each setting.

Filing a Ripsaw. The teeth of a ripsaw are shaped like a series of small chisels, and should be filed straight across (Figs. 32 and 246).

5. After the saw has been set, place it in a saw vise so that the gullets of the teeth are about ⅛ in. above the jaws of the vise. If a saw vise is not

Fig. 247. Filing a ripsaw held between boards in a bench vise

available, the saw may be placed between two pieces of wood in an ordinary bench vise (Fig. 247).

6. With the handle of the saw placed to the right, begin filing from the point or narrow end of the saw. Start in the first gullet to the left of the first tooth set toward you.

7. Hold the file level and at right angles to the saw blade, and push it straight across the teeth.

8. Repeat the process in every other gullet, until half of the teeth have been filed. Then reverse the saw, placing the handle at the left, and file the other half.

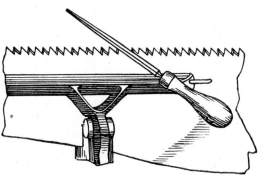

Fig. 248. Filing a crosscut saw

Filing a Crosscut Saw. The teeth of a crosscut saw (Fig. 249) are filed to a knife point. The process is the same as described for filing a ripsaw. The file is held level, but at an angle of about 60 deg. to the blade of the saw. In this way a bevel is filed on the front side of one tooth, while at the same time a corresponding bevel is filed on the rear side of the adjoining tooth (Figs. 248 and 249).

129. To Sharpen a Plane Iron. When a plane iron, gouge, chisel, or spokeshave blade has been nicked, or has been whetted on the oilstone so often that its bevel has become short, it is necessary to grind it on a grindstone or emery wheel. Ordinarily, a cutting iron may be whetted a few times before it is necessary to regrind it.

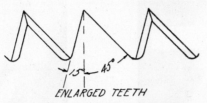

ENLARGED TEETH

Fig. 249. Enlarged crosscut-saw teeth

1. Remove the cap from the cutter iron, and grind the bevel on an old-fashioned grindstone until it is true, straight, and at right angles to the side of the iron. Move the iron back and forth across the face of the stone while grinding, and use plenty of water to prevent burning.

2. It is important that the bevel is ground flat or slightly concave, and that the iron is not burned while grinding. Burning means that the edge or part of it turns a blue-black color. When this happens, the temper of the steel is drawn or lost, and the edge will not stay sharp.

3. A device for holding chisels and plane irons steady and at the correct angle on a grindstone is shown in Figure 250. If an oilstone grinder is used, a tool holder, in which the iron is clamped, can be set to different angles and insures a straight and even bevel (Fig. 237).

4. The length of the bevel should be about twice the thickness of the tool. This gives a grinding angle of 25 to 30 deg. The tool with the holder is moved from side to side across the face of the stone. The stone should always revolve toward the tool, because it cuts faster that way and forms a smaller wire edge. Kerosene is used as a cooling liquid on oilstone grinders. On cup wheels the kerosene drops on the inside of the wheel through a small pipe (Fig. 237), and filters through to the surface of the stone.

5. It is extremely difficult to grind tools on a dry emery wheel without burning them, even though dipping them frequently in cold water. The tools should be tested for squareness of bevel with sides when they have been ground (Fig. 252).

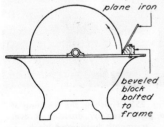

Fig. 250. Old-fashioned grindstone

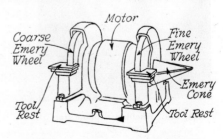

Fig. 251. A modern emery-wheel grinder

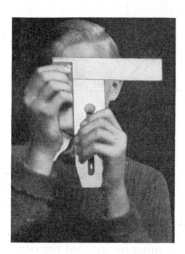

Fig. 252. Testing the edge of a
plane iron for squareness

Fig. 253. Whetting a plane iron,
bevel down

6. The wire edge formed during the grinding process is now removed by *whetting* the iron on an oilstone. Machine oil thinned with kerosene is used as a lubricant. Never use water on an oilstone, because it allows small particles of steel to be imbedded in its surface (glazing).

7. Place the bevel flat on the oilstone, raise the iron a little, and move it back and forth or with a circular motion, pressing on it with the left

Fig. 254. Whetting a plane iron,
bevel up

Fig. 255. Finishing the whetting of
a plane iron by drawing it over
a smooth hardwood block

hand (Fig. 253). Use the whole surface of the stone to wear it down evenly.

8. Reverse the iron, and place it flat on the oilstone, beveled side up. Press on it with the left hand, and move it back and forth a few times (Fig. 254). Be careful to hold it absolutely flat.

9. Repeat the process until the wire edge has been removed. This usually drops off on the oilstone and appears as a silvery thread.

10. Finish the whetting by drawing the iron a few times over a piece of leather belting which has been glued to a wooden block with the smooth side of the belting up. A smooth hardwood block without the leather will also serve (Fig. 255). Test the sharpness of the iron on the thumb nail. If the iron is sharp it takes ahold in the nail; if it is not sharp, the nail slides over it (Fig. 256).

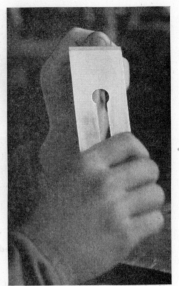

Fig. 256. Testing a plane iron for sharpness on thumb nail

Chisels and spokeshaves are sharpened in the same way.

A worn-down oilstone can easily and quickly be leveled off by rubbing it on an iron surface, using kerosene and powdered emery as an abrasive. It may also be rubbed down on a piece of level concrete with sand and water, or on a piece of coarse garnet paper.

130. To Sharpen Gouges. (1) Outside bevel gouges are ground on the outside only. Grasp the handle with the right hand, and hold the blade to the surface of the stone with the left hand. Move the gouge across the face of the stone with a rolling motion.

2. Inside bevel gouges are ground on a conical grinding wheel.

3. Both types of gouges are whetted on an oilstone having a wedge-shaped cross section and rounded edges (Fig. 270). Such a stone is called a "slip stone" (see Sharpening of Wood-Turner's Gouge, Art. 134).

131. To Sharpen and Adjust a Cabinet Scraper. (1) Grind and whet the cabinet scraper exactly as you would a plane iron (Art. 129). It is necessary to regrind the cabinet scraper every time it becomes dull.

2. Place the scraper in a vise, and bend the edge with a burnisher. Start the burnisher in contact with the whole bevel, and move it across the blade, pressing lightly. Elevate the handle of the burnisher gradually in the succeeding strokes until it forms an angle of about 15 deg. with the horizontal, and increase the pressure (Fig. 257).

An excellent burnisher can be made from an old triangular file by grinding away the teeth on a grindstone.

3. To adjust the blade in a cabinet scraper, loosen the three thumb-screws in the holder, place it on a flat wooden surface, and insert the blade from the bottom so that the bevel is toward the adjusting thumb screw in the center.

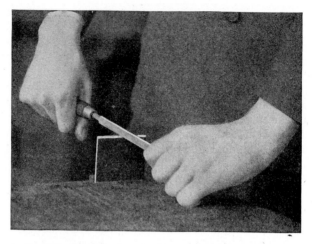

Fig. 257. Bending edge of cabinet scraper with burnisher

4. Tighten the two thumbscrews which clamp the blade to the holder, and turn the adjusting screw until it bears loosely against the blade. Turn it a fraction of a revolution at a time, until the scraper cuts a shaving of the desired thickness.

132. To Sharpen a Hand Scraper. (1) Fasten the scraper blade in the vise with one of the long edges up.

2. Grasp a triangular file with both hands, one at each end. Hold the file level and at right angles to the blade, and move it back and forth over the edge, longitudinally (Fig. 258). This method of using a file is called "drawfiling." Test the edge for flatness.

Fig. 258. Drawfiling hand scraper

3. When the two long edges have been drawfiled, the burr formed by the filing must be removed on the oilstone. Hold the scraper perpendicular to the face of the stone, and whet the edge (Fig. 259). Then place one side flat on the face of the stone moving it back and forth (Fig. 260), then the other side, and then again the edge until the burr has disappeared.

over the edge. This is done to cause the metal slightly over the
edge ( ) and so form a

Fig. 259. Whetting edge of hand scraper

Fig. 260. Whetting side of hand scraper

Fig. 261. Drawing metal over edge of hand scraper

4. Place the scraper flat on the bench near the edge and rub a burnisher over the sides in order to draw the metal slightly over the edges as in Figures 261 and 262.

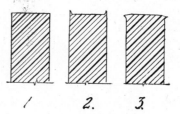

Fig. 262. Enlarged sections of hand scraper. 1. Sharpened on oilstone; 2. metal drawn over edge; 3. edges turned

5. The edges may now be turned in one of three different ways: (*a*) Place the scraper in a vise and turn the edges by rubbing a burnisher over them, tilting it slightly to alternate sides (Fig. 263). (*b*) Hold a triangular burnisher flat on the workbench and rub the scraper across it, tilting it slightly to alternate sides (Figs. 264 and 265). (*c*) Hold the scraper flat on the bench, so that its edge projects a little over the edge of the bench, and draw the burnisher slightly upward and toward you (Fig. 266). To produce an extra fine edge on a scraper, a drop of oil should be rubbed on the burnisher.

6. To resharpen a hand scraper, place it flat on the bench top, and flatten the turned-up edge carefully with the burnisher as in Figure 261. Then repeat the process described in the preceding paragraph.

A hand scraper may be resharpened with the burnisher several times before it needs to be drawfiled.

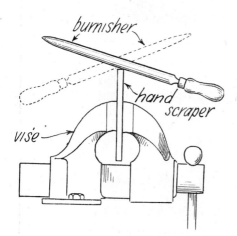

Fig. 263. Turning edge of hand scraper

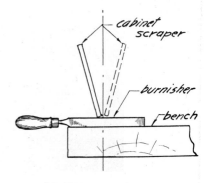

Fig. 264. Turning the edge of a hand scraper

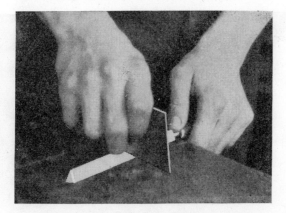

Fig. 265. Turning edges of hand scraper burnisher
on bench

133. To Sharpen an Auger Bit. (1) To sharpen the nibs, hold the bit against the side of the workbench so that the screw points upward. File the nibs on the *inside* only, with an auger-bit file, until the cutting edge is sharp (Fig. 267).

2. To sharpen the lips, rest the screw of the bit on the bench, and file the lips on the *upper* side only (Fig. 268). Remove an equal amount of material from both lips.

3. To straighten an auger bit that has been bent, roll it on a flat surface to determine where it has been bent. Strike light blows on the high side with a mallet until the bend has disappeared.

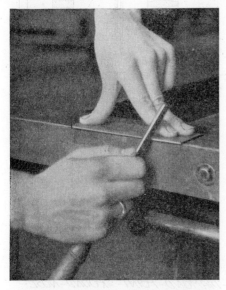

Fig. 266. Turning edge of hand scraper,
holding it flat over the edge of the bench

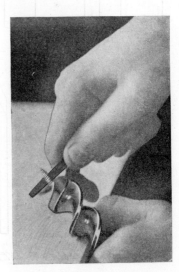

Fig. 267. Filing nibs on auger bit

Fig. 268. Filing lips on auger bit

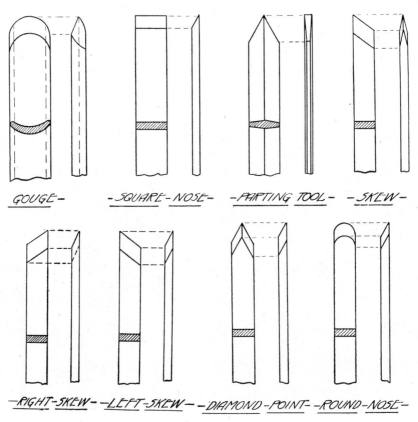

GOUGE –   – SQUARE – NOSE –   – PARTING TOOL –   – SKEW –

– RIGHT–SKEW – – LEFT–SKEW – – DIAMOND –POINT – – ROUND–NOSE –

Fig. 269. Turning tools

SHARPENING TURNING TOOLS

134. The gouge (Fig. 269), which is similar to an ordinary outside bevel gouge, is ground on a sandstone or an emery wheel.

1. The end of the gouge is ground to a semicircular shape, and the bevel should extend well around to the sides so as to leave no sharp corners as on the ordinary gouge. The bevel should be about twice as long as the gouge is thick.

2. Grasp the handle with the right hand, and hold the blade to the surface of the stone with the left hand. Move the gouge across the face of the stone with a rolling motion.

3. When the grinding has been completed, the gouge is whetted on an oilstone. The bevel is brought in contact with the stone, and the gouge moved back and forth, at the same time rolling it from one side to the other.

4. The wire edge, which is bent toward the inside by this process, is removed by rubbing the rounded edge of a slip stone back and forth over it (Fig. 270). Care should be taken to keep the whole edge of the slip stone in contact with the inside of the gouge during this operation.

135. The square-nose chisel is like an ordinary chisel, except that it is longer (Fig. 269). In fact, a common chisel, which is fairly heavy and has a long blade, may be used in its place. It is sharpened exactly in the same manner as a common chisel (Art. 129) except that the bevel should be shorter.

136. The skew chisel (Fig. 269) is ground so that two bevels are formed instead of one. The cutting edge should be at an angle of about 65 deg. with the side of the chisel. While grinding, grasp the handle firmly with the right hand, press down on the blade with the left, and hold the chisel at such an angle that the cutting edge is parallel to the axis of the grindstone or emery wheel (Fig. 271).

Fig. 270. Whetting inside of gouge with slip stone

Whet the chisel on the oilstone, and test for sharpness on the thumb nail.

137. The parting or cutoff tool (Fig. 269) has two bevels, which should be of equal length and meet in the ridge running through the center of the blade. If they do not meet at this point, which is the thickest point on the chisel, it will not cut itself free, but will bind and stick in the wood. The bevels should be ground straight and true. The wire edge is removed on the oilstone.

138. The round-nose chisel (Fig. 269) is ground very much like a gouge. As it has only one bevel, the opposite side is held flat on the oilstone in the same manner as a square-nose chisel.

139. The diamond-point or spear-point chisel (Fig. 269) is like a round-nose chisel except that it is pointed instead of rounded. It has two bevels, both on the same side of the chisel. While grinding, it should be held on the stone at an angle, so that its edge is parallel to the axis of the stone. It is whetted in the same manner as a square-nose and a round-nose chisel.

140. The right or left skew chisel or turning chisel is shaped like an ordinary skew chisel, but has only one bevel. It is sharpened like a spear-point chisel (Fig. 269).

141. To Clean a Rasp or a File. The old accepted method of cleaning files is to use fire, as follows:

1. When a rasp or file has been gummed up with particles of wood wedged between its teeth, it may be cleaned by dipping it in alcohol and setting fire to it. Hold the file by the handle, dip it into a bottle, or pour a little alcohol over it carefully. *Cork the bottle,* hold the wet file horizontally, light a match, and apply it to the file. The alcohol will burn with a small blue flame for about half a minute, and then die out.

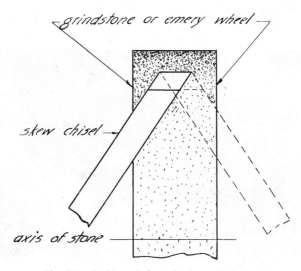

Fig. 271. Position of skew chisel on grindstone

Solid alcohol may be used instead of liquid alcohol. Hold the file in the flame for short periods at a time.

2. Brush the file with a file card (Fig. 272). This usually removes all traces of wood from the file. If the file is not clean after it has been brushed, a second application of alcohol is necessary.

Fig. 272. Brushing teeth of a file with a file card. The other side of this file card has a wire brush

In most cases, however, it is readily possible to clean files in a very satisfactory way by soaking them in hot water for an hour and then brushing them with a steel brush. The soaking swells the wood which is stuck between the teeth of the file and loosens it so that it may be readily removed with a brush. It is necessary, however, that files dry quickly to prevent rusting.

B. MACHINE TOOLS

It is even more important to sharpen machine tools than hand tools, because a dull tool driven by the force of a motor endangers the safety of the operator, is difficult to work with, and does not produce clean and accurate work.

142. Jointing Circular Saws. To joint a circular saw, lower it until its teeth barely project above the saw table. They should project just enough to score a piece of wood held flat on the table.

1. Start the saw, and pass an emery stone over the table above it. A lot of sparks will now fly. When they diminish, stop the saw and examine every tooth. If some of the teeth have not been touched by the stone, raise the saw slightly and continue jointing until every tooth has a bright point. The saw is then perfectly round.

2. Jointing is usually not done every time a saw needs sharpening, but as the job takes only a short time and the bright points help in filing a saw correctly, it is recommended to joint it often.

3. As the arbor hole is slightly larger than the arbor, the saw will not

run perfectly true unless replaced in the same position. Make it a habit to replace saws on the arbor with the manufacturer's name up.

143. Gumming a Circular Ripsaw. (1) After repeated filings, the gullets between the teeth become too shallow and clog up easily with sawdust. They must, therefore, be ground or filed down to their original depth. This operation is called "gumming" and is usually done with a thin emery wheel, mounted on a regular grinding machine, or in a lathe.

2. This grinding wheel should be about ¼ in. thick by about 8 in. in diameter. It should have a rather hard, medium grain. If it is to be used in a lathe, it is mounted on a mandrel having the same taper as the lathe center. Its other end has a small hole and runs on the dead center. The edge of the emery wheel is then shaped with an emery-wheel dresser to fit the shape of the gullets in the saw.

3. A wooden jig, as shown in Figure 273 is made to clamp to the lathe bed. The thick part is made equal to half the swing of the lathe. Its upper edge is grooved through the center and fitted with a stop block. The width of the groove is equal to the diameter of the arbor hole. A turned plug fits into the arbor hole. It slides in the groove until it butts up against the stop block. In this way all the gullets are ground to the same depth and angle.

4. Before adjusting the jig, the correct angle must be found. To do this, draw a circle halfway between the edge and the center of the saw. Then draw a tangent to this circle from any one of the tooth points (Fig. 274). This line gives the correct angle at which the front of the teeth must be ground. It is called the "rake." The lines may be drawn on the circular saw with a red pencil, chalk, or a fountain pen.

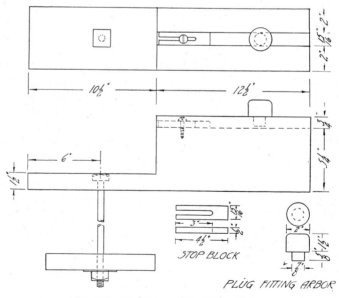

Fig. 273. Jig for gumming circular saws

5. The jig is now clamped to the lathe and the stop block is adjusted. Put a drop of oil on the dead center before starting the lathe (Fig. 275). Run it at a medium speed and be careful not to burn the saw. Crosscut saws are generally filed, but may be gummed with a very thin emery wheel.

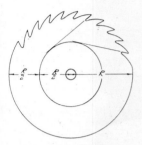

Fig. 274. Laying out the rake on a circular ripsaw

Fig. 275. Gumming a circular saw

144. Setting Circular Saws. (1) The next step in sharpening circular saws is to set or bend the teeth. Small saw blades are set with an ordinary saw set like those used for hand saws. Larger saw blades, from 10 to 16 in., are set by striking the teeth with a hammer.

2. A setting device consists of a beveled anvil fixed to a cast-iron base. At the other end is a movable pin over which the saw is placed. A cone-shaped casting fits over this pin and into the arbor hole of the saw, so that it will be accurately centered (Fig. 276).

3. The pin is then adjusted so that the outer third of each tooth projects over the beveled part of the anvil. Set every other tooth by striking a punch which is fixed above the anvil. Then reverse the saw and set the rest of the teeth. A trip-hammer saw set (Fig. 277) delivers a blow of exactly the same force every time.

4. Set only a small part of the teeth, because otherwise too much resistance to the passage of the wood will be encountered and the cut will be rough and uneven.

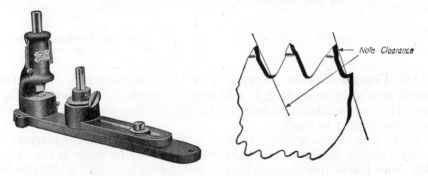

Fig. 276. Circular-saw set for smooth end trimming and work it produces

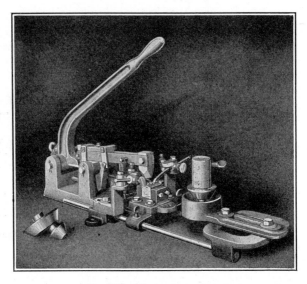

Fig. 277. Trip-hammer saw set

5. Miter saws are not set. They are hollow ground and therefore are thinner at the center than at the edge. Ripsaws over 16 in. in diameter are usually swaged like the inside cutter of a dado head. This means spreading the points of the teeth so that they will make a saw kerf wide enough to clear the rest of the saw. A tool called a saw swage (Fig. 278) is used.

Fig. 278. Saw swage

Fig. 279. Saw-filing vise for circular saws

145. Filing a Circular Ripsaw. (1) After gumming and setting, the saw is now ready to be filed. If a filing machine, such as is shown in Figure 291, is not available, a clamp for holding the saw while it is filed must be either bought or made.

2. An iron clamp or vise, as shown in Figure 279, is on the market; a wooden clamp, as shown in Figure 280, can easily be made in the shop. The front jaw of this clamp is hinged and slotted for a bolt which can be moved up or down in a similar slot in the rear jaw to which it is fastened.

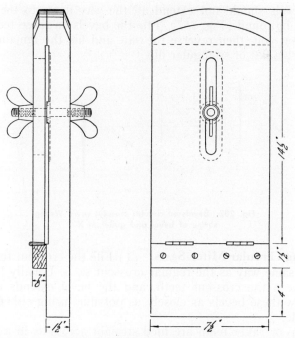

Fig. 280. Circular-saw filing clamps

In this way saws of different diameters may be accommodated. The bolt is turned from a piece of 1-in. stock and is threaded on both ends.

3. Use a flat mill file with rounded ends, hold the file level and take only light strokes. File the top of the teeth set away from you, then reverse the saw in the clamp and file the rest of the teeth. Some woodworkers prefer to bevel the teeth slightly on top.

4. If the saw has not been gummed, it is necessary first to file the front edge of each tooth. The rounded edges of the file keep the gullets round. Square gullets often cause the saw blade to crack (Fig. 281).

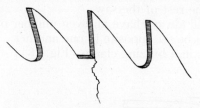

Fig. 281. Crack caused by square gullet
on circular ripsaw

146. Filing Circular Crosscut Saws. (1) As the crosscut saws have beveled edges like those of a handsaw, it is more convenient to file them when clamped in the iron saw-filing vise (Fig. 279) because that can be tilted to 45 deg.

2. The bevels should not extend all the way down to the gullets, as these should be round (Fig. 282). File the bevels on those teeth that are set away from you, then reverse the saw and file the remaining half of the teeth. Use a flat or triangular file.

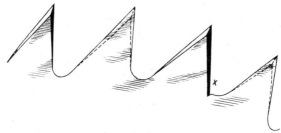

Fig. 282. Bevels on circular crosscut saws. Wrong shape of bevel and gullet at X

147. Filing Circular Miter Saws. (1) File the crosscut teeth of these saws in the same way as the regular crosscut saws. Usually there are no gullets between the crosscut teeth, and the bevel extends all the way down. Follow these bevels as closely as possible, using either a flat or a triangular file.

2. The rip or raker teeth are filed straight across as in a ripsaw, but they should be a trifle lower than the crosscut teeth. Test them by taking a shallow cut in a piece of wood. If the bottom of the saw cut is flat, the raker teeth are too high, and must be filed a little more, but if two sharp lines are scored in each side of the saw cut, it shows that the crosscut teeth are a trifle longer than the raker teeth. When the crosscut teeth are a little longer, a smoother cut will result.

148. To Braze Band Saws. (1) Straighten out any kinks or bends the saw may have received in breaking, and *scarf* the two ends to be soldered; i.e., file their sides to a taper for a distance equal to the length of one or two teeth (Fig. 283). This filing should be done carefully, so that the filed surfaces are perfectly flat and the finished joint is of the same thickness as the rest of the saw.

A band saw should always have an even number of teeth, so that succeeding teeth will all be set opposite to one another.

2. Clamp the saw in a brazing clamp (Fig. 284) so that it is perfectly

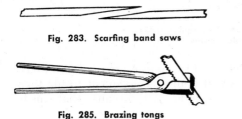

Fig. 283. Scarfing band saws

Fig. 285. Brazing tongs

Fig. 284. Brazing clamp

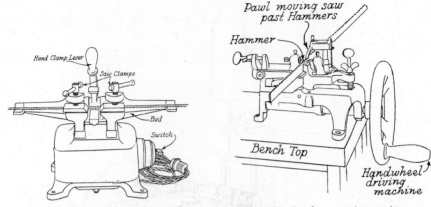

Fig. 286. Electric band-saw brazer   Fig. 287. Band-saw setting machine

aligned. Mix a little borax with water to form a paste, and coat the filed surfaces with this mixture.

This is called a "flux" which keeps the surfaces clean while the heat is applied. A specially prepared flux also may be used.

3. Cut a strip of silver solder the length of the scarf, coat it with the flux, and insert it between the surfaces to be soldered. Silver solder for band-saw brazing is manufactured in rolls of different widths.

4. Heat a pair of brazing tongs (Fig. 285) until they take a bright-red color, and clamp the joint together. The red-hot tongs heat the blade and melt the solder. Keep the tongs clamped on the saw blade until they turn black. If the joint is cooled too quickly, it does not hold. The joint also may be heated by a blowtorch, special brazing lamp, or electric current.

5. When using an electric brazer, Figure 286, the joint should be prepared and clamped as described above. When the current is turned on, heat is automatically applied to both ends of the saw blade. After a few seconds, the joint becomes red and the solder melts. The current is then turned off, and the center clamp is tightened for a few seconds to bring the ends of the joint close together. If a joint cools too quickly, as it is likely to do when the electric heater is used, it becomes very hard and brittle. To prevent it from breaking, reheat it to a dull red color.

6. Smooth the joint on both sides with a fine, flat file, then finish it with fine emery cloth.

149. Setting Band Saws. (1) Narrow band saws may be set by hand with an ordinary saw set, or by machine. Band-saw setters are either hand or motor driven. They have two hammers, which automatically bend the teeth to alternate sides, and a pawl, which moves the saw past the hammers (Fig. 287). The amount of set and pawl movement or feed is adjustable.

Fig. 288. Band-saw fitting wheels

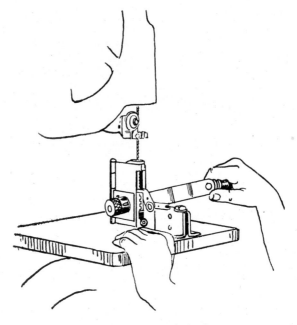

Fig. 289. Band-saw setting device for narrow
band saws

2. To use the setting machine, adjust the amount of set and the feed. Mark the point where the setting begins with chalk. Place the saw on a table or bench so that it can move freely through the machine.

Fitting wheels (Fig. 288), which are faced with leather, are very convenient for mounting the saw while it is being set or filed.

3. Another setting device for narrow band saws is shown in Figure 289. It may be clamped to the table so that the saw need not be removed from the wheels.

150. Filing Band Saws. Filing may be done by hand or by machine. Some machines do both the setting and filing operations. When filed by hand, it is very convenient to use a special vise 20 in. long in connection with the fitting wheels (Fig. 290). If this is not available, an ordinary bench vise may be used and the saw laid in the trough of the bench.

1. File the band saw straight across in the manner explained for filing hand ripsaws. Use a blunt triangular file with rounded edges, because this gives just the right hook to the front of the teeth on narrow blades. Place the file in each gullet so that it rests on the back of the next tooth, and thus files the front of

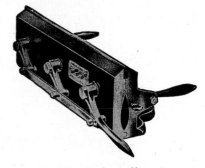

Fig. 290. Band-saw filing vise

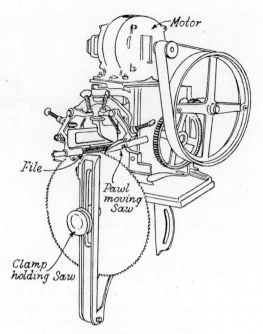

Fig. 291. Universal filing machine

one and the back of another at the same time. File all the teeth from one side of the saw.

The machine illustrated in Figure 291 can file practically any kind of saw, rip or crosscut, hand saws, circular saws, and band saws.

151. Grinding Jointer and Planer Knives. (1) On machines equipped with a knife-grinding attachment the knives need not be removed from the cutterhead. Instead, the cutterhead is locked with a pin, which brings

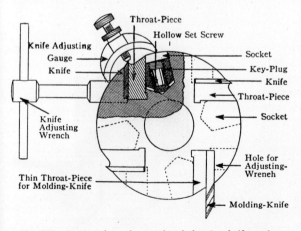

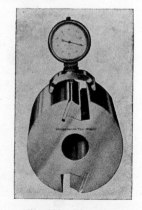

Fig. 292. Section through cutterhead showing knife-setting device

Fig. 293. Micrometer knife-setting gauge

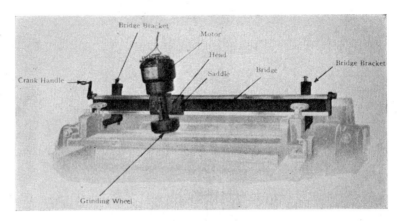

Fig. 294. Knife-grinding attachment

one of the knives into grinding position. All the bolts holding the knife are now loosened, after which it is moved up about 1/16 in. with a special adjusting wrench furnished with the machine (Fig. 292). Use the three-pronged knife-adjusting gauge or the micrometer gauge, shown in Figure 293, to set it as accurately as possible. The bolts are then tightened again and the next knife brought into position.

2. When all the knives in the cutterhead have been moved up the same distance, the grinding motor is bolted to a casting called the "saddle" which is moved back and forth on a steel bar (the bridge) by a continuous screw (Fig. 294).

3. Adjust the motor so that only a very light cut is taken and move it back and forth over the knife several times. Be careful to move it fast enough so that the knife is not burned. Repeat on the other knives, lock-

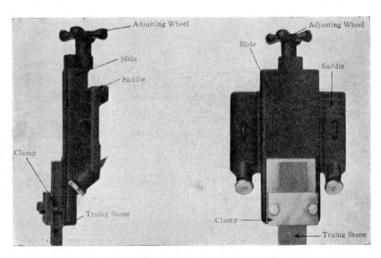

Fig. 295. Knife-setting and jointing attachment

ing the cutterhead with the pin, so that each one in turn is held firmly in the correct grinding position.

4. When the first knife is again brought into position, the motor is lowered slightly and again moved several times over the knife. Repeat on the other knives and lower the motor each time all the knives have been gone over until all nicks have been ground away and a perfect bevel has been obtained on every knife in the cutterhead.

5. Remove the motor from the saddle and bolt a jointing attachment to it. A jointing attachment has a fine whetstone clamped to its lower end which can be adjusted vertically by a screw (Fig. 295).

6. Set it so that it barely touches the knives. Revolve the cutterhead by hand to make sure, then start the machine and move the jointing attachment back and forth over the revolving knives.

7. Stop the machine and examine the knives. If they have not all been touched by the whetstone, move the stone down slightly and repeat the process. Be careful not to joint the knives too much, otherwise a rounded surface or "heel" will be formed behind the cutting edge. Too much heel is likely to cause the knives to pound, heat up, and produce a glazed surface. If this should happen, the heel may be ground away with a small portable grinder (Fig. 296) without touching the edge.

8. Knives on older or smaller machines which are not equipped with a knife-grinding attachment, have to be removed from the cutterhead for grinding. Knife-grinding machines have a carriage, which slides on a fixed bed and moves back and forth in front of a grinding wheel. The movement of the carriage is automatically reversed at each end of the bed so that the machine can be left running with only occasional adjustment (see Fig. 238).

Fig. 296. Removing the heel on molded knives with a portable grinder

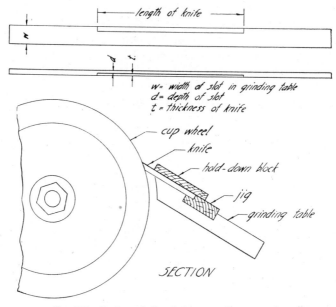

Fig. 297. Jig for grinding knives on oilstone grinder

9. The knife to be ground is clamped to the carriage and adjusted to the correct grinding bevel, which is from 30 to 40 deg. A pump sends a continuous stream of oil over the knife to cool it.

10. If a special knife grinder is not available, an oilstone grinder, as shown in Figure 236, may be used for grinding thin knives up to 12 in. in length.

11. A simple jig, as shown in Figure 297, consists of two sticks of close-grained hardwood such as birch or maple. One stick, which slides in the

Fig. 298. Grinding jointer knives on oilstone grinder

slot in the table, has a recess cut for the knife. The other is simply used to hold the knife against the stone and protect the fingers from the heat generated by the grinding (Fig. 298). This stick may be fastened to the first one with a couple of brads or small screws.

12. When all the knives have been ground, they are weighed on a special knife balance or scale (Fig. 299). If the knives are not exactly of

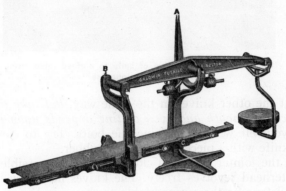

Fig. 299. Knife balance

the same weight, they will cause the cutterhead to vibrate and run noisily. This will produce an uneven cut and ultimately damage the bearings. If one or more knives, therefore, are too heavy, they must be reground until their weight equals that of the lightest knife.

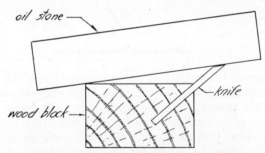

Fig. 300. Slotted wooden block for whetting jointer knives

13. Whetting is done on an ordinary flat oilstone. A jig, as shown in Figure 300, is helpful in whetting the beveled side. The flat side is whetted just like a plane iron.

14. To replace the knives in the cutterhead of a jointer, place a build-ers' level or a piece of hardwood with a straight edge on the outfeed table and line up the knives with it (Fig. 301). Screw the bolts in lightly and revolve the cutterhead by hand. If the knife lifts or moves the level, it is too high and must be tapped with a mallet to lower it. When the knife barely touches the level, it is at the correct height and the bolts should be tightened.

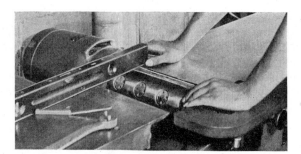

Fig. 301. Adjusting height of knife to outfeed table, using level or straightedge

15. Adjust the other knives in the same way, *but take time to do the job well, because smooth and even cutting depends upon it.* Be careful not to cut yourself when tightening the bolts. Try to cover the sharp edge of the knife with a piece of leather or rubber.

16. Move the jointer tables as close together as possible, but be sure that the cutterhead revolves freely. The knives may now be jointed by holding an oilstone on the outfeed table as shown in Figure 302. Wrap a

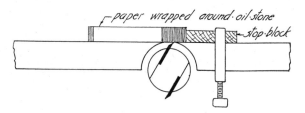

Fig. 302. Jointing knives on jointer

piece of paper around that part of the stone resting on the outfeed table, then bring the infeed table up to the same height and clamp a stop block to it. Turn on the power, hold the stone with both hands, and move it across the tables, pressing lightly on it. This will bring the knives to the exact cutting circle so that each one will do the same amount of work.

17. Similar jigs may be made for trimmer knives, which are sharpened in the same way.

152. Sharpening Shaper Knives and Router Bits. (1) Flat shaper knives with straight cutting edges are sharpened just like plane irons and chisels.

2. Flat shaper knives with curved cutting edges may be sharpened with various-shaped small emery wheels or with a grinding pencil (see Fig. 296) which can be held in the chuck of a portable router. A grinding pencil is an abrasive stone, shaped like a pencil point. The shape of the curves must first be carefully laid out from templates.

3. Three-lip shaper cutters also can be sharpened with a grinding pencil or small grinding wheels held in a router chuck. An attachment for holding the cutters while grinding them is made for some routers (Fig. 303).

Fig. 303. Grinding attachment for shaper cutters and bits for portable router or shaper

4. Milled shaper cutters (Fig. 199) are sharpened simply by grinding a flat bevel on them.

5. Router bits are sharpened on the inside with a special grinding wheel which fits in the chuck of a portable router.

153. Sharpening Hollow Chisels. (1) When hollow chisels become nicked or cracked, they can be reconditioned by grinding away the damaged part.

2. The square end produced as at A, Figure 304, is then milled out as at B. This may be done on a hand operated milling machine which has a clamp for holding the chisel in a vertical position while a milling cutter is rotated in its end (Fig. 305). Since the milling cutter has a pilot which fits the bore of the chisel, a different cutter must be used for each size chisel.

3. A wooden cone may also be turned in a lathe and covered with sandpaper. The cone is fastened to a screw chuck mounted on the live spindle and the upper end of the chisel is held on the dead center, which is gradually moved forward as the grinding progresses (Fig. 306).

4. The corners are then filed with a small triangular or auger-bit file as shown at C, Figure 304. Finally, remove the burrs by whetting the chisel on an oilstone.

5. If the chisel is not damaged but merely dull, it may be sharpened on the inside with a grinding pencil and file.

When grinding wheels clog up with particles of steel, oil, and dirt, they can be cleaned with one of three dressing tools: a diamond set in the end of a steel rod, a number of star-shaped wheels placed side by side

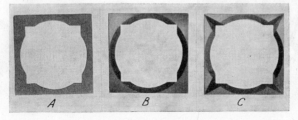

Fig. 304. End views of a mortising chisel. A, Ground flat; B, reamed; C, corners filed

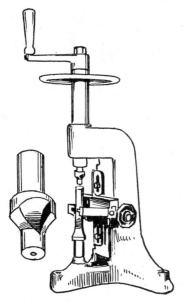

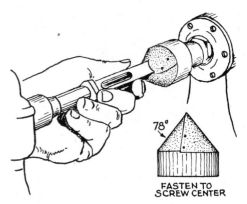

Fig. 306. Sanding cone for sharpening hollow chisels mounted in lathe

Fig. 305. Machine and milling cutter for sharpening hollow chisels

in a steel holder (emery-wheel dresser), or hard, abrasive stones, plain or circular (Fig. 307). Soaking in kerosene or heating in an oven cleans the wheel of dirt and oil. *When dressing or shaping an emery wheel, be sure to wear goggles.*

Rust Remover. A solution made from the following simple and inexpensive ingredients removes rust from tools and machines very readily: 1 cup lye, ½ cup washing soda, and ½ teaspoon potassium permanganate dissolved in 1 quart of water. Apply the solution liberally to the surface to be cleaned. Small tools may be placed in a large, flat glass tray, such as is used by photographers, and covered with the solution.

Fig. 307. Emery-wheel dressers

REVIEW QUESTIONS

A. Hand Tools

1. A handsaw is jointed with .... when the teeth ....
2. What is the difference between shaping and sharpening the teeth?
3. What is understood by the terms "set," "saw kerf," and "points to the inch"?
4. When filing a ripsaw, start the file ....
5. When filing a crosscut saw, hold the file ....
6. A grindstone or emery wheel should always revolve .... the tool.
7. What is understood by "burning" a tool?
8. When whetting a plane iron after grinding, ... is removed.
9. The length of a bevel should be equal to ....
10. When a plane iron has been sharpened, it should be tested for ....
    and ....
11. A gouge is whetted on the inside with a ....
12. How can the worn surface of an oilstone be made flat?
13. Kerosene should be used on an oilstone, because water ....
14. The edge of a handscraper is ....; that of a cabinet scraper is ....
15. The tool used for turning the edges of scrapers is called a ....
    It may be made from ....
16. An auger bit is sharpened on ....,......
17. Wood lodged between the teeth of a file may be removed by ....
    or ...., and then ....
18. How does a turning gouge differ from an ordinary gouge?
19. When grinding a skew chisel, hold it ....
20. A parting tool is ground ....

B. Machine Tools

21. It is important to sharpen machine tools because (a) ....;
    (b) ....; (c) ....
22. The four sharpening operations on a circular saw are: (a) ....;
    (b) ....; (c) ....; (d) ....
23. The rake of a tooth is ....; the gullet is ....
24. Square gullets are likely to cause ....
25. Circular saws may be set by (a) ....; (b) ....; (c) ....
26. The raker teeth on a miter saw must be .... than ....
    to prevent ....
27. Why are miter saws neither set nor swaged?
28. Scarfing a band-saw blade means ....
29. A flux prevents .... when ....
30. The metal used for brazing a band saw is ....; the flux is ....
31. Why should a band saw have an even number of teeth?
32. The teeth of a band saw are all filed .... side.
33. The saw may be heated for brazing with (a) ....; (b) ....;
    (c) ....
34. A knife-grinding attachment on a planer enables the operator to ....
    and .... knives without .... the machine.
35. Knives of uneven weight cause ....
36. Jointer knives are set to correct height in the cutterhead by using a ....
    or ....
37. Jointer knives removed for sharpening may be trued to exact cutting
    circle by ....

38. Common types of shaper knives are: (*a*) ....; (*b*) ....;
    (*c*) ....; (*d*) ....
39. A cracked, hollow mortising chisel may be reground with a ....
    or ....
40. Emery wheels may be cleaned or shaped with (*a*) ....; (*b*) ....;
    (*c*) ....

Chapter 5

PLANING AND SQUARING TO DIMENSIONS

Planing and squaring to exact dimensions is the ABC of all good woodwork. It must be thoroughly mastered before any other process can be undertaken successfully.

Fig. 313. Clamping a board for surface planing

156. To Square Small Boards to Dimensions. (1) Select the better of the two wider sides, and clamp the board end to end between the vise dog and a bench stop (Fig. 313). Never clamp a board side to side, because the pressure will bend it. If it is then planed so that it is flat, it will spring back when the pressure is released and will be curved. If the sides have been planed, it usually can be seen in which direction the face should be planed by observing the edge grain (Fig. 314). Note that

Fig. 314. Opposite surfaces are planed
in opposite directions

opposite surfaces are planed in opposite directions. Set the plane to cut a fine shaving, plane off just enough to clean off the surface, and make it perfectly flat. Test this surface with the try square, holding it lengthwise, crosswise, and diagonally at several points. This surface is called the "working face" (Fig. 315).

137

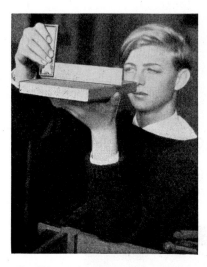

Fig. 315. Testing flatness of a surface with a try square

Fig. 317. Testing edge for squareness with a try square, holding the handle of the square firmly against the working face

2. Select the better of the two edges, and plane it until the surface is true and square to the working face. This edge is called the "working edge." Mark the working face and working edge with a pencil (Figs. 316 and 317).

3. Set a marking gauge to the desired width. With a rule measure the width from the spur of the gauge to the block. Hold the block of the marking gauge against the working edge, and mark a line on the working face, pushing the gauge away from you.

If the width of the board is more than 5 or 6 in., the marking gauge cannot be used. If a panel gauge is not available, measure the width with a ruler at two points, one near each end. Then, draw a pencil line, along a straightedge, through these two points.

4. Chisel off a corner outside the gauge line (Fig. 318), and plane the better end square to both working face and working edge (Figs. 319 and 320). The corner is chiseled off to prevent the wood from splitting when

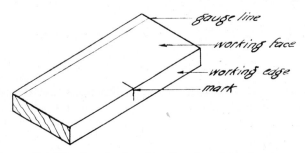

Fig. 316. Squaring board to dimensions. Steps 1 to 3

Fig. 318. Chiseling off a corner to prevent
splitting when planing end grain

Fig. 319. Testing end for squareness
from working edge

Fig. 320. Testing end for squareness
from working face

Fig. 321. Planing end wood. Corner cut off to
prevent splitting

planing end grain (Fig. 321). Plane from the working edge toward the unfinished edge. Never chisel off a corner on the working edge.

5. Measure the length of the piece from the end just planed, and square lines all around, using the try square and a knife or sharp pencil (Fig. 322).

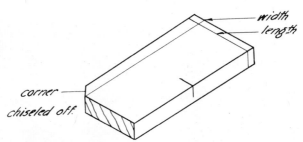

Fig. 322. Squaring board to dimensions. Steps 4 and 5

6. Saw off the surplus lumber outside this line, using a bench hook, or clamping the piece in the vise. Chisel off the corner as before, and plane this end to the line marked, so that it is square to both the working face and the working edge.

7. Plane the edge opposite the working edge to the gauge or pencil line, and square to the working face.

8. Gauge the thickness from the working face on both edges and ends (Fig. 323).

9. Plane the last face, opposite the working face, to these gauge lines.

In cases where the board is very narrow or already has the desired width, splitting of the end wood may be prevented if a piece of wood is placed in the vise behind the edge while planing the ends (Fig. 324).

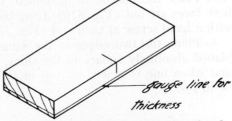

Fig. 323. Squaring board to dimensions. Step 8

157. To Joint Boards for Gluing. (1) Wide surfaces, such as table tops, are built up of two or more boards, whose edges are jointed and glued together. After enough boards have been cut to length to form the width, it is a good plan to arrange them so that the better surfaces of all are up and so that the grain, if possible, runs in the same direction and forms pleasing patterns.

Fig. 324. Planing end of narrow piece of wood

2. Mark the direction of the grain and the edges to be joined together. The faces are usually not planed until after the boards have been glued (Fig. 325).

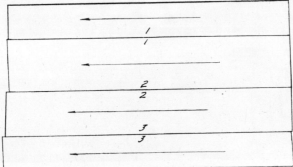

Fig. 325. Arranging boards for jointing

3. Place the boards to be joined, two and two, in the vise, so that both faces are out (Fig. 326). Long boards are further clamped together with a hand screw at each end (Fig. 327).

4. Plane the two edges at the same time. Even if the edges are not planed absolutely square to the sides, the angles of both are still equal, and when one is placed on top of the other (Fig. 326), the faces will be in line.

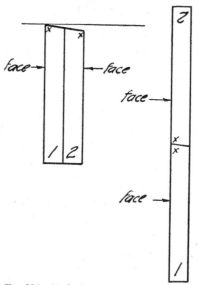

Fig. 326. Method of jointing two boards

5. It is of the utmost importance that the edges of both boards make a good joint at both ends, because wood dries faster at the ends, and, therefore, shrinks more rapidly, causing the joints to open. For this

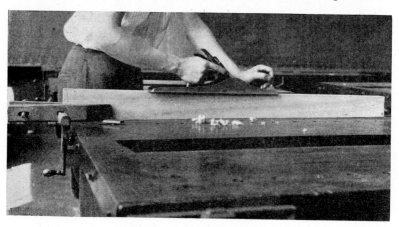

Fig. 327. Holding long boards in vise

Fig. 328. Testing an edge-to-edge joint before gluing

reason, it is advisable to plane the edges of the boards in such a way that when one is placed on top of the other the joint will be closed at both ends, but there will be a slight opening in the center.

6. If a single clamp is put on the boards in the center, they should come together over-all and the two ends should be tight (Fig. 328).

7. The other edges are jointed in the same way, two and two.

Directions for gluing are given in Article 216.

158. To Square a Table Top. (1) Select the better face, remove any surplus glue with a chisel, clamp the table top securely to the top of the bench, and plane it *across the grain*. Start planing at one end, continue toward the other end, and repeat (Fig. 329). It may be necessary to plane a small chamfer on the farthest end to prevent splitting.

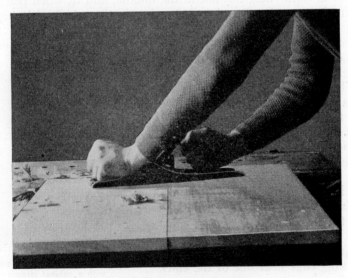

Fig. 329. Planing across the grain

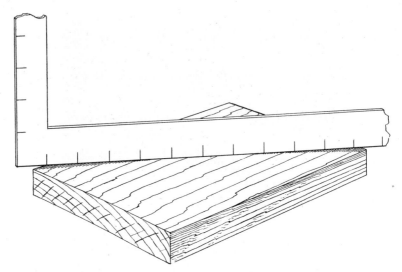

Fig. 330. Testing a board in "wind" with a steel square

Planing across the grain is especially recommended when working with cross-grained woods, like birch or mahogany, as it prevents tearing up the grain. Straight-grained woods, like white pine or cypress, may be planed lengthwise from the beginning of the work. Planing a surface across the grain is a good method of quickly evening it up and reducing it to size.

2. Test the surface frequently lengthwise, crosswise, and diagonally with a framing square (Fig. 330). If, when placing the square diagonally, it touches at both ends, but not in the middle, and if, when placed diagonally in the opposite direction, it touches in the middle, but not at the ends, it is an indication that the board is warped or in "wind." This is remedied by planing the board in the diagonal direction first mentioned, when the square touches at both ends, but not in the middle.

3. When the surface is true over-all, it is planed lengthwise just enough to remove the marks of the cross planing. Use a very sharp cutter, and set it to cut a fine shaving.

If the wood is very cross grained, it should be scraped with a cabinet scraper instead of planed (Fig. 331).

4. Plane the better edge true and square to the face, and test it as in Figures 332 and 333.

5. Square a line across the face from the working edge near one of the ends, using a framing square.

Fig. 331. Smoothing a flat surface with a cabinet scraper

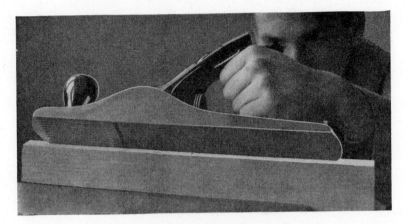

Fig. 332. Testing edge for straightness with plane

6. Saw off any surplus wood, and plane this end square to the working face and the working edge. Do not plane all the way across the end, but plane part way from both edges. Test for squareness with a framing square. Hold large boards while planing as shown in Figure 327. Clamp one side or end in the bench vise and support the other by fastening a hand screw to it and letting it rest on the bench top.

7. Measure the length from the squared end, square a line across the working face from the working edge, saw off the surplus wood, and plane the other end to the line in the same manner as the first one was planed (Fig. 334). Test for squareness with a steel square held against the working edge.

8. Measure the width at both ends, connect these points with a pencil line, and plane the other edge.

Fig. 333. Testing edge for squareness with try square

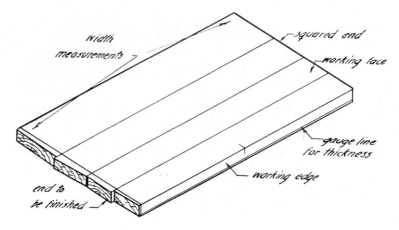

Fig. 334. Squaring a table top

9. Gauge the thickness on both edges and ends from the working face.

10. Fasten the board face down to the top of the workbench, and plane the last face or underside to the gauge lines, as explained in steps 1, 2, and 3.

159. To Make and Square a Table Top, Using Machine Tools. (1) Cut the number of boards, which are needed to make up the top on the swing cutoff saw, allowing about ½ in. on the length for squaring.

2. If the boards are not absolutely straight, but are a little in "wind," plane one of the faces of each board on the jointer until it is perfectly flat. Mark the direction of the grain on each board. Then plane the two edges square to this face, except on the outside boards, where only one edge needs to be planed.

3. Run all the boards through the planer to bring them to an even thickness. Remember that the grain runs in opposite directions on opposite surfaces.

4. Place the boards together, taking into consideration the matching of the grain and the direction in which it runs (Art. 157 and Fig. 325). Number the edges to be glued together.

5. Glue and clamp according to directions given in Article 216.

6. After the glued top is dry, plane it on the planer. Notice the direction of the grain, and take a light cut the first time. When this surface is smooth, reverse the top, and plane the other surface. Continue planing until the top has been reduced to the required thickness.

7. Plane one edge on the jointer, measure the length, and square lines across both ends. If the top is too large to be cut across on the circular saw, it may be cut on the band saw. If several tops are to be sawed, it will be worth while to make a jig of two boards nailed together as shown in Figure 335. The lower and narrower one should be a little thicker than the top to be sawed. Clamp the jig to the band-saw table so that the upper board touches the saw blade, then nail a strip of wood along the line

squared across the table top. When this strip is held against the jig, a perfectly straight saw cut will be made.

8. The ends may be squared on the jointer. Begin planing from the squared edge, take a light cut, and push the board slowly across the cutterhead. The grain may tear a little on the edge yet to be finished.

9. If the top has been planed to width, the end-planing should be stopped ½ in. from the last edge and this piece finished by hand. Never end-plane a board less than 12 in. wide.

10. If the top is not too wide, it may be ripped to width on the circular saw. In this case, the ripping fence is set to the proper width, and the top run through without further measurement.

11. When the top is wider, the width is measured from the planed edge, and a pencil line is drawn from one end to the other. The waste is sawed off on the band saw, and the edge planed on the jointer.

12. The top may now be sanded smooth on a belt sander, or with a portable sander. No hand planing or scraping is necessary when a sanding machine is available.

160. To Square Legs for Tables and Cabinets. (1) Cut the legs (usually four) to dimensions, allowing sufficient material for squaring. If the lumber is free from defects, from 1/16 in. to ⅛ in. on each side should be sufficient. For example, a leg that should measure 1½ in. square when finished, should be at least 1⅝ in. in the rough. It is well to allow ½ in. on the length.

2. Select the best two adjoining sides on each leg, and plane them true and square to each other. Test each surface planed for "wind" by placing it on a level surface (Fig. 336). Mark the sides squared.

3. When two faces have been squared on each leg, the marking gauge is set to width, and lines are gauged on all legs with the same setting of the marking gauge (Fig. 337).

4. The remaining sides are then planed to the gauge lines square to

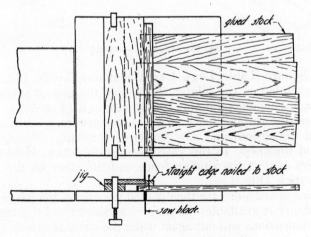

Fig. 335. Trimming ends of glued-up stock

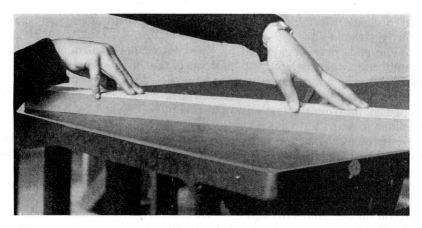

Fig. 336. Testing for "wind"

the first two sides planed. The ends are usually cut to exact length in a miter box.

5. Turned legs having square sections should be planed to finished dimensions in the same way and cut to length before they are put in the lathe. It is important to center them carefully, otherwise the square parts will be out of line.

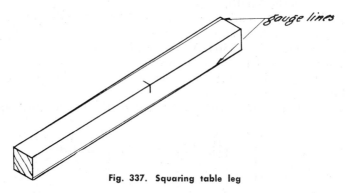

Fig. 337. Squaring table leg

161. To Square Table Legs, Using Machine Tools. (1) Plane one surface of each leg on the jointer. Then hold the planed surface against the fence and plane one adjoining side square to it (Fig. 338).

2. Now set the ripping fence on a circular saw to 1/32 in. more than the finished dimension, and saw the two remaining sides on each leg to width and thickness. In this case they are the same. Hold one of the squared sides against the ripping fence and the other on the saw table. Use a push stick (Fig. 130).

3. The two sawed sides are then planed smooth on the jointer.

4. If a planer is available, the unfinished sides can be planed directly to finished dimensions without again using the circular saw or the jointer.

5. In either case, the ends are squared and sawed to length on the

circular saw. First square one end on all the legs, using the universal gauge and cutting off as little as possible. Then clamp the stop rod in the universal gauge, adjust the stop and, holding the squared ends against it, saw all the legs to correct length.

162. **To Taper Square Legs for Tables and Cabinets.** (1) After the legs have been squared, as explained in Article 160, the part to be tapered is measured off and a pencil line squared all around each leg.

2. A marking gauge is then set to the amount of the taper, as for example ¼ in., and four lines are gauged on the end of each leg. The lines of taper are then drawn on two opposite sides with a straightedge from these points to the pencil lines (Fig. 339).

3. If the amount of material to be removed is considerable, it is advisable to saw it off before planing the sides true to the lines.

4. When two opposite sides have been tapered, the taper lines are laid out on the remaining two sides, and the processes are repeated.

163. **To Taper Square Legs for Tables and Cabinets on the Circular Saw.** (1) Suppose the legs are to be 2 in. square and 30 in. long; plane two adjoining edges on the jointer, set the ripping fence on the circular saw to 2 in. full, and rip with the planed edges always against the fence.

2. If the taper is to be ¼ in. on each side and begins 5 in. from the top, make a jig as shown at A, Figure 340. The notches, as will be seen, are ¼ in. each.

3. Square a line all around each leg 5 in. from the top. Place the other end of the leg in the inner notch as shown at B. Measure the combined width of the leg and jig, in this case 5 in., and set the ripping fence accordingly.

4. Rip two adjoining sides, then place these successively in the other notch, and rip the remaining two sides. The leg is now tapered equally on all four sides. Use the splitter guard to prevent the stock from being caught by the back teeth of the saw.

5. Smooth the legs with a cabinet scraper, or a belt or portable sander.

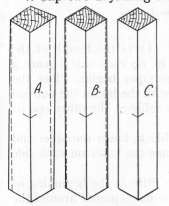

Fig. 338. Steps in squaring table leg on jointer and circular saw. A, Two adjoining sides planed square to each other; B, sawed on circular saw to within 1/16 inch of finished dimensions; C, sawed sides planed to finished dimensions

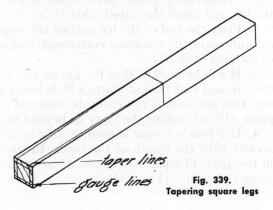

taper lines

gauge lines

Fig. 339.
Tapering square legs

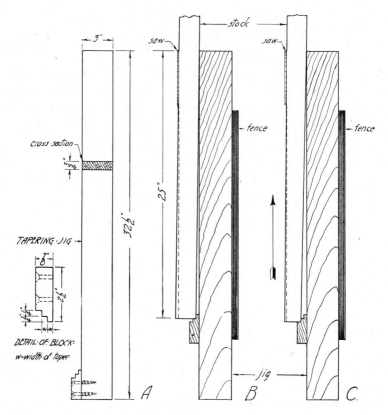

Fig. 340. Tapering table legs on a circular saw

164. To Taper Table Legs on a Jointer. (1) If the length of the taper is 25 in. and the leg is to be tapered ¼ in. on each side, square a line all around one leg at the point where the taper begins. Place the leg on the infeed table so that this line is even with the lip on the outfeed table. Then clamp a stop block to the fence or table at the other end of the leg, and lower the infeed table ¼ in.

2. Place the end of the leg against the stop block, lower the other end carefully over the revolving cutterhead, and plane the taper on each side of each leg (Fig. 341).

3. It will be noticed that the knives dig in a little at the beginning of the cut, and that the cut starts a little below the line squared around the leg. This unevenness can easily be removed with a few strokes of a hand plane without making the taper go beyond the line marked.

4. If a bench jointer is used, it may be found that the infeed table is shorter than the length of the taper. In such cases the taper is divided in two parts of equal length and a line is squared around the leg at this point (12½ in.) (Fig. 342).

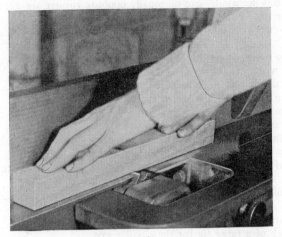

Fig. 341. Tapering leg using hand screw as stop block

5. Lower the table to half the amount of the taper (⅛ in.), and plane the lower half of the taper first. Then, with the same setting, make a second cut the full length of the taper. The leg will now have a ¼-in. taper, 25 in. long.

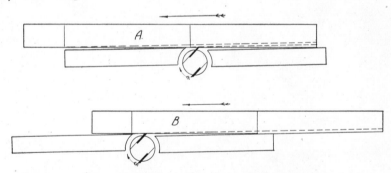

Fig. 342. Tapering long leg on small jointer. A, Cut started at middle of taper. B, Taking finish cut the full length of the taper

REVIEW QUESTIONS

1. When planing a narrow board, the grain may be prevented from splitting by .... or by ....
2. When squaring a small board, it should be planed to length before it is planed to width, because ....
3. The boards for a table top should be arranged according to .... The edges should be .... before gluing.
4. What is the advantage of jointing two edges at the same time?
5. When trying the fit of two jointed edges, why is it best to have a fine opening show in the center?
6. A cross-grained table top should be planed .... Afterward it is smoothed with a ....

7. When a board is in "wind," two diagonally opposite corners are .... and the other two ....

8. The uneven ends of a glued-up table top may be sawed off straight on a band saw by ....

9. When planing endwood on the jointer, the cut should be stopped .... and finished with ....

10. End-planing should not be done on a board narrower than ....

11. When planing a table leg it is tested for "wind" by ....

12. Turned legs with square parts should be .... and .... before they are put in the lathe.

13. When squaring legs on woodworking machinery, a thickness planer eliminates the following operations: (a) ....; (b) ....

14. The ends of the legs are squared and cut to length on a circular saw by using a .... and a ....

15. When legs are to be tapered, the amount of taper is marked on .... with a ....

16. Taper lines are laid out only on two opposite sides, because ....

17. Make a sketch of a taper jig for the circular saw.

18. When cutting tapers on the circular saw, the .... should be used to prevent ....

19. The line marking the beginning of a taper is placed .... of the outfeed table.

20. If a taper is twice as long as the infeed table and ¼ in. deep at the end .... cuts, each .... deep, must be taken.

Chapter 6

GROOVED JOINTS

Grooved joints are a group of joints which have the following characteristics in common: They all have a groove or recess cut into one member, either with the grain or across the grain, into which the edge or end, in whole or in part, of another member is fitted. This type of joint is used extensively in all cabinet construction, as for example, in door, panel, and drawer construction, in shelving, picture frames, built-in furniture, etc. The carpenter uses grooved joints in flooring, wainscoting, tank construction, concrete forms, store fixtures, etc.

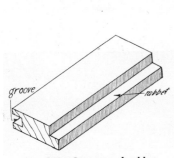

Fig. 346. Groove and rabbet

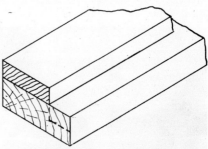

Fig. 347. Strip of wood clamped to board as a guide for the rabbet to be planed

167. To Make a Rabbet Joint. A rabbet is a groove cut on the edge or end of a piece of wood (Fig. 346). To make this joint by hand use the rabbet and fillister plane shown in Figure 53.

1. Adjust the plane iron to cut the proper thickness of shaving as in ordinary planing. Be sure that the blade projects evenly through the bottom of the plane. See that the edge of the blade is exactly in line with the side of the plane.

2. The spur, which is fastened to the side of the plane with a little screw, is now set to a cutting position. It is important to have it sharp.

3. Set the two gauges on the plane to the desired width and depth.

4. Clamp the board to be rabbeted to the bench. Hold the plane level, and press the width gauge against the edge of the board. Take every stroke evenly and carefully. The spur scores the wood so that the rabbet will be cut to an even width. Continue until the depth gauge bears against the upper surface of the board.

5. If the gauges cannot be used on a thin or narrow board, a strip

153

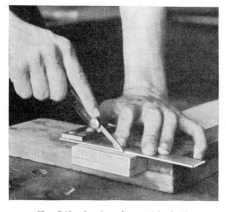

Fig. 348. Scoring line with knife

Fig. 350. Cutting triangular groove with chisel

Fig. 349. Scoring with a chisel

Fig. 351. Cutting triangular groove with bevel of chisel down

of wood can be nailed or clamped to the board as a width gauge. The depth should be marked along the edge with a marking gauge (Fig. 347).

6. On narrow boards it is easier to saw and chisel a rabbet than to plane one. Mark the width and depth of the rabbet with a marking gauge and then saw across the grain with a backsaw.

7. A straight saw cut can be made when a small triangular groove is first cut on the waste side of the line marked for the width. First score the line as deeply as possible with a knife or a chisel. Hold the try square right on the line when scoring (Figs. 348 and 349). The groove can now be cut with a chisel as shown in Figures 350 and 351.

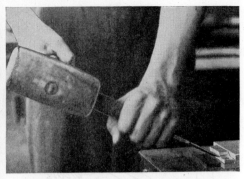

Fig. 353. Cutting end wood with chisel, bevel down

Fig. 352. Block hand-screwed to piece guiding backsaw

8. Another way to make a straight saw cut is to clamp a piece of wood right on the line (Fig. 352).

9. The rabbet is cut to depth with a chisel as shown in Figures 353 and 354. The final smoothing and cutting to uniform depth should be done with the bevel of the chisel up or with a router plane.

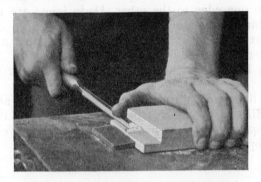

Fig. 354. Finishing rabbet with chisel, beveled side up

168. To Make a Groove. (1) A groove is a recess or slot cut along the grain (Fig. 346). It differs from a rabbet in having three surfaces — two sides and one bottom; the rabbet has only two — one side and one bottom. Grooves are cut on the sides and front of drawers for the bottom (Fig. 355). They are also made in the frame around a panel and in the edges of flooring and sheathing.

2. Grooves are planed with a matching plane (Fig. 54) or with a plow plane (Fig. 356). A matching plane makes a groove on the edge of one board and a tongue to match or fit it on another.

3. *Groove and rabbet joints,* as shown in Figure 357, are used a good deal in furniture construction, for example where the sides and legs of a

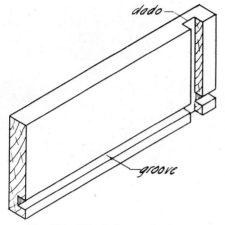

Fig. 355. Side of drawer showing
groove and dado

Fig. 356. Plow plane

cabinet are joined. The groove is first made in the legs, after which the rabbet is planed to fit it.

This joint is sometimes called a barefaced tongue joint.

169. To Make a Dado Joint. (1) A dado is a groove made across the grain from one edge to the other. Dado joints are used in shelves, bookcases, cabinets, stepladders, boxes, etc.

2. A practice joint (Fig. 358) may be made from a piece of wood squared to about 4 in. wide by 8 in. or more long.

3. Square a line across the center and saw the board in two with a backsaw.

4. Square a line across the center of one of the pieces at A, Figure 359, and lay out half the thickness of the other piece, B, on each side of this center line. Square lines across piece A at these points. Test the layout by placing B on top of A.

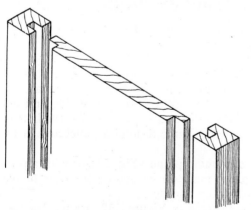

Fig. 357. Groove and rabbet or barefaced
tongue joint

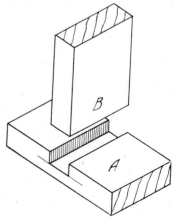

Fig. 358. Dado joint

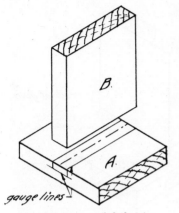

Fig. 359. Layout of dado joint

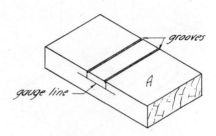

Fig. 360. Dado ready for sawing

Remember that a *dado is always cut across the grain* and never with the grain.

5. Saw on the waste side of the lines, using one of the methods described in Article 167 to obtain straight cuts (Fig. 360). Cut away the waste stock between the saw cuts with a chisel narrower than the dado, and finish the bottom of the cut with a router plane (Fig. 361). Chisel and plane from both edges toward the middle.

6. Fit the planed end of piece B, Figure 358, into the dado. If it is too loose, nothing can be done about it except to make a new joint. If it is too tight, a few shavings may be planed off piece B until it fits snugly into the dado.

170. To Make a Gain or Stopped Dado Joint. (1) A gain joint (Fig. 362) is a dado joint that does not go all the way across a surface. It is therefore also called a stopped dado joint. It is used for the same jobs as the dado joint, but is neater in appearance.

2. Square the piece, cut it in half, and lay out the joint as explained in Article 169. Lay off the distance where the dado stops on both members, which is about ½ in. from the front edge (Fig. 363).

Fig. 361. Finishing gain with router plane

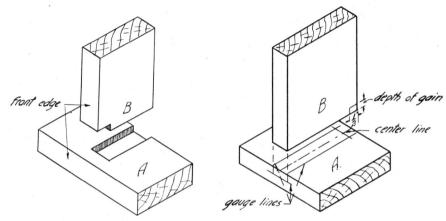

Fig. 362. Gain joint   Fig. 363. Layout of gain joint

3. Gauge the depth on the rear edge of piece A, and also on the front edge of piece B.

4. Chisel out the gain, using a ¾-in. chisel, and holding the beveled side toward the inside. Strike light blows with a mallet, being careful to follow the lines (Fig. 364).

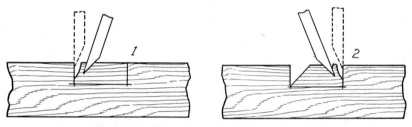

Fig. 364. Positions of chisel in chiseling gain joint

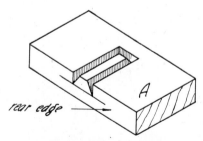

Fig. 365. Chiseling gain

5. Cut a small groove all around, and then go over it again striking heavier blows (Fig. 365).

6. Finish the gain with a chisel and router plane (Fig. 361).

7. Saw out the notch in the front edge of B, and fit the pieces together.

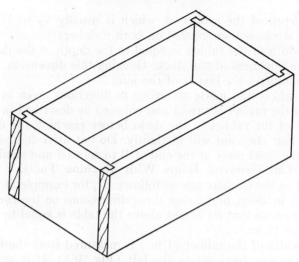

Fig. 366. Dado-and-rabbet joint

This joint is used on such pieces of furniture as bookshelves, where the plain dado joint would be unsightly.

171. To Make a Dado-and-Rabbet Joint. (1) This joint (Fig. 366) is similar to the groove-and-rabbet joint, except that it is made across the grain. It is used principally in boxes and boxlike construction as chests, cabinets, and drawers.

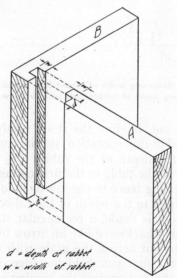

d = depth of rabbet
w = width of rabbet

Fig. 367. Dado-and-rabbet joint

2. The two pieces forming the joint are first squared to dimensions. The thickness of the rabbet member, A, is then gauged on the dado member, B, with a marking gauge (Fig. 367).

3. The depth of the rabbet, *d*, which is usually ½ to 2/3 the thickness of the stock, is then gauged on both members.

4. The width of the rabbet is equal to the depth of the dado or about one half the thickness of the stock. Gauging this dimension (*w*) on both members completes the layout of the joint.

5. The dado is first made according to directions given in Article 169, after which the rabbet is sawed and chiseled as described in Article 167. Try the fit of the rabbet in the dado before reaching the depth line to make sure that the joint will fit tightly. Do not drive it together as that will cause the short piece at the end of B to split off and spoil the joint.

172. To Cut Grooved Joints With Machine Tools. (1) *A rabbet* may be cut on the circular saw as follows: If, for example, it is to be 1 in. wide and ½ in. deep, first gauge these dimensions on the endwood. Then adjust the saw, so that its height above the table is equal to the depth of the rabbet or ½ in.

2. The width of the rabbet (1 in.) is measured from the ripping fence to one of the saw teeth set to the left (Fig. 368). If it were measured according to the scale on the table, the width of the rabbet would be increased by the width of the saw kerf.

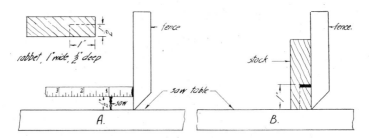

Fig. 368. A, Measuring width of rabbet from outside of saw blade to fence. B, Cutting depth of rabbet. Side with first saw cut against fence

3. Now make the cut, holding the stock firmly against the fence. As no guards can be used in this operation, special caution must be exercised.

4. When cutting the depth of the rabbet (½ in.), hold that face of the stock which was on the table in the first cut against the ripping fence. Measure from the ripping fence to the saw as before, and set the saw 1 in. above the table or equal to the width of the rabbet.

5. As the second cut is made, a rectangular strip of wood will be cut away. This is often shot backward like an arrow by the motion of the saw.

6. Rabbets may be cut across the grain with the same setting of the saw. When making the first cut, hold the edge of the stock against the universal gauge and the end against the ripping fence. When making the second cut, hold the piece vertically on the table, one face bearing against the ripping fence.

7. By using a dado head, rabbets may be made with a single cut. This saves time if many pieces have to be cut.

Fig. 369. Rabbeting on a router

Fig. 370. Cutting rabbets on sliding jig

Fig. 371. Cutting combination molding with two-wing cutters

8. Rabbets may be planed on the jointer as explained and shown in Figures 154 and 155.

9. Rabbets may also be cut on a shaper or a router. Straight work is held against the fence when rabbeting along the grain (Fig. 369). When rabbeting endwood the stock is clamped to a slide in the table (Fig. 370). Curved work is guided along a shaper collar (Fig. 371). A follower (Fig. 210) is used over the bit on a portable router. Curved work can only be rabbeted on a shaper or router.

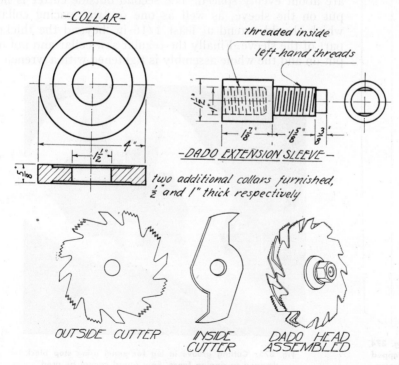

Fig. 372. Dado head

Fig. 373. Cutting a dado, using ripping fence as stop.
Saw guard cannot be used

10. *Grooves and Dadoes* on straight work are usually cut on the circular saw with a dado head (Fig. 372). The two outside cutters or saws alone will cut a full ¼ in. The inside cutters vary in thickness from 1/16 to ¼ in.

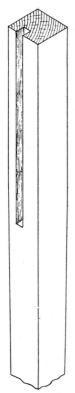

11. To set up the dado head, first screw the sleeve to the saw arbor. Remember it is a left thread. One outside cutter is then put on, and as many inside cutters as needed. The inside cutters should be distributed so that the cutting points are about evenly spaced. The second outside cutter is now put on the sleeve, as well as one or two spacing collars, which should extend at least 1/16 in. beyond the thickest part of the sleeve. Finally the regular saw collar and nut are put on and the whole assembly is tightened with a wrench.

Fig. 374.
Stopped
groove

Fig. 375. Cutting groove in leg for panel using stop block
clamped to ripping fence. Saw guard cannot be used

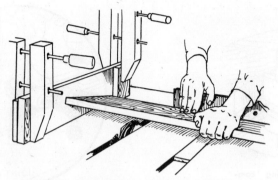

Fig. 376. Cutting stopped dado or gain using
two stop blocks

12. Be sure the dado head revolves freely before turning on the power. Set it to correct height over the table, and make a trial cut to check both depth and width of cut. If the cut is too wide or too narrow, the dado head must be reset. Sometimes a piece of cardboard, added to the inside cutters, will give just the right width needed. Grooving saws are used for narrower grooves. They may be obtained in different thicknesses.

13. Grooves are cut as in ordinary ripping. Dadoes are cut with the same setup of the dado head, but the edge of the stock is held against the cutoff gauge or the universal gauge. The ripping fence is used as a stop against which the end of the board slides (Fig. 373). There can be no danger of a kickback, because the cut goes only part way through the wood.

14. Stopped grooves are often made on the legs of cabinets, as in Figure 374. To do this, set the ripping fence and dado head to correct width and height. The width is figured from the outside surface of the legs. Measure the length of the groove to be cut from the front of the dado head toward the rear of the table, and clamp a stop block to the table at this point. Beginning the cut at the end, two of the legs can now be grooved with this setting. The other two must be cut from the point where the grooves stop toward the end of the leg. The length of the groove is therefore measured from the back teeth of the dado head toward the front, where a stop

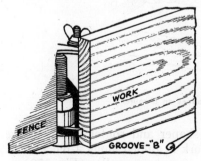

Fig. 377. Cutting grooves along fence

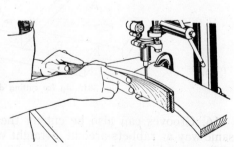

Fig. 378. Grooving curved stock

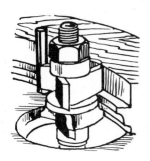

Fig. 379. Cutting compound molding with two three-lip cutters, showing starting pin

Fig. 380. Cutting dadoes. Board clamped to tenoning jig

block is clamped to the ripping fence (Fig. 375). Start the machine, hold the end of the leg against the stop block and its side against the ripping fence, and lower it slowly over the revolving dado head. Then push it forward until the cut has been completed. As no guard can be used, great care must be taken to avoid an accident.

15. Stopped dadoes are cut in the same manner (Fig. 376), holding the edge of the board against the universal gauge and using the ripping fence as a stop for the end of the board.

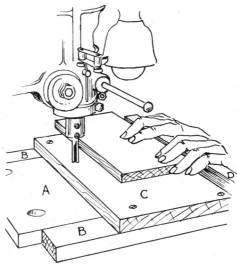

Fig. 381. Jig for cutting dadoes on a router

16. Grooves can also be cut on the shaper and router, much in the same way as rabbets are cut. Straight work is guided along a fence (Fig. 377), curved work along a jig (Fig. 378) or a shaper collar (Fig. 379).

17. Dadoes are cut on a shaper by clamping the stock in a vertical position to a sliding jig (Fig. 380). They may be cut on a router by making a jig that will slide across the table (Fig. 381).

18. The ends of stopped grooves and dadoes cut on a circular saw or shaper must be squared by hand with a chisel.

REVIEW QUESTIONS

1. The most common grooved joints are: (a) ....; (b) ....; (c) ....; (d) ....; (e) ....; (f) ....

2. Name ten jobs in which grooved joints are used.

3. To make a straight saw cut across the grain, the backsaw can be guided by .... or by ....

4. A groove differs from a rabbet by ....

5. A groove is cut ....; a rabbet is cut ....

6. The bottoms of grooved joints can be cut to uniform depth with ....

7. A stopped dado is also called a .... joint. It differs from a plain dado ....

8. Test the accuracy of the layout of a dado joint by placing ....

9. The following machines may be used for cutting grooves, rabbets, and dadoes: (a) ....; (b) ....; (c) ....

10. A stopped dado is used ....; a gain joint is used ....

11. The ends of stopped grooves and dadoes cut on a circular saw must be finished .... because ....

12. Rabbets and grooves on curved work can only be cut on a .... and a ....

13. Why is there no danger of a kickback when cutting dadoes on a circular saw?

14. The width of a groove can be increased slightly by placing .... dado head.

15. A dado may be cut on a router machine by ....

Chapter 7

DOWEL JOINTS

Dowels are used extensively in all modern furniture construction. They are used in re-enforcing boards glued edge to edge, in segment work, and as a substitute for the mortise-and-tenon joint. A dowel joint can be made more rapidly than a mortise-and-tenon joint, and does not require as much skill. When well made, it is much superior to a poorly made mortise-and-tenon joint. The patternmaker uses dowels in split patterns.

Dowels are round sticks of wood made of birch or maple. They are either smooth or grooved. The standard sizes measure from 3/16 to 1 in. in diameter and 36, 42, or 48 in. in length. They also may be obtained in usual working lengths, pointed, grooved, and ready for use. The purpose of the grooved surface is to allow glue and air to escape when the dowel is driven into the hole bored for it. It is also a good idea to countersink dowel holes slightly so that the wood will not be forced up around dowels when they are driven home.

175. To Make a Doweled Butt Joint. (1) Square the pieces to dimensions.

2. Gauge a line through the center of the ends and edges to be joined from the face of each piece.

3. Determine the position of the dowels, and set the marking gauge equal to the distance between the outside edge and the center of the dowel nearest to it. With this setting, gauge lines crossing the center lines on all the pieces (Fig. 388).

4. Now set the marking gauge equal to the distance between the outside edge and the center of the next dowel, and gauge lines as before. The important point to remember is always *to gauge from the same sides and edges.*

5. Bore holes with an auger or dowel bit of the same size as the

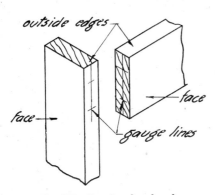

Fig. 388. Gauging for dowels

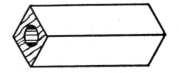

Fig. 389. Auger-bit gauge made of wood

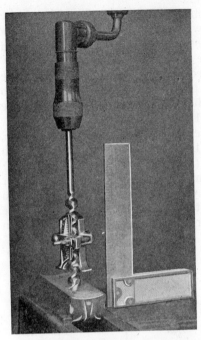

Fig. 390. Boring for dowel

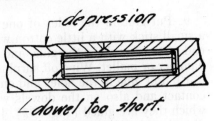

Fig. 391. Depression in surface caused by too short dowel

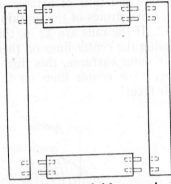

Fig. 392. Doweled frame ready for gluing

dowels, where all gauge lines on all the pieces intersect. The dowels should be of a diameter to give sufficient strength to the construction, without weakening the members to be joined. The diameter should be from one third to one half the thickness of the stock. Clamp an auger-bit gauge to the bit so that all the holes are bored to the same depth.

6. The ordinary auger-bit gauge is too long to fit on a dowel bit. For these bits a gauge can easily be made by running the bit through a small block of wood, which is then cut to the right length (Fig. 389). When this block of wood is slipped over the bit until it butts against the chuck of the brace, the bit should project the distance to which it is desired to bore the hole (Fig. 438).

7. Watch the boring carefully so that all holes will be perpendicular when finished. It is recommended to stop boring after every few turns, and sight the work to determine if the bit is perpendicular both to the side and end of the board (Fig. 390). Any error may then be corrected before the holes are bored to their full depth.

8. Cut the dowels about ⅛ in. less in length than the combined depth of the holes. Point them a little with a knife or coarse sandpaper so that they may enter the holes more easily. Cut a small groove along the side of the smooth dowels to permit glue and air in the bottom of the holes to escape. Avoid making the dowels too short, as the wood around the part of the hole, not filled, will shrink and make a depression in the surface (Fig. 391).

9. Put glue in the holes of one member with a small round brush, or a small stick with a little cotton waste wrapped around one end. Dip one end of the dowels in the glue, and drive them home with light blows of a hammer or mallet. Wipe off surplus glue with a piece of waste.

10. Put glue in the holes and on the edges of the members which make contact and also on the dowels which protrude from the members into which they are glued (Fig. 392). Join the pieces together and clamp (see directions for clamping, Arts. 216 and 218).

11. When the members of a joint are not to be flush as, for example, the legs and rails of a table or stool, the center lines are gauged with different settings of the marking gauge (Fig. 393).

12. If the rails are ¾ in. thick, the marking gauge is set to ⅜ in. for gauging the center lines on them. If they are to join the legs ¼ in. from their outer surfaces, this distance must be added to the setting of the gauge. The center lines on the legs are therefore gauged ⅝ in. from their faces.

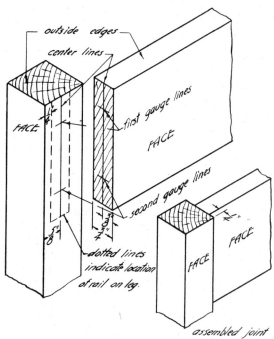

Fig. 393. Dowel joint between table leg and rail

176. To Make a Draw-Bolt Joint. Although this joint is not strictly a dowel joint, it may be described under this heading, because dowels are generally used for locating the parts (Fig. 394).

1. Draw-bolt joints are used in timber construction, in stands for motors or machines, in workbenches, and in other construction subject to strain and vibration. Its advantage over other joints is that it can be tightened when it works loose.

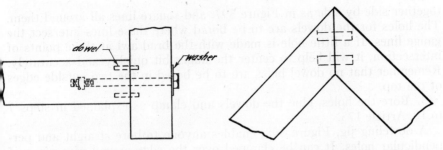

Fig. 394. Draw-bolt joint   Fig. 395. Doweled miter joint

2. The horizontal member or rail is joined to the vertical member with one or two dowels as explained in the previous article. The dowels are glued into the rail only.

3. The hole for the bolt is bored through both pieces while they are clamped together. It should be of the same size as the bolt and a little longer.

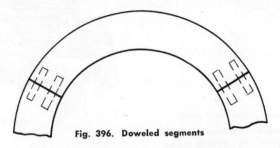

Fig. 396. Doweled segments

4. Another hole is then bored or chiseled in the rail for the nut of the bolt. If the rail is thin, the hole goes right through it, but if the rail is thick the hole should be only deep enough so that the nut will fit into it. It should be made so that the nut cannot move out of place and so that the end of the bolt will go through it and get a good grip. A washer should be placed under the head of the bolt to prevent it from digging into the wood.

Note that holes for dowels are always bored at right angles to the surfaces to be joined, even if these surfaces are not at right angles to the sides. Typical examples are rims for round tables, side rails for chairs, miter joints (Fig. 395), and segment work (Fig. 396).

177. To Dowel Boards Edge to Edge. (1) When boards for a table top are to be glued together, they are first placed side by side on a bench and arranged so that the grain forms pleasing patterns and runs in the same direction. They are then numbered as in Figure 325 and jointed two and two as in Figure 326. Do this job just as carefully as if no dowels were to be used, *because dowels will not hold poorly jointed edges together.*

2. When all the joints fit (Fig. 328), the edges are all gauged lengthwise in the center from the face of the boards. Clamp all the boards

together side by side as in Figure 397, and square lines all around them. The holes for the dowels are to be bored where these lines intersect the gauge lines. If a little hole is made with the brad awl at these points of intersection, it will help to center the auger bit quickly and accurately. Remember that no dowel holes are to be bored in the two outside edges of the top.

3. Bore the holes, glue the dowels and clamp as explained in steps 7 to 10, Article 175.

A doweling jig, Figure 398, enables anyone to bore straight and perpendicular holes. It can be clamped over the edge or end of a piece of wood and has cylindrical metal guides for $\frac{1}{4}$, 5/16, $\frac{3}{8}$, 7/16, and $\frac{1}{2}$-in. bits.

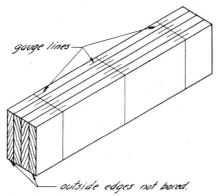

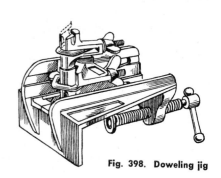

Fig. 398. Doweling jig

Fig. 397. Doweling boards edge to edge. Note how the boards are gauged across the lines from the face of each board

178. To Join Legs to a Turned Column With Dowels. (1) Sand the legs on a spindle sander or sanding cylinder mounted in the lathe. Support each leg on the tool rest, and move it from side to side until the desired curvature has been obtained, so that it fits snugly against the column (Fig. 399).

It is also important that the upper part of the leg, which fits against the column, is square with the lower part which is to stand on the floor. Test for squareness with a steel square (Fig. 400) before and after sanding in the lathe. If one of the legs should not be square, the column of the table would be out of plumb.

2. Gauge center lines on the ends of the legs as described in Article 175, step 2. It is important that these lines be gauged exactly in the center, because the legs are to fit against a cylindrical column. If the holes to be bored for the dowels are a little off center, the joints will be open on one side.

3. Lay out vertical lines on the column at the points where the legs are to join it. This may be done as follows: Wrap a strip of paper around the column and cut it so that the ends just meet. Remove it and fold it

Fig. 399. Sanding end of leg to fit against turned column

into three or four equal parts, depending upon the number of legs to be doweled into the column. Wrap the paper strip around the column again, and mark these divisions on it with a pencil (Fig. 667). Place the column in the lathe, move the tool rest of the lathe close up against it, and mark the lines along its upper edge from these points (see also directions for reeding, Art. 265).

4. Make a template of cardboard of the same length as the joint, mark a center line on it, and punch two holes where the dowels should be (Fig. 401).

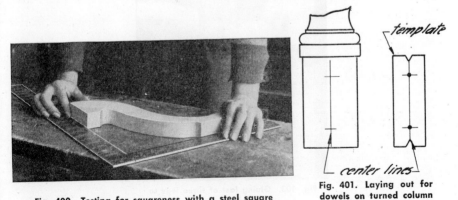

Fig. 400. Testing for squareness with a steel square

Fig. 401. Laying out for dowels on turned column

Fig. 402. Leg to be joined to turned column with dowels

5. Place the template on the column and legs so that the center lines coincide, and mark the position of the dowels.

When the underside of the column is flat as in this case, the horizontal gauge lines may also be gauged on both column and legs by holding the block of the marking gauge against their lower edges (Art. 175, step 4).

6. Bore holes for the dowels as explained in Article 175 (Figs. 389 and 402), and glue the legs to the column as described in Article 222.

Fig. 403. Gluing last of three legs to turned column

179. To Bore Dowel Holes With Machine Tools. (1) Holes for dowels can be bored on a boring machine, a mortiser with boring attachment, a drill press, or a router. However, only shallow holes can be bored on the router, because router bits are very short.

2. When boring holes in the edges of boards for a table top, an auxiliary fence should be made and screwed to the regular fence. This is then adjusted and clamped to the table, so that the holes will be bored in the center of each edge. Lay out the holes on one board, and bore a spacing hole for each dowel in the auxiliary fence, which should extend beyond the table (Fig. 404).

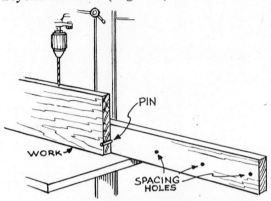

Fig. 404. Boring dowel holes in the edges of boards to be glued together

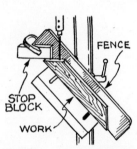

Fig. 405. Boring dowel holes in mitered frame

3. A pin is put in the first spacing hole, the end of one of the boards butted against it, and the first dowel hole bored. The pin is then put in the second spacing hole, the board moved against it, and another dowel hole bored. In this way all the holes will be spaced exactly alike on all the boards without any further laying out.

4. Holes in 45-deg. miter joints may be bored with the table tilted to 45 deg. (Fig. 405). Similarly, holes may be bored in surfaces at other angles by tilting the table the required number of degrees and supporting the work on jigs and stop blocks.

5. Holes may be bored in a turned column, by making a cradle for it and clamping it to the fence as shown in Figure 459.

REVIEW QUESTIONS

1. Dowels are made of .... or .... and manufactured in lengths of ....•...
2. Dowels are grooved on the surface, so that ....
3. If a dowel is too short for the hole bored, the wood is likely to ....
4. Dowel holes are countersunk slightly to prevent ....
5. Center lines should be gauged from ....
6. A gauge for a dowel bit may be made ....
7. A doweling jig is .... Holes .... in diameter can be bored with it.

8. A draw-bolt joint is used on (*a*) ....; (*b*) ....; (*c*) ....
9. Name five kinds of work in which dowels are used.
10. When gluing up a table top, it is important that the joints fit well, because dowels ....
11. Holes for dowels are always bored at right angles to ....
12. By segments is understood ....
13. Holes for dowels may be bored with the following machine tools: (*a*) ....; (*b*) ....; (*c*) ....; (*d*) ....
14. An auxiliary fence is made of .... and fastened to ....
15. Dowel holes in a turned column are laid out ....

Chapter 8

LAP OR HALVING JOINTS

In lap or halving joints, half the thickness of each member is cut away, so that when they are joined together their upper and lower surfaces will be flush. These joints are used in carpentry, in patternmaking, and cabinetmaking. The carpenter uses lap joints in framing the timbers forming the sill and plate of a house and where timbers cross each other. The patternmaker uses them in making the arms for pulleys, etc. The cabinetmaker uses them in connecting crossrails to the sides of a cabinet, in chair seats, in picture frames, in joining stretchers which cross diagonally, in molded work, and faced-up grounds for doors. These joints also have many other applications.

180. To Make an End-Lap Joint. (1) For a practice joint, square one piece of stock to the following dimensions: ¾ in. thick, 2 in. wide, and 12 in. long. Cut it in half and mark the face of each member plainly.

2. Lay out the width (2 in.) from one end of each piece, and square lines all around.

3. Place one piece on top of the other in the position they are to occupy with the face of both pieces up (Fig. 411).

4. Then set a marking gauge to half the thickness of the pieces (⅜ in.) and gauge a line around the end of each piece *from the face of both pieces.*

5. The parts to be cut away are then marked. It is the lower part of the top piece and the upper part of the bottom piece.

6. If the lines were not gauged exactly in the center, the two pieces when cut would still be flush, because if too little were cut from one

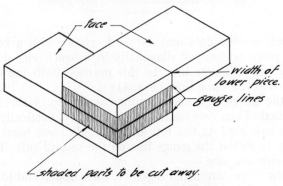

Fig. 411. Layout of end-lap joint

175

Fig. 412. Sawing with a backsaw on waste side
of the line

piece, proportionately more would be cut from the other. The most important thing in laying out lap joints, therefore, is to *gauge from the face of both members*.

7. The shoulder cuts across the grain are now made on both pieces. As it is very important to make them straight, perpendicular, and to the line, it is best to cut triangular grooves in which to start the backsaw, or to clamp a piece of wood as a guide right on the line (Figs. 348, 350, 351, 412, and 413).

Fig. 413. Block hand-screwed to piece guiding
backsaw

8. The cheek or side cuts may be made either with a backsaw or a ripsaw. Each piece is clamped diagonally in a bench vise and sawed on the waste side of the gauge line. In this position both the end and one side can be seen at the same time (Fig. 414).

9. Follow the gauge line and continue sawing until the shoulder cut has been reached. Then reverse the piece, clamp it vertically in the vise, and finish the saw cut. As the top and one side have been sawed, it is only necessary to follow the gauge line on the second side. The first saw cut helps to guide the saw.

10. When the pieces are fitted together, their upper and lower surfaces should be flush, and the side of one should fit accurately against the

shoulder of the other (Fig. 415). Any adjustment can be made with a chisel.

181. To Make an End-Lap Joint With Rabbet. This joint is used when framing a mirror, a wooden panel, or a pane of glass.

1. If possible, square a piece of wood long enough for the whole frame, plane the rabbet, and saw into lengths.

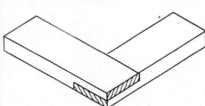

Fig. 415. Finished end-lap joint

Fig. 414. Sawing cheek cut of end-lap joint

2. The joint is laid out as an ordinary end-lap joint, except that the width of the rabbet is subtracted on one piece (B) when laying out the shoulder cuts (Fig. 416).

3. The pieces are gauged *from the face* so that the gauge lines are even with the rabbet.

4. The shoulder cuts are made as explained in the previous article. When the side cuts are made, the piece from which the upper part is

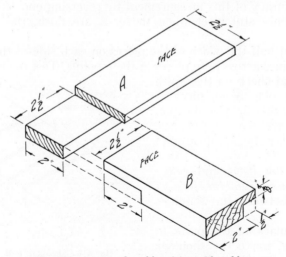

Fig. 416. Layout of end-lap joint with rabbet

cut away (A) will be reduced in width by the width of the rabbet, while the other piece (B) still has its full width.

182. To Make a Cross-Lap Joint. In cabinetmaking this joint is used more than any other lap joint. Some typical examples are: crossrails, both plain and shaped, for taborets, tables, stools, and cabinets, as well as crosses for hall trees, flower-pot stands, trellises, etc. The pattern-maker uses cross-lap joints when making spokes for wheels and pulleys, and the carpenter also uses them in various timber constructions.

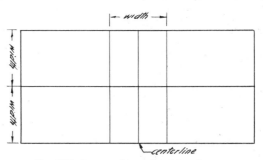

Fig. 417. Layout of cross-lap joint; first step

1. The members of a cross-lap joint generally are of the same thickness and width, and cross each other in the middle at right angles. Cross-lap joints, however, may be made at different angles and the parts may also be of different dimensions. To make one of the common cross-lap joints, square a piece of stock, long enough for both parts, to dimensions.

2. If the joint is to be in the center, cut the pieces to exact length, place them side by side, and square a line across them in the center (Fig. 417). Test the accuracy of this measurement by reversing one of the pieces. If the center lines still meet when the ends are flush, the measurement is correct.

3. Lay out half the width of the pieces on each side of the center line, and square lines across both pieces at these points. Test the measurements as before and check on the width of the cut by placing one piece on top of the other in the position these pieces are to occupy. Square these shoulder lines all around each piece.

4. Mark the faces and *gauge the depth lines from the face* of each piece between the shoulder lines.

5. After marking the parts to be cut away, make the shoulder cuts as explained in Article 180,

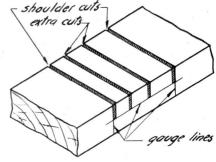

Fig. 418. Shoulder and center cuts for middle- or cross-lap joints

Fig. 419. Chiseling middle- or cross-lap joint, bevel down.
Roughing cut

and Figures 348, 350, 351, 412, and 413. It is better to make these so that they are a trifle too small, and then plane a few shavings off the edges until they fit perfectly.

6. To aid in chiseling away the waste stock, a few extra saw cuts should be made between the shoulder cuts (Fig. 418). These will serve as a depth gauge and prevent splitting off chips below the depth line. Hold the bevel of the chisel down and begin cutting well above the gauge line (Fig. 419). Chisel from both edges toward the middle. Finish the cut with the bevel of the chisel up (Fig. 420) or with a router plane (Fig. 421).

7. Cross-lap joints are also made on the edges of the stock as shown in Figure 422. The procedure is the same.

8. *Middle-lap joints* (Fig. 423) are used especially in house framing and timber construction. One member is made as an end-lap joint and the other as a cross-lap joint. They are usually made at right angles to

Fig. 420. Chiseling middle- or cross-lap joint,
bevel up. Finishing cut

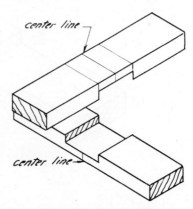

Fig. 421. Cross-lap joint

each other, either in the center of one piece or at some other point between the ends. They are laid out and cut exactly as end-lap and cross-lap joints.

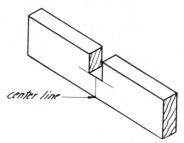

**Fig. 422. Cross-lap joint on edge
of board**

183. To Make a Dovetail-Lap Joint. (1) This joint (Fig. 424) is a modified middle-lap joint. As it cannot be pulled apart, it is used especially where there is a pull or tension strain. It is used a good deal in such pieces of furniture as cabinets and chests of drawers, which have an upper rail connecting and holding the two sides together (Fig. 425).

2. The joint is laid out as an ordinary middle-lap joint after which the angle of the dovetail is marked on the upper piece B, Figure 426.

3. The angle is obtained as follows: Square a line across a board, and step off six equal spaces on it. From the end of the sixth space, step off one to the right and parallel to the edge of the board (Fig. 427). A line drawn from this point to the starting point of the first line gives the correct angle for dovetails. Set a sliding T bevel to this angle and lay it out on the end of piece B.

4. Make the shoulder cut as explained in Article 180, but continue it around both edges to the line of the dovetail.

5. Then make the cheek cut as in a regular end-lap joint. Finally saw along the lines marked for the dovetail.

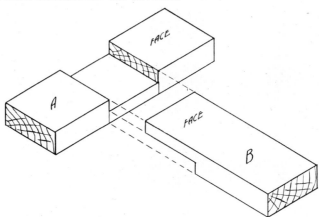

Fig. 423. Middle-lap joint

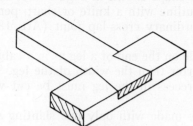

Fig. 424. Dovetail-lap joint

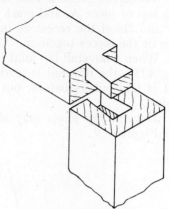

Fig. 425. Dovetail-lap joint (open)

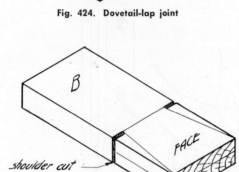

shoulder cut
gauge line for cheek cut

Fig. 426. Shoulder cut on dovetail-lap joint

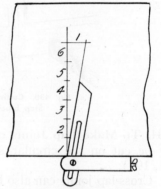

Fig. 427. Laying out angle of dovetails

Fig. 429. Pin of dovetail-lap
joint with one straight edge

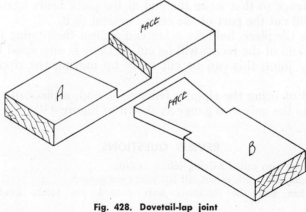

Fig. 428. Dovetail-lap joint

6. The upper piece B now has the shape shown in Figure 428. Place it on top of piece A, and mark its outline with a knife or sharp pencil. Saw and chisel the recess as in an ordinary cross-lap joint (Art. 182). Then fit the pieces together.

7. When a dovetail-lap joint is made on the end of a leg as in a cabinet (Fig. 425), the dovetail is made shorter than the width of the leg. The joint is laid out as before, but the recess in the leg must be cut with a chisel.

8. Dovetail-lap joints may also be made with only one slanting side as in Figure 429.

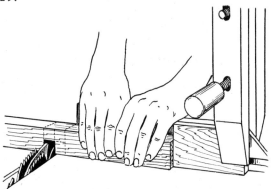

Fig. 430. Cutting cross-lap joint with dado head.
Stop block clamped to miter gauge

184. To Make Lap Joints on the Circular Saw. (1) End-lap joints may be cut on the circular saw in the same way as tenons are cut (Art. 194).

2. Cross-lap joints can also be cut on the circular saw, but in this case a dado head is used.

3. Set the dado head to the correct height above the table and hold each part of the joint with one edge against the universal gauge. Adjust the ripping fence so that when the end of the piece bears against it, the dado head will cut the part of the recess nearest to it.

4. Reverse the piece, hold the other end against the ripping fence, and the opposite end of the recess will be cut. If there is any wood left in the center of the joint, this can be cut away by moving the ripping fence to the right.

5. Instead of using the ripping fence as a stop, a piece of wood may be clamped to the universal gauge as shown in Figure 430.

REVIEW QUESTIONS

1. Lap joints are also called halving joints, because ....
2. When gauging for depth of cut, all lap joints are gauged ....
3. If less than half the thickness were gauged, lap joints would still be flush if ....
4. The two cuts made on an end-lap joint are called: (a) ....; (b) ....

5. In a rabbeted end-lap joint, the end of one member is wider than the other, because ....

6. The cabinetmaker uses cross-lap joints in ....
   The patternmaker uses them in ....

7. How are shoulder cuts made?

8. When laying out a cross-lap joint, the .... is first marked.

9. If the recesses in a cross-lap joint are too narrow, the .... until it fits.

10. One member of a middle-lap joint is like a ....; the other member is like a ....

11. The dovetail-lap joint is a modified ....

12. Show how the correct angle of a dovetail is laid out.

13. Where is a dovetail-lap joint used in furniture construction?

14. Saw cuts made between the shoulder cuts on a cross-lap joint help to .... and ....

15. Chisel a recess in a cross-lap joint from .... and hold the chisel .... Finish the cut with .... or ....

16. Which member is cut first when making a dovetail-lap joint?

17. Some dovetail-lap joints have only one ....

18. When cross-lap joints are cut on the circular saw, the .... should be used.

19. The machine used for cutting end-lap joints is ....

20. The recess for a dovetail-lap joint in endwood is cut with ....

Chapter 9

MORTISE-AND-TENON JOINTS

The mortise-and-tenon joint is without exception the most important and most used joint in cabinet construction. It is made with several variations. Some of the most important of these are: blind, pinned, haunched, barefaced, through, wedged, slip, and keyed joints.

A carpenter uses a mortise-and-tenon joint both in timber construction and in interior woodwork.

187. To Make a Blind Mortise-and-Tenon Joint. This type of mortise-and-tenon joint is used in most cabinetwork, because it is neater in appearance than other joints. It requires three principal operations to make any mortise-and-tenon joint. These operations are: laying out, making the mortise, and making the tenon.

Laying out. (1) Square the pieces to dimensions, and mark their faces plainly.

2. Determine the length of the tenon, i.e., the distance it is to enter the other member, and square a line all around its end at that point which is the shoulder.

3. Mark the total width of the tenon member on the mortise member at the point where they are to be joined.

4. Determine the thickness of the tenon; it is usually from one third to one half the thickness of the stock. Set the points of a mortising gauge to this distance, and adjust the block of the gauge, so that the double lines will be marked in about the center of the piece.

5. Gauge *from the face* on the end and edges as far as the lines which mark the shoulder (Fig. 433).

6. If the faces of the members are to be flush, gauge the mortise with the same setting of the gauge from the face of the piece. If the mortise member is thicker than the tenon member, as for example in a table leg, and the rail or tenon member is to be set in, for example ¼ in. from the face of the leg, the block of the mortise gauge must be moved accordingly, *but not the setting of the two points.*

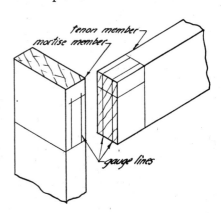

Fig. 433. Layout of mortise-and-tenon joint

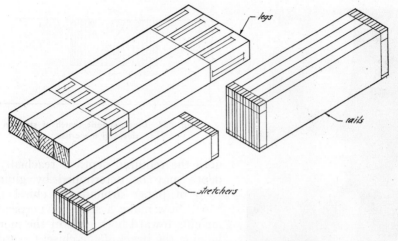

Fig. 434. Layout of mortises and tenons for small table

7. A tenon is rarely made the full width of the member, but an additional cheek cut is laid out, making it narrower. If the mortise is near the end of a piece, at least ½ in. should be taken from the width of the tenon so that the end wood of the mortise will not tear out when it is chiseled. Lay out this cheek cut on both tenons and mortises.

8. In a mortise-and-tenon construction there usually are several joints with the same dimensions. *These must all be laid out at the same time with the same setting of the gauge* in order to produce accurate work (Fig. 434). In addition, mortises in legs should always be gauged from the outside or face surfaces. When four legs are required, as in tables, stools, or cabinets, it will make it more convenient if they are placed in the position they are to occupy and are marked left front, right front, left back, and right back. Furthermore, all outside faces may be marked "out" (Fig. 435).

If a mortising gauge is not available, an ordinary marking gauge may be used. Set it first to mark the gauge lines nearest the faces of the pieces, then set it to mark the farther gauge line, and mark all the pieces again from the face of each.

Making the Mortise. The mortise can be made in two ways, either by chiseling the hole with a mortising chisel, or by boring a number of adjoining holes and then cutting away the waste between them.

9. In the first method, a mortising chisel of the same width as the mortise to be chiseled is used. Clamp the piece on top of the bench and begin by cutting out wedge-shaped pieces in the center of the mortise

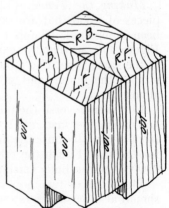

Fig. 435. Marking table legs before laying out mortises

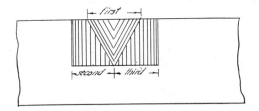

Fig. 437. Diagrammatic sketch of steps in chiseling a mortise

Fig. 436. Chiseling mortise. Note paper strip glued to chisel for depth gauge

until the required depth is reached. This depth may be determined by gluing a strip of paper around the chisel (Fig. 436). Now make a series of perpendicular cuts toward both ends of the mortise, holding the bevel of the chisel toward the center of the mortise. Break the shavings loose by moving the handle of the chisel toward the center of the mortise. Pare the ends of the mortise (Fig. 437).

10. In the second method, a series of adjoining holes are bored with an auger or dowel bit of the same diameter as the width of the mortise (Fig. 438). Clamp an auger-bit gauge to the bit, or make one of a block of wood (Art. 175, step 6) so that the hole bored will be slightly deeper than the length of the tenon. Be careful to bore the holes perpendicularly (Figs. 390 and 438).

11. Clamp the pieces firmly in the vise or on top of the bench, and chisel out the pieces of wood left between the holes bored. Chisel perpendicularly until the gauge lines have been reached (Fig. 439).

Making the Tenon. (12) If the cheek cuts are made first, the thin pieces of wood that are sawed off will not split away before the cut has been completed. Clamp the piece diagonally in the vise as shown in Figure 440, so that the gauge lines on the end and one side can be seen at the same time. Use either a backsaw or a ripsaw, depending upon the size of the tenon, and saw until the line marking the shoulder cut is almost reached.

13. Then reverse the piece in the vise, clamp it in a vertical position, and finish the saw cut. It is necessary to watch only the gauge line in front of you, because the diagonal saw cut already made serves as a guide for the saw. Finish the other cheek cut in the same manner, but do not saw below the lines marking the shoulder cut.

14. If one or two more cheek cuts reduce the width of the tenon, these should also be sawed as shown in Figure 441.

15. The shoulder cuts are made in the same way as those on lap joints. Score the lines all around with a sharp knife (Fig. 442) or a chisel (Fig.

Fig. 438. Boring series of holes for mortise

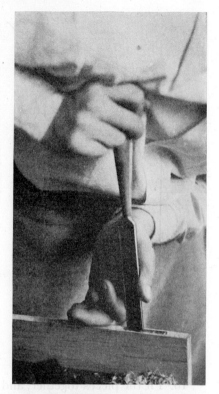

Fig. 439. Cleaning out bored mortise with chisel. Pressure of the shoulder forces the chisel into the wood

Fig. 440. Sawing cheek cuts of tenon

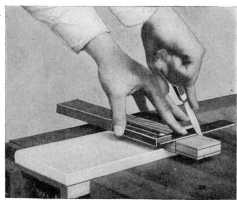

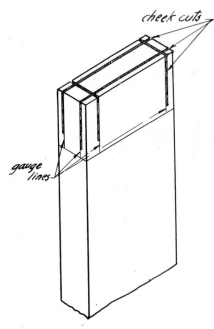

Fig. 441. Cheek cuts on a tenon partly sawed

Fig. 442. Scoring line with knife

444). Then make a shallow triangular groove in which to start the backsaw, either as in Figure 443 or as in Figure 351. When sawing the shoulder cuts, hold the piece of wood on a bench hook (Fig. 445) or clamp it in a vise. Trim off any unevenness with a sharp chisel, and bevel the edges of the tenon (Figs. 446 and 447).

16. Fit the pieces together, and make any necessary adjustments.

Only hand pressure should be necessary to bring the members of the joint together. Excessive force may cause the mortised member to split.

When the tenoned member of a blind mortise-and-tenon joint has only two cheek cuts, it is called a "stub mortise-and-tenon joint."

17. If the shoulder cuts are not perfect, the tenoned member will not fit snugly against the edge of the mortised member. A poor shoulder cut may be repaired by scoring a new line all around it (step 15). Cut as deeply with the chisel as possible (Fig. 444), and then make perpen-

Fig. 443. Cutting triangular groove in which to start the saw

Fig. 444. Cutting line around shoulders of tenon with sharp chisel

Fig. 445. Sawing shoulder cut

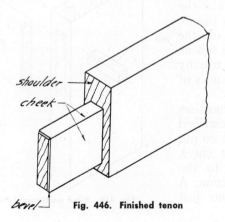

shoulder

cheek

bevel — **Fig. 446. Finished tenon**

Fig. 447. Straightening uneven
shoulder cuts with chisel

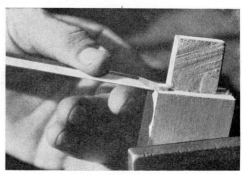

Fig. 448. Removing remaining parts on
shoulder with chisel

dicular chisel cuts on this line from both sides as in Figure 447. Finish by clamping the piece in a vise with the tenon up, and cut from the edges with a $\frac{1}{2}$-in. chisel (Fig. 448).

18. As this trimming naturally shortens the tenoned member, corresponding members must be shortened the same amount, even if their shoulder cuts are perfect. *Tenoned members of equal length must measure exactly the same between shoulders.*

19. A blind mortise-and-tenon joint is sometimes strengthened by driving a pin through it. On reproductions of Elizabethan or Jacobean tables, benches, or stools, such pins are a feature of the design and are usually made square or triangular. When the appearance is unimportant, ordinary dowels are used. Such joints are called "pinned mortise-and-tenon joints" (Fig. 449).

188. To Make a Haunched Mortise-and-Tenon Joint. (1) This joint is used in panel construction. First make the grooves in all the pieces. These must be of the same width as the tenons are to be, which is usually one third the thickness of the members.

2. Lay out the mortises and tenons, as described in Article 187, but do not extend the upper cheek cut all the way to the shoulder of the tenon. A piece of the tenon just

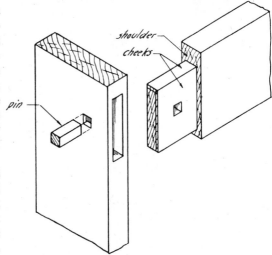

Fig. 449. Blind mortise-and-tenon joint with pin

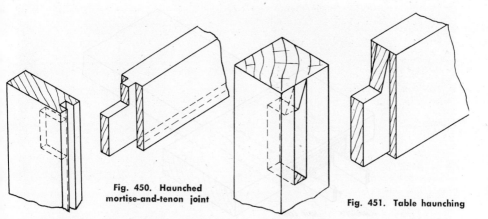

Fig. 450. Haunched
mortise-and-tenon joint

Fig. 451. Table haunching

large enough to fill up the groove is left at this point (Fig. 450).
The object of this joint is to give lateral stiffness.

3. A modified haunched joint is the table- or taper-haunched joint (Fig.
451). This is used on tables to give stiffness to the rails, or in places where
the appearance of the regular haunched joint would be objectionable.

4. A double tenon is made on the lower rail of a door if the rail is
more than 8 in. wide. The joint is haunched both on the ends and between
the tenons (Fig. 452).

189. To Make a Barefaced Mortise-and-Tenon Joint. When the
rails and legs of tables and stools are made flush, very little wood is left
between the mortise and the face of the leg if a regular tenon is used.
To strengthen the joint in such cases, the tenon is made on the inside
part of the rail and therefore has only one shoulder (Fig. 453). Note
that barefaced mortise-and-tenon joints can be used only when the
mortise member is thicker than the tenon member.

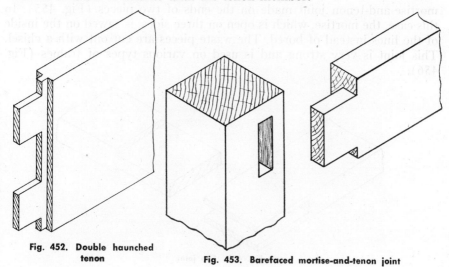

Fig. 452. Double haunched
tenon

Fig. 453. Barefaced mortise-and-tenon joint

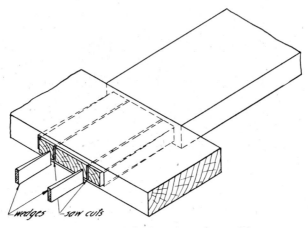

Fig. 454. Wedged mortise-and-tenon joint

190. To Make a Through Mortise-and-Tenon Joint. (1) This joint is laid out and made in the same manner as a blind mortise-and-tenon joint (Art. 187) except that the tenon extends through the mortise member and therefore is made a little longer than the mortise is deep. The mortise is chiseled from both edges.

2. The tenon is either planed off flush with the mortise member, or is rounded off and left to project a little.

3. "A wedged mortise-and-tenon joint" is a through mortise-and-tenon joint in which wedges are driven into the end of the tenon so that it cannot pull out. The end of the mortise is chiseled a little wider. When the wedges are driven home, the tenon will spread and fill the hole completely (Fig. 454).

191. To Make a Slip Joint. (1) A slip joint is simply a through mortise-and-tenon joint made on the ends of two pieces (Fig. 455). In this case, the mortise, which is open on three sides, is sawed on the inside of the lines instead of bored. The waste pieces are cut out with a chisel. This joint is very strong and is used on various types of frames (Fig. 456).

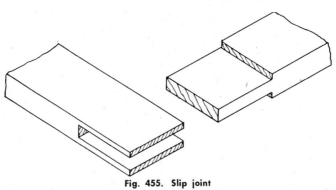

Fig. 455. Slip joint

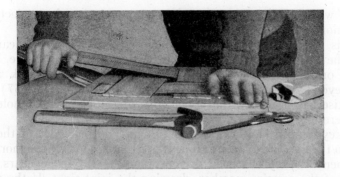

Fig. 456. Slip joint on chair seat

192. To Make a Keyed Mortise-and-Tenon Joint. This joint differs from the other mortise-and-tenon joints in that it can be taken apart. It can also be tightened by driving in the key. It is therefore used much in the same way as a draw-bolt joint (Fig. 394), on benches and other heavy wood construction.

1. The keyed joint is a through mortise-and-tenon joint with a tenon at least twice as long as the mortise.

2. Make the through mortise-and-tenon joint as explained in Article

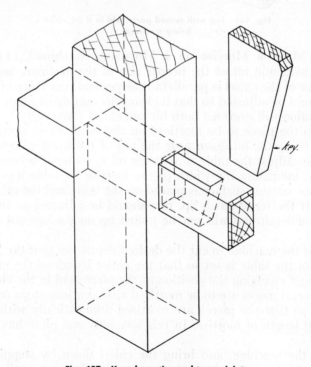

Fig. 457. Keyed mortise-and-tenon joint

190, and when that fits, lay out a through mortise on the projecting end of the tenon.

3. This mortise should be rectangular in shape. The end nearest the end of the stock must be slanted a little toward the underside, but the opposite or inner end should be perpendicular and cut back at least $\frac{1}{8}$ in. beyond the face of the large mortise member (Fig. 457). When the mortise has been cut, the upper edge of the rectangular hole in the tenon therefore should be a little longer than the lower edge.

4. A key is now made to fit this mortise. The rear edge of the key is square to the two ends, but its front edge is tapered to fit the mortise.

5. When this key has been driven home, its rear edge bears against the face of the mortise member, drawing the joint tight. If the mortise, made through the tenon, had not been cut back $\frac{1}{8}$ in., the joint could never be tightened, because the wedge could not be driven in any farther.

Fig. 458. Leg with turned parts held in a jig while being mortised

193. To Make a Mortise on a Mortising Machine. (1) Insert a mortising chisel and bit of the proper size in the machine, and see that the rear edge of the chisel is parallel to the vertical rear fence of the table. The bit should be adjusted so that it clears the cutting edges of the chisel, because friction will overheat both bit and chisel (Art. 110).

2. Clamp the piece to be mortised on the table. Press down the foot pedal, and bring the bit down near the top of the wood without starting the machine. Adjust the table so that the bit is centered between the two gauge lines, indicating the width of the mortise. If table legs are to be mortised, one outside surface is placed on the table and the other against the fence. If the fence has a lip, this should be adjusted so that the leg just slides under it and will not be pulled up on the upward movement of the ram.

3. Adjust the machine to cut the desired depth, see that the lengthwise movement of the table is set so that the entire length of the mortise can be cut without changing the position of the piece held in the clamp.

When several pieces are to be mortised alike, various stops on the table can be set so that the pieces are mortised automatically with the same spacing and length of mortise. In this way only one piece has to be laid out.

4. Start the machine, and bring the chisel down by stepping on the foot pedal. Make successive cuts next to the first cut until the entire

Fig. 459. Cutting mortises in circular stock

length of the mortise has been chiseled. The first cut should be made to only half the depth, because the chisel is likely to bind in the wood, so that the spring on the machine cannot return the ram to its first position. This would cause overheating. Make the last cut the full width of the chisel; otherwise the chisel may slide sideways and be bent.

5. Pieces that will not lie flat on the table as, for instance, legs with turned parts, must be held on a flat base as in the jig shown in Figure 458.

6. When mortises are to be cut in turned stock, it is of the utmost importance to clamp the stock in the machine in such a way that the mortise, if continued, would pass right through the center of the turned piece. This may be accomplished as shown in Figure 459. A rectangular block of the same width as the diameter of the turned piece is cut on the

Fig. 460. Making shoulder cuts on circular saw

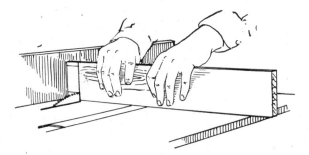

Fig. 461. Sawing shoulder cut on upper edge of table rail

band saw, so that it forms a rest or cradle for the cylindrical piece to be mortised. A line is marked in the center of the block as shown.

Lay out the mortises on the turned column as explained in Article 178, Figure 401. From these points draw lines across the end of the column. Each line passes through its center and continues to the opposite side.

Place the column in the cradle, so that the lines coincide, as shown in Figure 459. Clamp securely and adjust the table so that the chisel is centered over the line marked on the side.

This method may also be used when legs are to be doweled to a turned column (Fig. 402).

194. To Cut Tenons on the Circular Saw. (1) When a number of tenons have to be cut to the same dimensions, the pieces must all be planed or sawed to the same thickness and the ends squared and cut to exact length.

2. Lay out only one piece and make the shoulder cuts first. Set the crosscut saw to correct height above the table, and, using the ripping

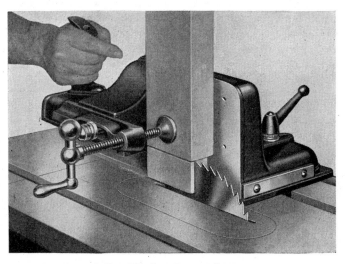

Fig. 462. Tenoning attachment

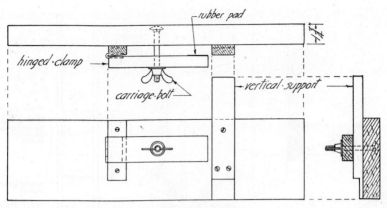

Fig. 463. Tenoning jig

fence as a stop, measure the length of the tenon from the fence to any saw tooth set to the left (Fig. 460).

3. Hold the edge of the piece against the universal gauge and cut both sides and edges (Fig. 461). On table rails and similar pieces the edges of the tenons are cut deeper on top (Fig. 441). In such cases the sides and one edge are cut first on all the pieces. The saw is then raised higher over the table and all the upper edges are cut (Fig. 461).

4. The cheek cuts are made with a ripsaw. If an attachment like that shown in Figure 462 is not available, a jig illustrated in Figures 463 and 464 should be made. With such a jig, cheek cuts can be made quite safely.

5. Clamp the pieces in the jig, and adjust the ripping fence so that the saw cut will come on the outside of the gauge lines farthest away from the ripping fence. When the jig now is held against the ripping fence and pushed past the saw, the waste wood from the cheek cut will fall on the table.

6. Reverse the piece in the jig, and make the other cheek cut. The waste pieces on the edges may be cut off by hand or on a band saw.

7. If the stock is not of exactly the same thickness, it is necessary to make both cheek cuts from the same side. In this case, make the outside

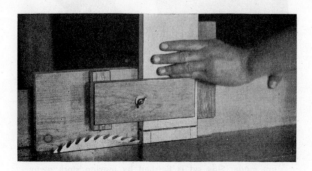

Fig. 464. Making cheek cuts using homemade jig

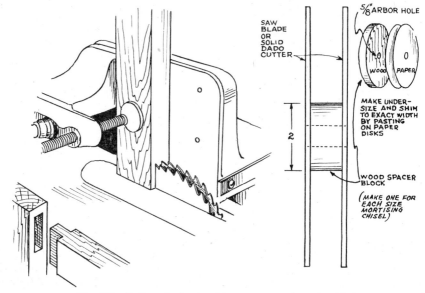

Fig. 465. Making cheek cuts with two saws and spacing block

cheek cut first on all the pieces and then reset the ripping fence to make the second cheek cut.

8. It is possible to make both cheek cuts simultaneously if two saws of the same diameter and with a spacing block between them are put on the saw arbor (Fig. 465).

9. The mortise member of a slip joint may be cut in the same manner. The saw cuts are made on the inside of the lines, and any waste wood remaining between them may be removed by one or two extra saw cuts in the middle.

10. The mortise on a slip joint may be made in a single cut by using a dado head.

11. Tenons may also be cut with a dado head. In this case the edge

Fig. 466. Cutting tenons with dado head. Ripping fence is used as stop so that shoulders and part of side cut are made. Side cut is finished by moving stock away from ripping fence. Saw guard cannot be used

of the piece is held against the universal gauge and the end against the ripping fence. The ripping fence is adjusted so that the dado head will cut just outside the shoulder line.

12. Set the dado head accurately to height and make the first cut. This will take in both the shoulder cut and part of the cheek cut (Fig. 466). Move the piece to the left and make one or two more cuts, but *do not change the setting of the ripping fence.* Make the other cheek cut in the same way.

13. When cutting tenons by this method, the stock must be planed to exactly the same thickness and the dado head set very carefully to height above the table, otherwise tenons will be either too thin or too thick.

REVIEW QUESTIONS

1. The blind mortise-and-tenon joint is used more than any other mortise-and-tenon joint in furniture construction, because . . . .
2. When a tenon member comes flush with the endwood of a mortise member, the tenon must . . . . to prevent . . . .
3. The thickness, width, and length of a tenon corresponds to the . . . . of a mortise.
4. When making a table, all . . . . and all . . . . at the same time with the same . . . .
5. When laying out, the four legs in a table should be marked . . . .
6. A mortise is made by hand either by . . . . or by . . . .
7. The shoulders of a tenon are . . . . ; the cheeks are. . . . .
8. A straight cut across the grain can be made with a backsaw by . . . .
9. The exact length of tenoned members should be measured between . . . .
10. Name and sketch three types of haunched mortise-and-tenon joints.
11. A blind mortise-and-tenon joint is strengthened by . . . . ; a through mortise-and-tenon joint by . . . .
12. A slip joint is a . . . .
13. A keyed mortise-and-tenon joint differs from the other mortise-and-tenon joints, because it can be . . . . and . . . .
14. A poorly made shoulder may be repaired by . . . .
15. When mortising on a machine, the outside faces of table legs are placed on . . . . and . . . .
16. The table of the mortising machine is adjusted three ways:
    (*a*) . . . . ; (*b*) . . . . ; (*c*) . . . .
17. When making cheek cuts on a circular saw, the safe way is to . . . .
18. Cheek and shoulder cuts may be made simultaneously on a circular saw by using . . . .
19. When cutting tenons of equal thickness on stock varying in thickness, the cheek cuts must be . . . .
20. A hollow chisel may be overheated if (*a*) . . . . ; (*b*) . . . . It may be bent if . . . .

Chapter 10

MITER JOINTS

Miter joints are used in picture frames, in furniture construction, and in moldings around panels, doors, mirrors, windows, interior and exterior trim.

A miter joint is a neat but weak joint, because its surfaces only butt against each other and in most cases contain about 50 per cent endwood. As glue does not hold well in endwood, miter joints are usually reinforced in various ways. The making of a miter joint may be divided into the following three principal operations: cutting, gluing, and reinforcing the joint.

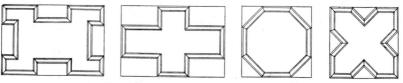

Fig. 472. Panels decorated with moldings

197. To Cut a Miter Joint. (1) Most moldings fit around a square or rectangular surface and are therefore cut at 45 deg. (Fig. 472). The angles for other polygons are found by dividing the number of sides into 180 deg. and subtract the quotient from 90 deg. Examples: pentagon, $90 - \dfrac{180}{5} = 54$ deg.; hexagon, $90 - \dfrac{180}{6} = 60$ deg.; octagon, $90 - \dfrac{180}{8} = 67\frac{1}{2}$ deg.

2. In any case the miter cut of any angle may be found by bisecting the angle as shown in Figure 473.

3. Having determined the angle of the cut, the length of the piece to be mitered is the next to be found. If it is a molding for a picture frame, take the length of the picture or glass and add to that twice the width of the molding less the rabbet (Fig. 474). Directions for making moldings are given in Article 273.

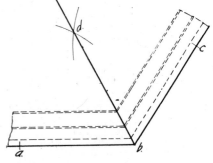

Fig. 473. Bisecting an angle. Lay off ab equal to bc. Draw arcs with equal radius from centers a and c, intersecting at d. Angle abd is the miter

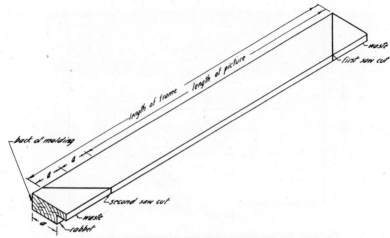

Fig. 474. Finding length of picture-frame molding

4. A miter box of wood or metal is used when cutting miters by hand. The iron miter box has the advantage over the wooden one in that it can be set to cut the most common angles and its saw runs in metal guides which hold it perpendicular. It is well to clamp the stock to be mitered to the back of the miter box while making the saw cuts (Fig. 475).

5. If the joints should not fit exactly, they may be touched up by planing, sawing, or sanding. Planing a miter joint is difficult and should be attempted only by the more experienced workers. Sawing a miter joint to fit is done as follows: Bring the two members of the joint as close together as possible, and clamp them to a board at right angles to each other. Then saw right through the joint, using a backsaw or a crosscut saw. The saw cuts away the high spots on both pieces so

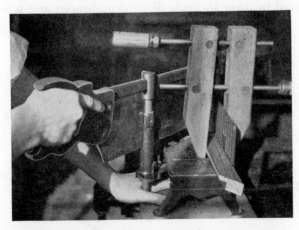

Fig. 475. Sawing picture-frame molding in miter box. Molding clamped to side of box with a hand screw

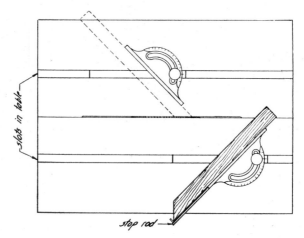

Fig. 476. Cutting miters using two miter gauges. First cut to right of saw, second cut to left, using stop rod in miter gauge

that, when they are unclamped and brought together again, they will fit perfectly. Sanding can only be done when a disk sander is available.

6. Miters may be cut on the circular saw by removing the ripping fence and using the two universal gauges in the slots milled in the table. If a 45-deg. miter is to be made, set both gauges to 45 deg., as shown in Figure 476. Make the first cut with the gauge to the right, set a stop rod to length in the gauge to the left, and cut the second miter.

7. If the mitered pieces are to be short as in Figure 472, this method cannot be used. Instead, a jig, as shown in Figure 477, should be made. It is made of ⅜ or ½-in. plywood. Two cleats, which fit in the slots in the saw table, are glued and screwed to its underside. A piece of 1½-in. stock is mitered to form an angle of 90 deg., braced and screwed to the upper side.

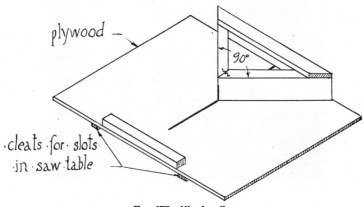

Fig. 477. Mitering jig

Fig. 478. Mitering molding using jig. Note stop block fastened
with a nail

8. The pieces to be mitered are held first against one side and then against the other as the jig is pushed over the saw. Do not saw into the jig any farther than necessary. A mitered stop block may be nailed along one side as shown in Figure 478. Both long and short, wide and narrow pieces can be accurately mitered on this jig, but only at an angle of 45 deg. (Fig. 479). Miters may also be cut on the wood trimmer.

198. To Glue Mitered Frames. (1) The best way to glue mitered frames, especially the larger ones, is to use four bar clamps as shown in Figure 480.

2. Since the mitered ends contain about 50 per cent end grain, the glue is likely to be absorbed and sink into the open pores in the endwood very quickly, thus leaving little glue on the miters and causing what is called a "starved" joint.

3. To avoid this it is recommended to first "size" the mitered ends. Sizing means to apply a rather thin coat of glue, which will run into pores and fill them up. When the sizing coat has set, the regular glue is applied to the pieces which are laid on the bench or other flat surface. Place a

Fig. 479. Jig for mitering moldings on the circular saw

Fig. 480. Clamping mitered frame while gluing

piece of paper under each joint to prevent it from sticking to the bench
and protect its surface from glue spots.

4. Place the first two clamps on their sides, so that the clamp dogs
are close to the mitered corners. The other two clamps are placed with
their notched backs up. Tightening one or two clamps and loosening
others will gradually bring all four miter joints in line. If the miter joints
are not flush on top, place a dowel on the piece that is high and drive it
down even with the others.

5. Smaller frames may be clamped in a jig like the one shown in
Figure 481. Four cleats are nailed or screwed to each other to a board.
Two sides of the frame are placed against two of these cleats. The other

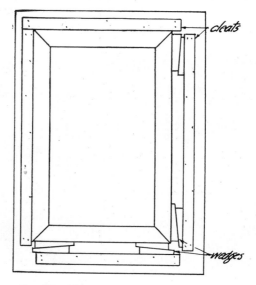

Fig. 481. Gluing a picture frame by wedging

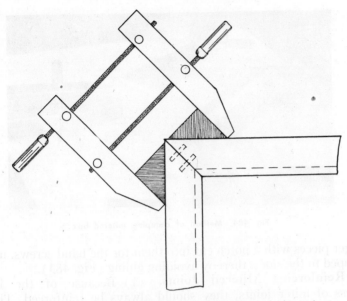

Fig. 482. Clamping mitered corner with hand screw. Triangular blocks glued to outside edges

two sides of the frame are forced tightly against the first two by driving double wedges between them and the other cleats.

6. Mitered frames may also be clamped with a hand screw on each corner as in Figure 482. In this case triangular blocks are first glued to the outside edges of the frame, two to each corner. If pieces of paper are placed between the blocks and the frame, the blocks will be easy to chisel off after the frame has been glued, because the paper will split. This method of gluing is particularly useful when long miters are made on the edges and ends of boards, as for example on mitered columns, boxes, chests, etc. (Fig. 483).

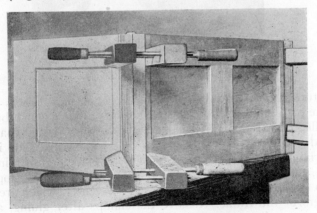

Fig. 483. Gluing a spline miter joint

Fig. 484. Method of clamping mitered box

Longer pieces with a notch cut into them for the hand screws, may also be clamped to the sides, thereby avoiding gluing (Fig. 484).

199. Reinforcing Mitered Joints. (1) Because of the inherent weakness of miter joints, they should always be reinforced. The most common methods of reinforcement are: nails, slip feathers, splines, and dowels.

Fig. 485. Making saw cuts for splines

2. Picture frames are always nailed together by glaziers and others who make picture frames to order. The joints are not glued, but the nails used, called picture points, have greater holding power than ordinary brads and finishing nails. Furthermore, the commercial shop is equipped with special cutting and clamping devices. This method of reinforcement, therefore, is not very satisfactory for school or home workshops.

3. Slip feathers are thin pieces of wood or veneer, which are glued into the corners of the frame. Remove the clamps after gluing, and handle the frame carefully so that the joints do not open up. Then clamp the

frame in a bench vise so that one corner projects over it, and make a saw cut as shown in Figure 485.

4. Glue and insert a piece of veneer into the saw cut. The veneer should fit tightly and its grain run at right angles to the miter joint. Clamp each corner with a hand screw as in Figure 486.

Fig. 486. Gluing splines

5. When dry, chisel off the projecting ends of the veneer and smooth the edge of the frame with plane and sandpaper. This joint is called a *slip-feather miter joint* (Fig. 487).

6. These saw cuts may also be made on the circular saw by holding the frame in a homemade jig as shown in Figures 488 and 489.

7. On wide moldings, such as casings of door frames, the reinforcing piece of veneer may be entirely concealed within the joint. A cut is made in the center of each mitered surface with a very small circular saw like those made for shaper spindles. The veneer is cut to fit the circular hole (Fig. 490) and is glued at the same time as the miter joint.

8. Splines are thin pieces of wood used to reinforce beveled edges and ends. The bevels may be planed by hand or on a jointer, or they may be sawed on a circular saw by tilting the ripping fence, the saw, or the saw table (Fig. 491). In the latter case the ripping fence is moved to the

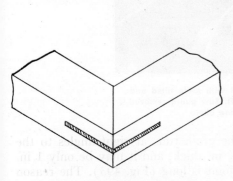

Fig. 487. Slip-feather miter joint

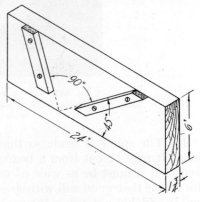

Fig. 488. Jig for cutting mitered frame for slip feather

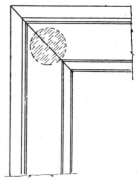

Fig. 489. Spline cuts made on circular saw

Fig. 490. Door casing with concealed slip feather

left of the saw, so that the stock being beveled will rest against it, thus preventing a kickback.

9. The ripping fence is then moved up to the saw, and a shallow cut is made in the edge at right angles to the bevel (Fig. 492).

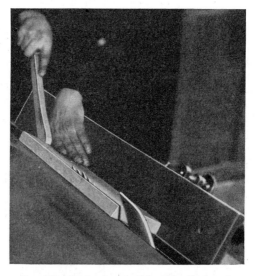

Fig. 491. Cutting bevel with table tilted and ripping fence to the left. Saw guard removed while taking photo

10. The spline is made so that the grain runs at right angles to the joint. It may be cut from a board ⅛ in. thick, and it may be only 1 in. long, but it must be as wide as the joint is long (Fig. 493). The reason for this is that wood will withstand a pull or tension along the grain from end to end, but not across the grain from edge to edge. This joint is called a *spline miter joint*. It is glued as shown in Figure 483.

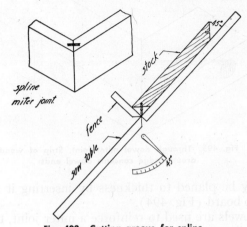

Fig. 492. Cutting groove for spline

A spline may be placed for thickness, inserting it into a groove of dado made in a board (Fig. 492).

11. When dowels are used to reinforce a miter joint, the holes are laid out as on an ordinary ... Find a center line length ways and two lines are made that ... line at the points of inter section and at right angles ... the surface returns ... the depth gauge. Cut the dowels to length, ... in each end, and glue them into one member of each joint. Glue ... clamp as explained above, and shown in Figure 492.

12. If it does not matter that the ... shows above on the out side edge of the frame, miters can be ... the frame as in Figure 493. Glue each ... the frame to the top of the ... and set the ... cut a line to the one edge to the other ... and mark ... (Fig. 495). Thru the ends of the dowel ... each ...

13. Picture frames are joined with ... rectangular strip of wood nailed in and the ... such ... generally conceals the dowel (Fig. 493).

20a. To Cope Moldings. A ... joint often open up in the inside part of the joint. (Fig. 493) ... the wood dutches across the grain, but not along the grain ...

2. To overcome this ... is sometimes coped that ... section is cut out of the end of one member so that it fits exactly al ...

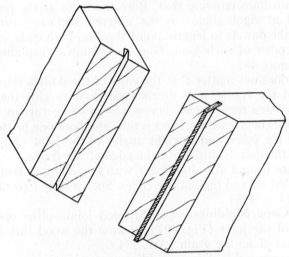

Fig. 493. Spline miter joint

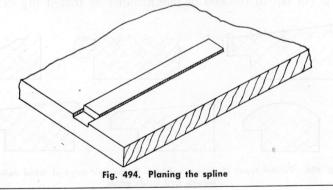

Fig. 494. Planing the spline

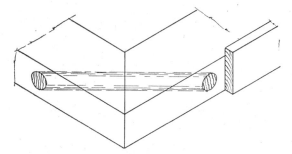

Fig. 495. Through dowel miter joint. Strip of wood
around edge conceals dowel ends

A spline may be planed to thickness by inserting it into a groove or dado made in a board (Fig. 494).

11. When dowels are used to reinforce a miter joint, the holes are laid out as on an ordinary dowel joint (Art. 175). Gauge a center line lengthways and two lines crossing that. Bore the holes at the points of intersection and at right angles to the mitered surfaces, using the depth gauge. Cut the dowels to length, point them on both ends, and glue them into one member of each joint. Glue and clamp as explained above and shown in Figure 482.

12. If it does not matter that the ends of the dowels show on the outside edge of the frame, it is much easier first to glue the frame as in Figure 480. Then remove the clamps, fasten one corner at a time to the top of the workbench with a hand screw, and bore one or two holes from one edge to the other and at right angles to the joint (Fig. 495). Trim the ends of the dowels flush with the edge of the frame.

13. Picture frames are often made with a molding or rectangular strip of wood nailed around the outside edges. Such a strip effectually conceals the dowels (Fig. 495).

200. To Cope Moldings. (1) Mitered joints often open up in the inside part of the joint (Fig. 497) because the wood shrinks across the grain, but not along the grain (Art. 331).

2. To overcome this defect, moldings are sometimes coped, that is, a section is cut out of the end of one member so that it fits exactly over

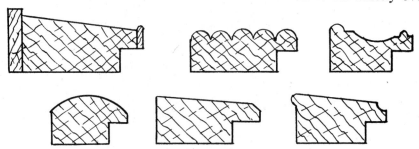

Fig. 496. Various types of picture moldings. Upper left: strips of wood nailed to
outside and inside edges

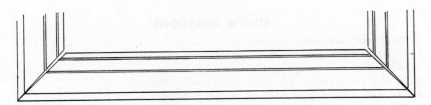

Fig. 497. Open miter joints due to shrinkage

the curves and flat surfaces of the other member (Fig. 498). This is done as follows:

3. If the moldings to be fitted form an angle of 90 deg. with each other, square the end of one of the members, and miter the other in the usual way at an angle of 45 deg. (A, Fig. 498). The mitered part of this mem-

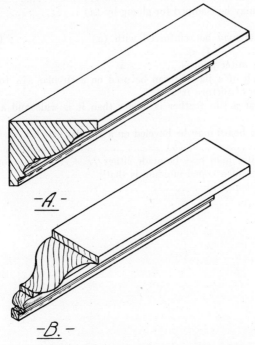

Fig. 498. A, Molding mitered at 45 deg. B, The same molding coped

ber is now cut away with a coping saw. The saw is held so that its blade is at right angles, or slightly less than a right angle, with the back of the molding. The line of the miter cut on the face of the molding must be followed closely in sawing the coping (B, Fig. 498). If the cut is made carefully, the coped member will now fit accurately over the squared member, and the joint will look exactly like a mitered joint. The same method is followed in coping moldings at other angles.

REVIEW QUESTIONS

1. Miter joints are weak, because ....
2. Making a miter joint involves the following principal operations:
   (a) ....; (b) ....; (c) ....
3. In what constructions are miter joints used? (Name 5.)
4. The angle for mitering moldings around a decagon is ....
5. The length of one side of a picture frame molding is equal to ....
   plus ....
6. The advantages of an iron miter box over a wooden one are:
   (a) ....; (b) ....
7. Faulty miter joints may be repaired by (a) ....; (b) ....;
   (c) ....
8. Long pieces of molding may be cut on the circular saw by ....
9. Short pieces of molding can be cut on the circular saw by ....
10. A starved joint is ....
11. Sizing means to ....
12. Miter joints may be clamped for gluing by (a) ....; (b) ....;
    (c) ....
13. Mitered joints may be reinforced with (a) ....; (b) ....;
    (c) ....; (d) ....
14. A slip-feather miter joint is ....
15. Make a sketch of a jig that can be used on a circular saw for making saw cuts
    in the corners of picture frames.
16. Is it true that a slip feather is longer than it is wide and a spline wider than
    it is long?
17. The edge of a board may be beveled on a circular saw by
    (a) ....; (b) ....; or (c) ....
18. A doweled miter joint may be made either .... or ....
19. The advantage of a coped molding is that ....
20. A molding is coped by ....

Chapter 11

DOVETAIL JOINTS

This type of joint is the strongest and neatest of all joints used in cabinetmaking. As it takes both time and skill to make dovetail joints, they are used only in the better class of work. Dovetail joints are used mostly in drawer construction, in carcase work, and in box construction.

203. To Make a Through, Multiple, Dovetail Joint. (1) Square the pieces to dimensions.

2. Square a line around the end of each member equal to a trifle more than the thickness of the other member.

3. Determine the number of dovetails to be cut, and divide the end of one piece into that number of equal spaces (Fig. 501).

The strongest joint is one having the tails and pins equal, but for the sake of appearance, the tails are usually made larger than the pins.

4. Square lines across the end of the board at the points of division. From these lines and from the sides of the piece, lay out a distance that is equal to one half the greatest width of the pin (Fig. 501).

5. Lay out the angle of the dovetails as follows: Square a line across a board, and step off six spaces with a divider (Fig. 502). At the sixth point, erect a perpendicular parallel to the edge of the board. Lay out one space on the perpendicular, and draw a line from this point to the edge of the board where the first line begins.

6. Set the sliding T bevel to this angle, holding the stock against the edge of the board and adjusting the blade to coincide with the line.

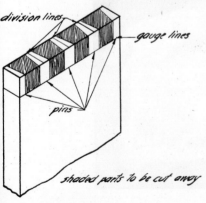

Fig. 501. Laying out the pins

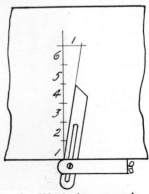

Fig. 502. Laying out angle of dovetails

213

7. Mark the pins from the points laid out on the end of the board, as shown in Figure 501.

8. Square these lines down on both sides of the board.

9. Mark plainly the parts to be cut away (Fig. 501).

10. Saw on the waste side of the lines with a dovetail saw or a fine backsaw.

11. Chisel away the waste pieces, cutting halfway through the board from one side, and

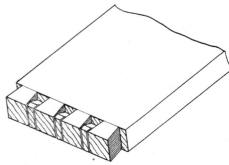

Fig. 503. Chiseling away waste pieces on tail member

then reverse the board and finish chiseling from the other side (Fig. 503). Be careful to make these cuts perpendicular, and do not go beyond the line.

12. Having finished the pins, lay the other board on the bench with the working face up. Place the board with the pins on the end of this board, so that the widest part of the pins is on the gauge line.

13. Mark the shape of the pins with a scratch awl, knife, or fine pencil point on the side of the other piece (Fig. 504).

14. Square these lines across the end of the board with a try square and pencil, and also mark the angles with the T bevel on the other side of the board (Fig. 505).

15. Mark the waste pieces, and saw and chisel as before (Fig. 503).

16. Fit the pieces together, but do not force them so as to break or fracture any of the tails or pins (Fig. 506).

Some woodworkers prefer to lay out the tails first, especially if duplicate pieces are to be made.

Fig. 504. Marking tails

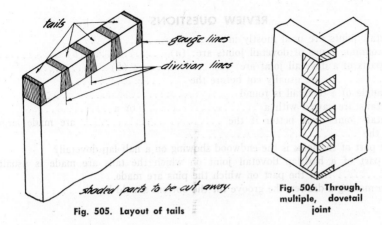

tails

gauge lines

division lines

shaded parts to be cut away

Fig. 505. Layout of tails

Fig. 506. Through, multiple, dovetail joint

204. To Make a Half-Lap, Multiple, Dovetail Joint. This joint (Fig. 508) differs from the through dovetail joint in that the tails do not extend all the way through the joint and, therefore, do not show on one side. It is used in drawer construction.

1. Gauge a line on the end of one member, A, Figure 507, indicating the distance the tails are to extend.

2. With the same setting of the marking gauge, mark lines around the end of the other member, B, holding the block of the gauge against its end. These lines indicate the length of the tails.

3. Lay off the thickness of the member having the tails, B, on the other member, A. B is usually thinner than A.

4. Lay out, cut, and fit the pins and tails as explained in Article 203.

When constructing a drawer, the groove for the bottom should be plowed before the pins are laid out so that it will fall within one tail. (Art. 207).

shaded parts to be cut away

gauge lines

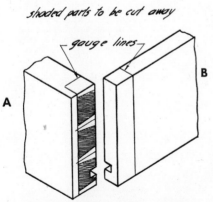

A

B

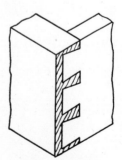

Fig. 507. Layout of half-lap, multiple, dovetail joint

Fig. 508. Half-lap, multiple, dovetail joint

REVIEW QUESTIONS

1. Dovetail joints are used mostly in ....
2. The common types of dovetail joints are: (*a*) ....; (*b*) ....
3. The parts of a dovetail joint are: (*a*) ....; (*b*) ....
4. The .... are usually cut before the ....
5. The angle of a dovetail is found ....
6. Dovetails are sawed with a .... or a ....
7. Dovetail joints look better if the .... are made larger than the ....
8. What part of the joint is the endwood showing on a half-lap dovetail?
9. The part of a half-lap dovetail joint on which the tails are made is usually .... than the part on which the pins are made.
10. When making a drawer, the groove for the bottom should be ....

Chapter 12

MISCELLANEOUS CONSTRUCTIONS

207. To Make a Drawer. Drawers are made in different ways according to their use and the grade of workmanship demanded.

1. The first step in all drawer construction is to fit the front piece carefully to the opening which the drawer will occupy. It should fit rather tightly in this opening in order to allow for smoothing after the drawer has been put together.

2. The two sides and the back are then squared to dimensions, after which a groove is plowed in the front and side pieces for the bottom. The groove is usually made ⅜ in. from the lower inside edge of the sides and the front.

3. One of the simplest kinds of drawers has a rabbet cut on each end of the front piece. The sides are glued and nailed into these rabbets. The nails are set below the surface so that the sides can be planed after the drawer has been assembled (Fig. 511). An improvement on this joint, called the rabbet and tongue, is shown in Figure 512. It is both neater and stronger.

4. The bottom is pushed into the grooves cut for it in the sides and

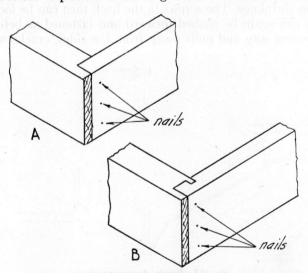

Fig. 511. Plain rabbet and rabbet-and-tongue joints in drawer construction

217

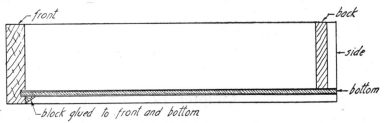

Fig. 512. Typical drawer section

the front. It should extend to the ends of the sides to allow for shrinkage. *It should never be glued into the grooves,* because it must be allowed to expand or contract under different climatic conditions. It should preferably be made of 3/16 or ¼-in. plywood, because this does not shrink or swell as much as solid wood.

5. The back is joined to the sides with dado or dado-and-rabbet joints. Its lower edge rests on top of the bottom which is fastened to it with a few small, flathead screws.

6. The bottom may also be held in place with triangular blocks glued to its underside and to the lower inside surface of the front. In this way it can never pull away from the front (Fig. 512).

7. If the bottom is made of solid wood, the grain should always run from side to side and never from front to back, and that is regardless of the shape of the drawer. The reason for this is that when the wood shrinks and the grain runs from front to back, the bottom becomes narrower and therefore no longer fills the grooves cut for it in the sides. If made with the grain from side to side it will pull out of the front groove upon shrinkage. The screws in the back then can be loosened, and the bottom can again be pushed forward and fastened as before. If it is made the wrong way and pulls away from the sides, cracks will appear.

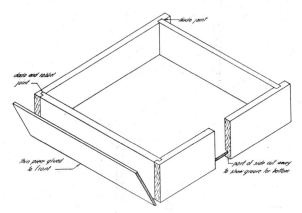

Fig. 513. Simple drawer construction, showing dado, groove, and dado-and-rabbet joints

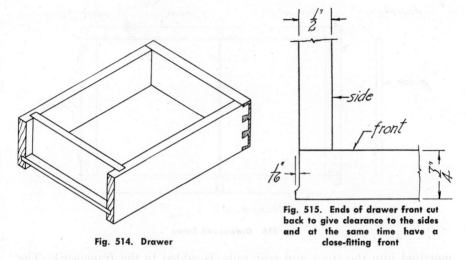

Fig. 514. Drawer

Fig. 515. Ends of drawer front cut back to give clearance to the sides and at the same time have a close-fitting front

The only remedy for this is to glue another piece to the bottom to make it wider.

8. When gluing the front, sides, and back together, be sure that the drawer is square and that its lower edges are level. It is a good plan to place it on a level surface while the glue is drying. See also Article 220.

9. A better drawer is shown in Figure 513. In this drawer the front is joined to the sides with dado-and-rabbet joints. The back, bottom, and sides are joined together as previously explained.

10. After gluing and planing the drawer, the endwood on the front may be concealed by gluing a $\frac{1}{4}$ or $\frac{3}{8}$-in. board to it. It may be planed flush or it may be rounded and extended about $\frac{3}{8}$ in. over the sides and upper edge.

11. On the better home and office furniture the front and sides of drawers are always joined with half-lap, multiple, dovetail joints (Fig. 514). On the very best work, the back and sides are also joined with through, multiple, dovetail joints. Such a drawer cannot possibly come apart. The sides of dovetail drawers are usually made of hardwood and their upper edges are rounded.

12. The pins on the drawer front often are cut back about 1/16 in. in order to give clearance to the sides and still have them fitting closely in the drawer opening (Fig. 515).

208. To Make Drawer Rails and Guides. The weight of a drawer is carried or supported on a framework called the "rails." Its movement is controlled by narrow cleats called "guides," which are fastened to the rails.

1. The rails usually consist of the front rail or division rail, the rear rail, and two side rails or bearing rails, mortised or doweled together. A $\frac{1}{4}$-in. plywood panel is generally framed in between these rails, at least in the bottom frame where it helps to keep out dust (Figs. 516 and 517). When the drawer to be supported is very wide, an extra central rail,

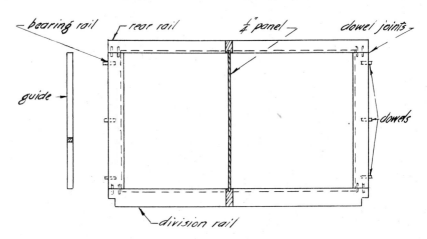

Fig. 516. Drawer-rail frame

mortised into the front and rear rails, is added to the framework. The frames may be joined to the sides of the cabinet with dowels or dado joints.

2. Drawer guides may be made of two narrow cleats of wood nailed to the bearing rails, one on each side of the drawer. This method of guiding can only be used when there is sufficient room for the guides between the front and rear legs as in Figure 517.

3. Another method which will serve in all cases, is to make a single guide in the center. A thin piece of wood, about 1 to 1½ in. wide, is glued and screwed to the underside of the drawer. It runs from front to back and is planed flush with the lower edge of the drawer front (Fig. 518).

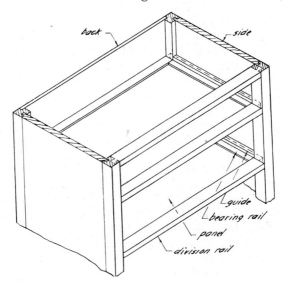

Fig. 517. Framing of drawer rails into cabinet

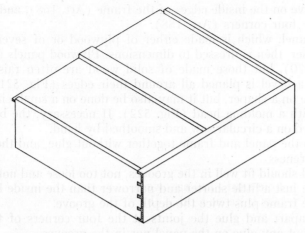

Fig. 518. Strip of wood glued to underside of drawer for guide

4. A corresponding grooved board is notched over the front and rear rails and fastened to them with screws (Fig. 519).

5. The guides should be fitted so that the drawer runs easily and smoothly. A well-fitted drawer can be pushed in by pressing lightly on either side of it with only one hand.

6. Small blocks should be glued either to the rear or front rails for the purpose of stopping the inward movement of the drawer at the right point.

209. To Make a Panel Structure. The object in panel construction is to provide a means by which a large surface of wood can shrink or swell within a comparatively narrow frame, which also will prevent it from warping or twisting. Panel construction is used a great deal in furniture work and in doors, wainscoting, and other interior trim.

The best type of frame is joined with the haunched mortise-and-tenon joint (Fig. 450), but the slip joint (Fig. 456), the end-lap joint (Fig. 416), and the miter joint (Fig. 487) also are used.

1. Square the pieces forming the frame to dimensions (Art. 156).

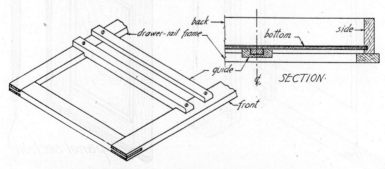

Fig. 519. Isometric and sectional view of central drawer guide

Plow a groove on the inside edges of the frame (Art. 168), and make the joints in the four corners (Art. 188).

2. The panel, which is made either of plywood or of several boards glued together, then is dressed to dimensions. Plywood panels are always flat (Fig. 520), but those made of solid wood are often raised, which means that a bevel is planed all around their edges (Fig. 521). This is usually done on a shaper, but it may also be done on a small circular saw equipped with a molding head (Fig. 522). If necessary, the bevels may also be sawed on a circular saw and smoothed by hand.

3. Clamp the panel and frame together without glue, and then test for fit and squareness.

The panel should fit well in the grooves, not too loose and not too tight. It should be just a little shorter and narrower than the inside length and width of the frame plus twice the depth of the groove.

4. Take apart and glue the joints at the four corners of the frame, but do not put any glue on the panel nor in the grooves.

5. Frames for panels may also be molded on the edges around the panel. This work, which is called "door sticking," is done on the shaper.

6. Two cutters are put on the spindle at the same time, one shapes the edge and the other cuts the groove for the panels.

7. The reverse of these cutters are then put on the spindle and the ends of the horizontal members or rails shaped. One cutter makes a tenon to fit in the groove and the other copes a molding that will fit perfectly over the shaped edges of the stiles or vertical members (Fig. 523).

8. The tenon is made only long enough to fill the groove. This is suffi-

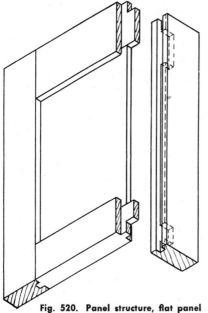

Fig. 520. Panel structure, flat panel

panel section

Fig. 521. Raised panel

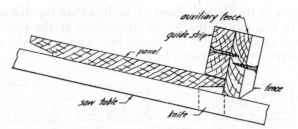

Fig. 522. Panel raising with molding head using square knives

cient for light work, but if greater strength is needed the joints may be reinforced with dowels.

9. If a shaper is not available, a small molding may be made, mitered in the corners and glued or nailed to the inside edges of the frame.

210. To Make a Rule Joint. This joint is used on table tops, whose size is extended by means of drop leaves hinged to it. A table of this kind usually has one fixed part and two leaves. The rule joint, because of its neater appearance, is used instead of the butt joint on the better class of tables (Fig. 524).

1. Square the pieces to dimensions, being particularly careful to see that the two edges are square and true.

2. Set the marking gauge to half the thickness of the knuckle of the hinge; then gauge lines on the end grain of the boards on both ends, holding the block of the gauge against the underside of the boards (Fig. 525).

3. The hinges are like butt hinges, but one leaf is longer than the other. The screw holes are countersunk on the rear side of the hinges, so that the knuckle can be set into the wood and come flush with the underside of the top. This type of hinges is called "back flaps." If they are not obtainable, serviceable ones can be made from ordinary hinge hasps (Fig. 566).

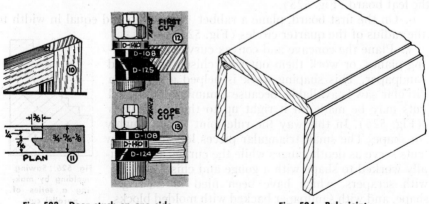

Fig. 523. Door stuck on one side   Fig. 524. Rule joint

4. Set a pair of dividers to about ⅛ in. less than the distance from the gauge line to the top of the board. Beginning at the end of the fixed board, lay off this radius on the gauge line, and mark the center; then scribe a quarter circle as shown in Figure 525.

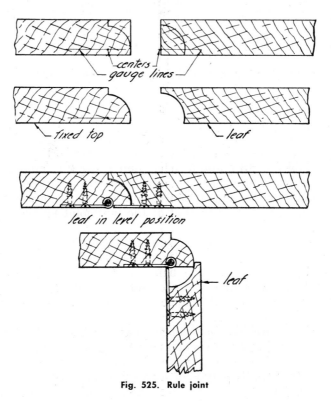

Fig. 525. Rule joint

5. With the same radius, but using the point of intersection of the gauge line and the end of the board as centers, scribe a quarter circle on the leaf board (Fig. 525).

6. On the first board, plane a rabbet ⅛ in. deep and equal in width to the radius of the quarter circles (Fig. 525).

7. Plane the concave and convex curves with molding planes, or work them out with chisel, gouge, and sandpaper. This shaping work is helped greatly if a circular saw is available, because a number of parallel cuts may be made on it right up to the gauge lines (Fig. 526). In this way the rule joint is cut roughly to shape. The small triangular pieces left by the saw cuts serve as depth gauges while the curves are gradually worked to shape with a gouge and chisel. Smooth with scrapers, which have been filed to the right shape, and with sandpaper backed with molded blocks.

Fig. 526. Sawing molding by making a series of parallel cuts

8. The concave curves on the leaves must be cut slightly below the gauge lines so that the two members of the joint will not rub against each other. Continue working on the joint until the two pieces fit together.

Fig. 526a

9. Place the pieces face down on a bench, and gauge a line for the hinges on the board with the convex edges. The gauge line is made directly over the centers and parallel to the edge. The knuckles of the hinges are placed on this line and the outline of the hinges are marked.

10. Chisel the gains so that the hinges will be flush with the wood, and cut grooves for the knuckles.

If the top has two leaves, as is usually the case, it follows that the two rule joints are laid out and worked at the same time.

11. To avoid having the gains show when the leaves are folded, it is recommended to bend the hinge hasp so that it will clear the edge of the fixed top (Fig. 526a).

12. A rule joint can be made much easier on the shaper if cutters of the right shape and size are available. Lay out the joint as explained in the foregoing and cut the quarter-round shape on both edges of the fixed centerboard.

Fig. 527. Early English gate-leg table

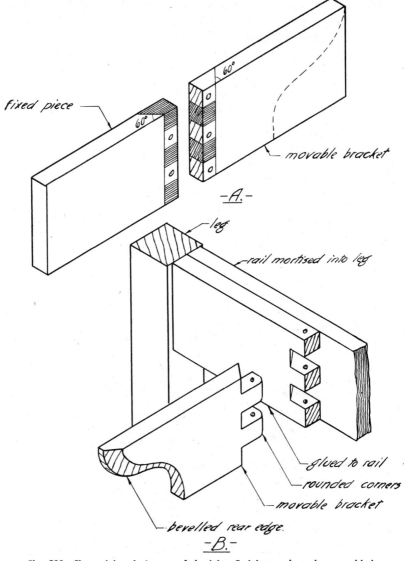

Fig. 528. Finger joint. A, Layout of the joint; B, joint ready to be assembled

13. The cutter for the leaves should be of the reverse shape and have a radius about 1/32 in. larger, so that the leaves, when hinged, can be opened without squeaking and rubbing off the finish on the convex edges.

211. To Make Supports for Table Leaves. For centuries cabinet-makers have devised methods of extending or increasing the area of table tops when occasion demanded. One of the oldest and most common extension tables is the gate-leg table. The leaves are supported on a swinging **leg** joined to a movable rail called a "fly-rail" (Fig. 527). Other types of extension tables have hinged, sliding, and pivoted supports for their leaves.

1. *The finger joint* is a movable, interlocking joint made of wood. It has two parts, the movable bracket and the fixed piece, which is fastened to the table rail (Fig. 528).

2. Square the two pieces to dimensions, and divide the width of the boards into five equal parts. Lay off these divisions on one end of each board, and square lines across the ends from these points.

3. Set a marking gauge equal to the thickness of the boards, and with this setting, gauge a line on the face of both boards, holding the block of the marking gauge against the ends of the boards just marked.

4. From these gauge lines, lay off lines at an angle of 60 deg. across the upper edges of the board. From the points where the 60-deg. lines meet the rear edges, gauge or square lines across the rear faces of the boards.

5. The division lines squared across the ends are now carried around on both faces of the boards until they intersect the gauge lines.

6. The boards should then be placed end to end, the parts to be cut away should be marked, and saw cuts made on the waste side of the lines. Use a backsaw or a dovetail saw for this work, and chisel out the waste pieces.

7. Fit the joint together, and mark the center where the hole is to be bored for the pin. Place the pieces at right angles, and bore the hole. A 5- or 6-in. nail or a ¼-in. dowel may be used as a pin.

It is advisable to bore the hole on a boring machine or in a drill press, if one is available, in order to insure perpendicularity.

8. When the joint is pinned together, it will be seen that the "fingers" on the movable piece will project a little when it is half open. These ends should now be rounded off as shown in the drawing.

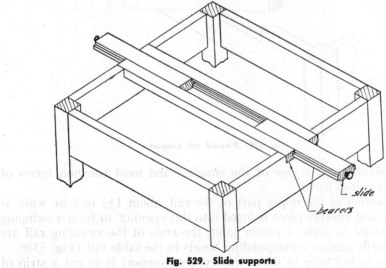

Fig. 529. Slide supports

9. The end of the movable part of the bracket is usually shaped and beveled on its rear side, so that it may be easily grasped with the hand.

10. The other part of the bracket is glued or screwed firmly to the fixed rail of the table.

A piece of a continuous hinge is sometimes substituted for a finger joint, but is not as strong nor as neat looking.

1. *A slide support* for a hinged table leaf consists of three narrow boards, each about 1½ in. wide and 1 in. thick. The length depends upon the size of the leaf.

2. A tongue is cut on each edge of the central board, or "slide," and a corresponding groove is cut in one edge of each of the other two boards, or "bearers." The tongues should fit in the groove, so that the slide will move easily between the bearers (Fig. 529).

3. The bearers are fastened to the rails as well as to the underside of the top.

4. A notch is cut in the table rails for the slide and bearers.

5. A stop usually is placed both on the slide and on the leaves. These stops limit the movement of the slide.

6. The front edge of the slide is either shaped or provided with a knob by which it can be pulled out under the leaf of the table.

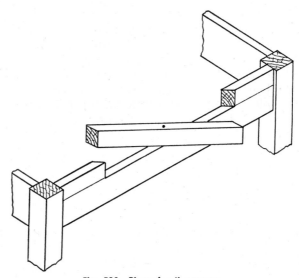

Fig. 530. Pivoted rail support

1. *A pivoted rail* is one of the simplest and most common forms of support for drop leaves.

2. A section of the upper part of the rail, about 1½ to 2 in. wide, is cut away and another piece is fitted into this opening, to form a swinging rail. In order to make a neater joint, the ends of the swinging rail are beveled to fit against corresponding bevels in the table rail (Fig. 530).

3. The easiest way to make this type of support is to cut a strip of

wood a little longer than the side rails and equal in width to the swinging rail. Lay out the length and 45-deg. angles of the swinging rail in the center of this piece, and then saw on these lines. The two shorter end pieces are now glued to the edge of another board after which it is planed to the same width as the other rails, cut to length, and joined to the legs with haunched mortise-and-tenon joints.

4. The swinging rail can then be fitted to the opening and pivoted in the center. Use a ¼- or a 5/16-in. dowel for a pivot, and let its end extend a little up in the underside of the fixed part of the table top.

REVIEW QUESTIONS

1. The bottom in a drawer should preferably be made of .... because ....
2. If the bottom is made of solid wood, the grain should run from ...., because ....
3. The bottom is fastened to the .... with .... or to the .... with ....
4. The bottom should never be glued into the grooves, because ....
5. When gluing a drawer, check for .... and ....
6. In the best drawer construction the sides are joined to the front with .... and to the back with ....
7. The bottom should be as wide as .... to allow ....
8. The sides of dovetailed drawers are made of .... and have ....
9. Clearance is given to the side of a drawer by ....
10. Drawers run on a .... joined to the sides of a cabinet with ....: or ....
11. A central drawer guide consists of ....
12. A raised panel is made of .... and .... on the edges.
13. Panel construction is used in (a) ....; (b) ....; (c) ....
14. Door sticking means ....
15. The horizontal members of a paneled structure are called .... and the vertical members are called ....
16. Why is a back board of a drawer narrower than the sides?
17. A rule joint is used .... instead of ....
18. The hinges used on a rule joint are called .... The screw holes are ....
19. .... may be used as a substitute for rule-joint hinges.
20. A rule joint can be cut on a .... or a ....
21. Drop leaves may be supported on (a) ....; (b) ....; (c) ....
22. A fly-rail is ....
23. A pin for a finger joint may be made from (a) .... or (b) ....
24. A .... is often substituted for a finger joint.
25. The concave part of a rule joint should be made .... than the convex part, because ....

Chapter 13

GLUING AND CLAMPING

Gluing and clamping is one of the most important phases of the woodworker's art, because the strength and appearance of the finished product is in direct proportion to the skill and accuracy with which this job has been done. Methods of clamping vary a good deal according to the work in hand, and often special blocks or fittings have to be devised.

214. Properties and Uses of Glue. (1) Several kinds of glue are used commercially, of which the most important are: animal glue, casein glue, resin glue, vegetable glue, and blood-albumen glue.

2. *Animal glue* is made from the hide parings, bones, sinews, and other waste parts of cattle, horses, pigs, sheep, etc. This offal is soaked in lime water for several weeks and then washed and boiled several times. A foam, which is skimmed off, forms at each boiling. The finished product is a gelatinous mass which is dried and sold in sheets, flakes, or coarse powder. Good grades of animal glue are brittle and transparent.

3. Animal glue must be soaked in cold water overnight before it is ready to be heated. Sheet glue, which is very hard and brittle, must be broken into small pieces with a hammer. The sheets should be put into a bag or cloth during the breaking-up process, otherwise the glue will be scattered all over the floor. The pieces are then put into a double-boiler glue pot, covered with water, and allowed to soak overnight. If it is a good grade of glue, the small hard pieces, when examined the following day, should have absorbed most of the water in which they were soaking. They should also have swelled to several times their original size, and be soft and jellylike.

4. The proportions of glue and water vary according to the grade of glue and the kind of wood to be glued. A certain standard grade of glue is mixed in the proportions of 1 part of glue to 2 parts of water for hardwoods, but only 1½ parts of water for softwoods.

5. Obtain these proportions from the manufacturer, weigh the glue and water, and let it soak in the glue pot overnight. Be sure to clean both glue pot and brushes thoroughly, because old scraps of glue will pollute a new batch. The old-style glue pot was just a cast-iron double boiler with water in the outer vessel. Very often, when it was not watched, the water would boil away and then the glue would boil over and spoil.

6. It was found that when glue was heated to more than 145 deg., its binding powers were greatly diminished. This led to the invention of the modern glue pot, which has no water jacket, but is heated electrically

and automatically to only 145 deg. It is recommended to use a type that has a lid, because that helps to prevent evaporation.

7. Repeated heatings weaken the glue and it also becomes thicker through evaporation. As the glue should be quite thin and run freely from the brush, more water has to be added and this further weakens the glue.

8. *Casein glue* is made from the curds of skimmed milk to which an alkali is added. The finished product is a fine, yellow powder.

9. This powder is mixed with an equal amount of cold water by volume. The glue powder is poured into the water while stirring briskly for about a minute. The mixture then is allowed to stand for about 15 minutes, after which it is again stirred for a minute.

10. The glue is now ready to use. It is much thicker than animal glue, but squeezes easily out of a joint when it is pressed together. Casein glue does not set for 15 to 20 minutes and therefore gives the operator plenty of time to glue and clamp his work.

11. Casein glue is water resistant and can be used in temperatures below 70 deg. It is used for all ordinary gluing jobs, in veneering, and in gluing up beams, partitions, and other structural forms used in modern carpentry.

12. As the glue is mixed fresh every day, it is always of uniform strength. It has the disadvantage of staining all wood. There is a casein glue, however, that is stainless, but it is less water-resistant.

13. *Resin glue* is made of formaldehyde, uric acid, and other chemicals. The finished product is a fine, white powder resembling casein glue. One type of resin glue is mixed with cold water and used like casein glue.

14. Resin glue is waterproof and stainless, and makes a perfect bond on surfaces that fit well together. It cannot be used in temperatures below 70 deg. Another type of resin glue is made for hot pressing. Resin glue is used in the manufacture of plywood and molded veneer work on airplanes, gliders, etc. It is also most satisfactory for ordinary cabinetwork.

15. *Vegetable glue* is made by grinding the wood of the cassava bush* into a fine, flourlike powder. This powder is mixed with water to which a quantity of caustic soda is added (usually 3 per cent by weight). The mixture is then heated. Vegetable glue is used cold, but is so viscous and stringy that it can only be applied by mechanical glue spreaders. It is not suitable for shopwork, but is used in the plywood industry and for laying linoleum.

16. *Blood-albumen glue* is made of beef blood to which an alkali is added. It is made into flakes which readily dissolve in water after a preliminary soaking of about an hour. It is used to glue plywood panels which must be heated while being clamped. As this glue is waterproof, it is also used in the manufacture of canoes and airplanes. It is not suitable for shopwork.

215. General Directions for Gluing. *Animal Glue.* When using animal glue the work must be done very quickly, because the glue sets

---

*The cassava bush grows in Brazil, Africa, the Malay States and in other tropical countries. It is from the root of this plant that tapioca is obtained.

and chills so fast. The whole gluing job must therefore be well thought out and planned in advance.

1. Have all pieces to be glued ready so far as tool operations are concerned. Mark them plainly to show how they are to be joined.

2. Prepare blocks needed to protect the finished surfaces from being marred by clamps or hand screws. Have a few extra ones on hand.

3. Adjust all necessary clamps and hand screws to the right opening or width between jaws.

4. Place them in a convenient position together with the framing squares, try squares, mallets, rules, chisels, or other tools necessary for the gluing job.

5. Clamp the pieces together without glue, in order to make sure that every part fits as it should and to find out the best way to apply the clamps.

6. Close all doors and windows so that no cold draft chills the glue while it is being applied. In the wintertime, it is well to warm the pieces to be glued by placing them on or near a steam radiator, because glue applied to a cold surface chills immediately. Chilled glue does not penetrate into the pores of the wood, nor can it be squeezed out of a joint. It, therefore, makes a poor bond, and such a joint comes apart when the glue later hardens and dries.

7. Apply the glue quickly to both members of each joint, but be careful not to smear it or get glue spots on finished surfaces. As far as possible hold each part over the glue pot while applying the glue so that the excess can drip back into the pot (Fig. 533).

8. Clamp the pieces together as quickly as possible and then check the job for squareness or flatness as the case may be.

9. Scrape off the surplus glue with a dull chisel after it has set but before it has dried hard.

It is usually advisable, and very often necessary to have one or more helpers when gluing.

Casein and Resin glue. (10) When using casein or resin glue the

Fig. 533. Holding work over glue pot while applying the glue

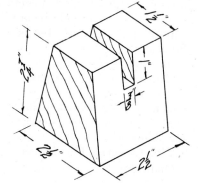

Fig. 534. Block in which to place bar clamp

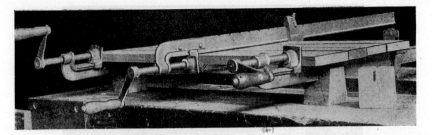

Fig. 535. Gluing boards edge to edge

method of procedure is about the same, except that speed is not so important as these glues set slower (in about 15 minutes).

11. With regard to temperature, the same precautions should be taken with resin glue, but casein glue can be used just as well in a cold room and on cold wood. Clean off casein and resin glue with a piece of clean cotton waste moistened with hot water.

216. To Glue Two or More Boards Edge to Edge. (1) Joint the edges as explained in Article 157, and number the boards in the order they are to be placed.

2. Prepare four blocks, as shown in Figure 534, for the two clamps to be placed underneath the boards at each extremity.

Fig. 536. Applying glue simultaneously
to the edges

3. Place the boards on top of these clamps, and put a third clamp on top of the boards in the center (Fig. 535). Tighten up the center clamp only, and see if the joints are tight all along and especially at the ends. The joints should be so tight at the ends that it is impossible to move the boards up or down by pressing on them with the hands.

4. Loosen the center clamp, and adjust the other two to the right opening.

5. Apply glue simultaneously to the two edges by holding the boards in a vertical position (Fig. 536).

Fig. 537. Testing glued boards for flatness

6. Tighten the center clamp on top of the boards first, and then the two underneath at either end.

7. Bring the surfaces of the boards to the same level by striking them with a mallet. This should be done after the clamps have been tightened.

8. Test for flatness with a framing square (Fig. 537). If the boards bulge in the center, this condition usually can be corrected by clamping them to the iron clamp below with one or two hand screws.

9. Sight along the boards to see that they have not been sprung out of shape in the gluing process.

10. When large table tops consisting of several boards are to be glued, it is necessary to use three or more clamps below and two or more above. Two or more heavy pieces, as 2 by 4 in., with one straight edge are also clamped across the top with hand screws so as to make it level (Fig. 538).

11. As boards glued together to form tops must be planed after gluing, no particular care need be taken in this case to protect the surfaces or outside edges.

12. When the gluing process has been completed, the boards with the clamps attached may be lifted out of the gluing blocks (Fig. 535) and placed against a wall to dry.

217. To Glue Bookshelves. (1) Finish and sandpaper the inside faces of the sides and both faces of the shelves, and try them together before applying the glue. Number all the joints.

2. Prepare short heavy blocks about 2 by 2 in. and as long as the sides are wide. Two blocks and two clamps are needed for every shelf. Each

Fig. 538. Planks clamped across glued-up table top
to make it flat.

block should have one planed side. Blocks, as shown in Figure 539 will not bend when clamped and therefore keep sides flat.

3. Place one of the sides flat on the bench with the inside face up. Apply glue to the dadoes with a small brush and to both ends of the shelves.

4. Insert the shelves in their corresponding dadoes, apply glue to the dadoes in the other side, and place that side on top of the shelf ends so that each enters in the dado cut for it.

5. Drive the joints together by striking on the upper side with a mallet, protecting this side from being marred by placing a piece of wood over each joint while it is being driven together.

6. Place the bookcase in an upright position, and apply the clamps. The heavy blocks extending across the sides will prevent them from bulging in the middle, which they are very likely to do when clamps are forcing the front and rear edges together, especially when the joints are tight.

7. Try for squareness by placing a try square on both ends of each

Fig. 539. Squaring bookcase by placing the clamps obliquely

shelf. If the shelves are not quite square with the sides, this defect can easily be remedied by changing the clamps from their horizontal position to an oblique one (Fig. 539).

8. Clean off the surplus glue, both on the upper and lower parts of the shelves as explained in Article 215.

218. To Glue a Frame or Panel. (1) Place two clamps in the blocks as explained in Article 216.

2. Number the mortise-and-tenon joints, and try them first without glue.

3. Apply glue both to the mortises and tenons. For the mortises a small, flat brush is needed. A small stick wrapped with a piece of waste or rag at one end may also serve the purpose. Protect finished sides by placing small blocks between them and the clamps.

4. If a panel is to be inserted between the four members of the frame, no glue should be applied either to the panel or the groove into which it fits. A panel should be free to expand or contract in accordance with the moisture it absorbs or gives off to the surrounding air.

5. Test the frame for squareness by placing a try square in the inside

Fig. 540. Two paneled sides of a cabinet clamped and
held together with hand screws

Fig. 541. Measuring diagonals

corners. Correct any angles being out of square by shifting the clamps or, in extreme cases, by applying a clamp diagonally. Also test for flatness and "wind" by placing a steel square across the rails and glued points. Correct any unevenness by clamping heavy pieces across the frame.

6. In cabinets, or stools, having two opposite sides alike, each side is glued up as explained before, after which they are clamped together with hand screws, inside faces together (Fig. 540). This tends to correct any twisting of legs or rails, and will insure perfectly square joints when the cabinet or stool finally has been assembled.

7. Clean off the surplus glue with a chisel or waste moistened in hot water as explained in Article 215.

219. To Glue a Cabinet. (1) Plane, scrape, and sand the two sides which were glued as explained in Article 218, and fit the back, bottom, and front rails in place. It is easier to finish the sides before gluing the cabinet, because they can be clamped to the bench. Clamp without gluing to test accuracy of construction.

2. Glue, as explained before, with one side flat on the bench. Place the cabinet in the natural position and apply clamps, being careful to protect the finished sides with small blocks preferably of softwood.

3. Test for squareness with a framing square and by measuring the diagonals (Fig. 541). Adjust any inaccuracy by moving the clamps so that they are close against the sides at one end, and away from them at the opposite end. This is the same principle as is shown in Figure 539.

4. If the error cannot be corrected by any movement of the clamps,

another clamp may be fastened diagonally on the corners having the longest diagonal, and tightened until the diagonals are even. A stick of the correct length also may be placed between the corners having the shortest diagonal.

5. Clean off the surplus glue as explained in Article 215, steps 9 and 11.

220. To Glue a Drawer. (1) Fit the pieces together without glue, and have clamps and blocks ready. All the inside surfaces of the drawer should be finished and sanded.

2. Glue the dovetails first, and then the rear piece.

3. Place a piece of paper over the dovetails so as to prevent the blocks from sticking to the sides. The blocks should be fairly heavy and as long as the width of the sides. One or two clamps are necessary at the front and rear, depending upon the depth of the drawer.

4. Measure the diagonals very carefully, and insert a stick if necessary as explained in Article 219.

5. Place the drawer on a flat surface to make sure it is level. If two corners are high, adjust the clamps until it is level. In extreme cases, clamp the drawer to the flat surface, or place weights on it until all four corners touch.

6. Clean off all surplus glue, and set the drawer away to dry.

7. The bottom is slid into the groove and fastened to the underside of the rear board with brads or screws. In case of shrinkage, these screws can be removed and the bottom pushed farther toward the front. Some people prefer to glue the bottom to the front of the drawer (Fig. 512).

221. To Glue a Chair. (1) Glue the back and front separately, and set them away to dry.

2. After cleaning and sanding, fit the side rails and stretchers, if any, in place.

3. Apply glue to the mortises and tenons as explained in Article 218, and clamp them together, using blocks to protect the finished surfaces from being marred by the clamps.

4. Measure the diagonals very carefully, and adjust the clamps until they are even.

5. Clean off all surplus glue, both inside and outside. Blocks are usually glued and screwed to the inside corners to strengthen the joints.

222. To Glue Doweled Joints and Segments. (1) Point all the dowels a little so that they will enter their corresponding holes easier.

Fig. 542. Gluing segments

Fig. 543. Clamping a simplified circular table with column clamp and hand screws

Also cut a small V groove along the side of each dowel so that the air and glue may escape when the dowel is driven into its hole (Art. 175).

2. Put glue in one set of holes with a small brush or stick. Dip one end of each dowel in the glue and drive it in place with a hammer. Wipe off surplus glue with a piece of dry waste or rag.

3. Put glue in the other set of holes, on the projecting ends of the dowels, and on the edges of the wood to be joined together.

4. Clamp as explained in Article 218, if the work is straight.

5. If segments or curved pieces are to be clamped, a strong rope or strip of leather is wound twice around the work and twisted by means

Fig. 544. Gluing irregular shape

of a short piece of dowel rod, until the tightening of the rope brings the joints together (Fig. 542). It is advisable to use sash cord, because of its strength.

Special clamps, called "column clamps" (Fig. 102), consisting of an iron chain and screw, are recommended for this type of gluing job (Fig. 543). Place small pieces of wood between the chain and the finished surfaces.

6. Legs may be glued to a turned column by clamping a hand screw firmly to each leg near the joint. This hand screw affords a hold for two other hand screws, which force the leg tightly against the column (Fig. 403).

7. Glue one leg at a time, and allow it to dry before attempting to glue the next one. Fasten the column in a vise during the gluing process.

8. Irregular shapes are glued much in the same manner, except that the blocks must be shaped to fit the curves (Figs. 540 and 544).

REVIEW QUESTIONS

1. The best known glues are: .... (name five) ....
2. Animal glue is made from .... and sold in (a) ....;
   (b) ...., or (c) ....
3. Animal glue must be .... before it is ready to heat.
4. Temperatures higher than .... the glue.
5. The modern glue pot is heated by .... and should have a ....
   to prevent ....
6. Repeated heatings .... and .... the glue.
7. The advantages of casein glue over animal glue are: (a)...................;
   (b) ....; (c) ....; (d) ....
8. Casein glue is made of .... Resin glue is made of ....
   Vegetable glue is made of .... Blood-albumin glue is made of ....
9. Chilled animal glue does not ...., nor can it ....
   out of a joint.
10. The proper time to remove surplus animal glue is ....
11. It is necessary to have the following tools ready for a gluing job (name six).
12. Boards glued edge to edge can be made absolutely flat by ....
13. When clamping a bookcase, the shelves can be squared with the sides by
    ....
14. When gluing a cabinet or table, glue the .... first and clamp
    them ....
15. Check a glued cabinet for squareness by ....
16. Irregular shaped surfaces can be clamped by ....
17. The circular rim of a table is clamped with .... or ....
18. Why should thick gluing blocks be used across the sides when clamping a bookcase?
19. The glued sides of a cabinet should be .... before gluing the
    whole cabinet, because ....
20. Resin glue is mixed and handled like ...., but can only be used
    in temperatures ....

Chapter 14

METAL FASTENINGS

Although wood very frequently is fastened with glue, it is also fastened together with nails, screws, and bolts. Different kinds of hardware as hinges, locks, door bolts, catches, casters, drawer pulls and knobs, escutcheons, etc., are used on movable parts as doors, table leaves, drawers, etc.

225. Nails are used in house framing, roofing, interior trim, box making, upholstery, and for many other purposes. They are, therefore, made in many shapes and of different materials as steel wire, iron, brass, copper, etc. Some of the most common nails used in the woodworking industry are wire nails, box nails, casing nails, finishing nails or brads, cut nails, and tacks (Fig. 547).

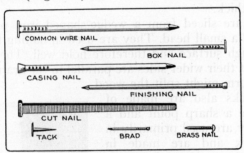

Fig. 547. Nails

1. Common wire nails are made with a large, flat head in lengths from 1 to 6 in. Larger sizes are usually called spikes. The length of common wire nails is generally given by the word "penny" instead of in inches.

2. The penny system originated in England, but there is some difference of opinion as to its original meaning. Some claim that the word penny meant pound and that it referred to the weight of 1000 nails. Therefore, 1000 nails weighing six pounds were called sixpenny nails. At any rate, the relation of the length in inches to the penny system is as follows:

2-penny nail is 1 in. long	8-penny nail is 2½ in. long
3-penny nail is 1¼ in. long	9-penny nail is 2¾ in. long
4-penny nail is 1½ in. long	10-penny nail is 3 in. long
5-penny nail is 1¾ in. long	12-penny nail is 3¼ in. long
6-penny nail is 2 in. long	16-penny nail is 3½ in. long
7-penny nail is 2¼ in. long	20-penny nail is 4 in. long

3. Each length of common wire nails is made from a standard thickness of wire. In colonial days, nails were forged from iron and were therefore scarce and expensive. In modern times wire nails are made on a machine, which straightens the wire as it is fed from a roll, cuts it to length, forms the point and head, and ejects it from the machine.

4. Common wire nails are sold by the 100-lb. keg and are used mostly in house carpentry and in rough construction work.

5. Box nails are made like common wire nails, but are thinner than wire nails of the same length. To make them hold better, box nails are sometimes barbed or coated with resin or cement.

6. Casing nails have the same wire gauge as box nails. They are used for interior trim and can be set below the surface of the wood, because they have a small head.

7. Brads or finishing nails are made in lengths from ⅜ to 3 in. They are used like casing nails and have a very small head. The same length of brad is obtainable in different thicknesses. They are packed in 1-lb. cardboard boxes on which both length and thickness are marked, as for example 1¼ in. by 16 or 1¼ in. by 18. The last number refers to the thickness of the wire or wire gauge. *The higher the number, the thinner the nail.* An 18-gauge nail is about 1/20 in. thick; a 12-gauge nail is about 1/10 in. thick.

8. Cut nails are sliced from a wedge-shaped iron plate. They have a blunt end and a small head. They are used in nailing flooring, because they have a rough surface and therefore hold well. They should always be driven so that their wider sides are parallel to the grain otherwise their wedge-shaped form might split the wood.

9. Carpet tacks also are made of iron. They have a sharp point and a large head. They are used primarily in upholstery work and are made in lengths from 3/16 to 18/16 in. Their size is also indicated in ounces. An 8-oz. tack, for example, is ½ in. long. Like penny, ounce is an old term which originally meant the weight of 1000 tacks.

10. Shingle nails, plaster-board nails, and felt-roofing nails are short nails with very large heads. Because workmen are in the habit of putting such nails in their mouths, they are sterilized by dipping them in muriatic acid. This gives them a blue color.

11. Brass, copper, and galvanized iron nails are used on work which is exposed to the weather and therefore likely to be damaged by rust.

Fig. 548. Boring hole in hardwood with a nail

226. Rules for Driving Nails. (1) Glue, grease, or dirt on the face of a hammer will cause it to glance off when striking a nail. Clean it with a piece of fine sandpaper.

2. Nails driven in a line following the grain may cause the wood to split. The best way is to stagger them.

3. When driving thin nails in hardwood, it is recommended first to bore holes for them. As a bit, use the same size nail as the one to be driven, cut off its head, and hold it in the chuck of a hand drill (Fig. 548).

4. Always clinch a nail with the grain, because its point can then be driven in between the wood fibers. This cannot be done if the nail is bent across the grain.

5. If the point of a nail comes outside the surface, drive it back with a nail set until its head projects enough above the wood to be pulled out with a hammer.

6. A nail has a tendency to follow the grain of the wood. Blunting its point with a hammer helps to drive it in a straight line.

7. Place a block under the head of a claw hammer to protect the surface of the wood when pulling a nail (Fig. 549).

Fig. 549. Pulling nail with claw hammer. Block placed under hammer head to protect the surface of the wood

227. Screws for Fastening Wood are superior to nails, because they hold better, look better, and can be removed easily and without damage to the wood. Like nails, screws are made in many different shapes and sizes and of different materials as brass, soft steel, and iron. Screws are also brass or nickel plated, or galvanized. The most common screws are: flathead, roundhead, oval-countersunk head, Phillips head, lag screws, drive screws, screw eyes, screw hooks, and cup hooks (Fig. 550).

1. Screws are made in lengths from ¼ to 5 in. and in wire gauges from 0 to 24. The wire gauge for screws runs opposite to that for nails — *the higher the number, the thicker the screw.* No. 5, for example, is ⅛ in. thick and No. 14 is ¼ in. thick. Screws are packed in cardboard boxes

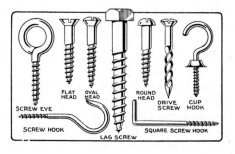

Fig. 550. Screws

Fig. 551.
Phillips head
screw

which hold one gross each. The length and wire gauge are marked on the box as for instance, 1¼ in. by 9.

2. Flathead and roundhead screws are the most commonly used. Flathead steel screws are bright, and roundhead screws generally are blue. In places where screws might rust, brass, brass-plated, nickel-plated, or galvanized-iron screws are used.

3. Phillips head screws have a flat or oval head with two slots at right angles to each other, but not extending to the edge of the screw head (Fig. 551). They can be driven only with a special screw driver, but faster and easier than ordinary screws and with less slipping of the screw driver.

4. Lag screws are made of iron. They have a square head like a bolt and are from ¼ to 1 in. thick and from 1 to 16 in. long (Fig. 550). They are used mostly in construction work and for expansion bolts (see Art. 229, step 8).

5. Drive screws have a very steep thread and can, therefore, be driven with a hammer instead of a screw driver. They are used instead of nails on such jobs as fastening galvanized iron sheets, etc. (Fig. 550).

6. Screw hooks, screw eyes, and cup hooks are made of steel, brass, and galvanized iron (Fig. 550). They are manufactured in many sizes and are used principally in the household for hanging pictures, curtains, kitchen utensils, keys, etc.

228. Rules for Driving Screws.   (1) When two boards are to be fastened together with screws, a hole of the same diameter as the shank of the screw must be bored through one, and a smaller hole, equal to the root diameter of the screw, must be bored part way into the other. The root diameter of a screw is the thickness of the central part around which the threads are cut. The sizes of holes for different screw gauges are given in Figure 552.

2. In hardwoods the small hole or pilot hole must be bored as deep as the screw enters; in softwoods it may be bored to half this depth or it may even be omitted. The large hole must be big enough to permit the screw to be pushed through with the fingers. Its upper end must be countersunk when flathead or oval-countersunk screws are used.

3. Soap or wax rubbed on the threads of a screw reduces friction and

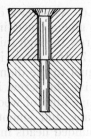

Gauge No. of Screw	4	5	6	7	8	9	10	11	12
Dia. of First Hole	$\frac{1}{8}$	$\frac{1}{8}$	$\frac{5}{32}$	$\frac{5}{32}$	$\frac{3}{16}$	$\frac{3}{16}$	$\frac{3}{16}$	$\frac{7}{32}$	$\frac{7}{32}$
Dia. of Second Hole	$\frac{3}{32}$	$\frac{3}{32}$	$\frac{1}{8}$	$\frac{1}{8}$	$\frac{5}{32}$	$\frac{5}{32}$	$\frac{5}{32}$	$\frac{5}{32}$	$\frac{5}{32}$

Fig. 552. Table showing size of holes in inches to be bored for screws of various gauges

makes it much easier to drive. It therefore also reduces the danger of "twisting off," which means that the screw breaks when too much force is applied to drive it in place. It always breaks at the point where the threads end, and the threaded part remains imbedded in the wood. Such broken parts are almost impossible to remove without greatly damaging the surface.

4. As brass screws are softer than steel screws, they twist off more easily. It is, therefore, a good plan to drive a steel screw of the same size first, especially in hardwoods, then remove it and drive the brass screw. In this way the steel screw cuts the threads in the wood for the brass screw.

5. It is important to use a screw driver that fits the slot in the screw and whose sides and end are flat and square. A screw driver that is too thin or has rounded edges constantly "climbs" out of the slot and damages it so that the screw becomes more and more difficult to drive and ruins its appearance (Fig. 553).

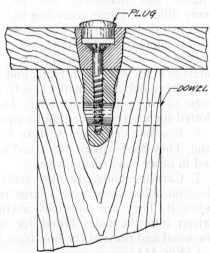

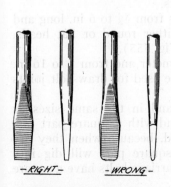

Fig. 553. Right and wrong shapes of the end of a screw driver

Fig. 554. Screw in end wood passing through dowel. Screw set below surface and hole plugged

6. As screws do not hold well in endwood, it is sometimes advisable to glue a dowel into the wood a short distance from the end. Driving the screw through this dowel makes the joint very strong (Fig. 554).

7. If a screw is to be concealed in the wood, first bore a shallow hole equal to the diameter of the head, then bore the regular screw hole and drive the screw in place. Now cut a plug with a plug cutter from the same kind of wood, and glue it into the hole above the screw. When dry, plane and smooth it level with the surrounding surface. Plugs with rounded heads may be bought in hardware stores (Fig. 554).

229. Bolts are used in woodwork where great strength is required as when timbers are bolted together, in draw-bolt joints (Fig. 394), or when wood is fastened to metal or masonry.

1. Bolts differ from screws in that they do not taper to a point, but are of the same diameter from one end to the other. A head is made on one end of a bolt. The other end is threaded for a nut, which is usually square or hexagonal.

2. Washers or metal plates are usually placed between the work being clamped and the head and nut of the bolt. When great pressure is not required, a wing-nut (Fig. 555), which can be screwed off or on by hand, is sometimes used.

3. Threads on bolts are not nearly as steep as those on wood screws. They are cut by hand with a steel die, by machine on an engine lathe, or on a special thread-cutting machine.

4. Bolts are made in different lengths and diameters and in many different forms according to the work they are to do. The ones most commonly used by the woodworker are stove bolts, iron bolts, carriage bolts, expansion bolts, and toggle bolts.

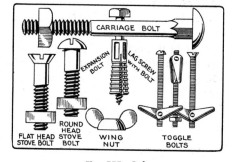

Fig. 555. Bolts

5. Stove bolts are small, cheaply made bolts from $\frac{3}{8}$ to 6 in. long and from $\frac{1}{8}$ to $\frac{1}{2}$ in. in diameter. They have either round or flat heads, slotted for a screw driver, and a square nut (Fig. 555).

6. Iron bolts are from 3/16 to $\frac{3}{4}$ in. in diameter and from 1 to 16 in. long. They have square heads and nuts and are used for draw-bolt joints and in other construction work.

7. Carriage bolts are also made of iron and in the same sizes as the iron bolts. They have a large rounded head with a square part just below it. They are especially useful for wood, because when they are driven into the holes bored for them, the square part will dig into the wood and prevent the bolt from turning. Carriage bolts have a square nut (Fig. 555).

8. Expansion bolts are used in brick, stone, and concrete. They consist of two parts, a lag screw and a shield (Fig. 555). The shield is a

split, cast-iron cylinder threaded on the inside for the lag screw, and corrugated on the outside so that it will hold in brick or concrete when expanded. When timbers or machines are to be fastened to masonry, holes to fit the shields are first drilled with a star drill. When the lag screw then is driven into the shield, its two halves expand in the hole. Shields are made in sizes corresponding to diameters of lag screws.

9. Toggle bolts are used to fasten wood or metal to hollow partitions and hollow-tile walls. The bolt is a stove bolt with a special nut made of two pieces of bent sheet iron hinged together (Fig. 555). When the hole

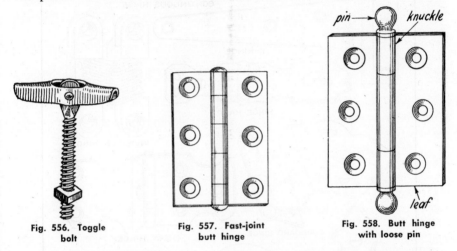

Fig. 556. Toggle bolt   Fig. 557. Fast-joint butt hinge   Fig. 558. Butt hinge with loose pin

is made in the thin wall of hollow tile, the two wings of the nut are folded together, and the bolt is inserted in the wall. As soon as it is through the hole, a spring spreads the wings of the nut apart. Another type of toggle bolt has just a single bent-iron nut which is heavier in one end than in the other. When it is pushed through the hole the heavy end drops down at right angles to the bolt (Fig. 556).

230. Hinges are used a great deal both in cabinetwork and in carpentry. They are, therefore, made in many different shapes and of different materials as iron, galvanized iron, brass, brass plated and nickel plated.

1. The most common hinges used in cabinetwork are: butt hinges, chest hinges, desk hinges, continuous hinges, screen hinges, pivot hinges, invisible hinges, and card-table hinges.

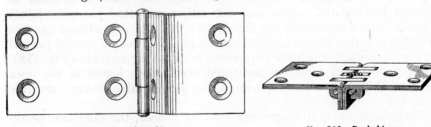

Fig. 559. Chest hinge   Fig. 560. Desk hinge

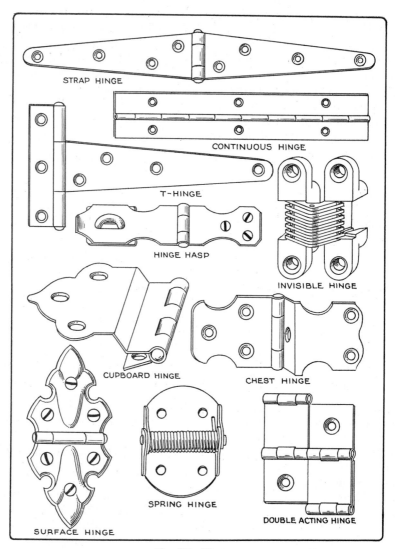

STRAP HINGE

CONTINUOUS HINGE

T-HINGE

HINGE HASP

INVISIBLE HINGE

CUPBOARD HINGE

CHEST HINGE

SURFACE HINGE

SPRING HINGE

DOUBLE ACTING HINGE

Fig. 561. Hinges

2. The butt hinge is the type most frequently used. It is made in different lengths and widths and has either a riveted pin (fast-joint) (Fig. 557) or a removable pin (loose-pin). A butt hinge always has two rectangular leaves joined together with a pin. The round, central part of the hinge, through which the pin passes, is called the knuckle (Fig. 558). The width of butt hinges is measured across both leaves in the open position. Butt hinges are used on doors, boxes, table leaves (see rule joint, Art. 210), etc.

When loose-pin butt hinges are used on a door, the door can be removed by simply taking out the pins.

3. The chest hinge is a butt hinge with one leaf bent at right angles in the center (Fig. 559).

4. The desk hinge is also a butt hinge used for hinging the lid of writing desks or secretaries. It is always made of brass (Fig. 560).

5. The continuous hinge is another butt hinge sold by the foot of length. It is always used for hinging the lids on pianos (Fig. 561).

6. The screen or double-acting hinge (Fig. 562), has three knuckles and can, as its name implies, open both ways.

7. The pivot or pin hinge (Fig. 563) consists of two flat, narrow, rectangular pieces of iron. One of them has a pin which fits into a hole in the other. The part having the pin is screwed into the ends of the door, and the other part into the frame. Two hinges are needed for each door, one on top and one on the bottom. Pivot hinges, which are invisible, are used on cabinet doors and also on doors that open both ways, as for example between the kitchen and the dining room.

8. Invisible hinges, also named Soss hinges after the inventor (Fig. 564), are used principally on small cabinet doors. They are mortised into the edge of the door and the door frame. They are quite easy to apply, but are not very strong, because they are cast.

9. Card-table hinges are narrow brass hinges riveted together (Fig. 565). They are set into the edges of the two leaves of a card table.

10. Besides the butt hinge, a carpenter also uses a surface hinge, cupboard hinge, spring hinge, strap hinge, T hinge, and hinge hasp.

11. The surface hinge is shaped to give it a more decorative appearance. It is used on boxes and small doors and is generally brass or nickel plated (Fig. 561). A surface hinge is simply screwed to the wood surface without cutting any recess for it.

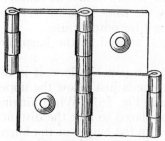

Fig. 562. Double-acting hinge

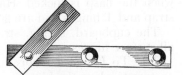

Fig. 563. Pivot or pin hinge

Fig. 565. Card-table hinge

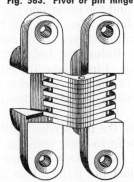

Fig. 564. Invisible hinge

12. One leaf of the cupboard hinge is like a butt hinge and is fastened to the framework of the cupboard. The other is offset or bent over the edge of the door and shaped (Fig. 561). Cupboard doors usually have a rabbeted edge.

13. The spring hinge is used on light-weight doors which are to close automatically, such as screen doors. It has a coil spring wound around the pin (Fig. 561).

14. The strap hinge (Fig. 561) has long tapered leaves and is used mainly on rough work such as cellar or garage doors or large tool boxes.

15. The T hinge is used in the same way as the strap hinge. One of its leaves is like a butt hinge and the other like a strap hinge. Both of these hinges are made of plain and galvanized iron (Fig. 561).

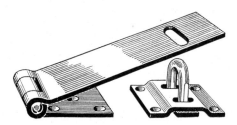

Fig. 566. Hinge hasp

16. The hinge hasp (Fig. 566) has two parts — a square plate to which a heavy wire loop is riveted, and a hinge, one leaf of which has screw holes and the other a slot that fits over the wire loop. The hasp is a locking device used with a padlock. The leaf which is screwed to the wood is covered by the slotted leaf, so that the screws cannot be removed when the hasp is locked. Hasps are used in the same type of work as strap and T hinges and are generally galvanized for outdoor use.

The cupboard, spring, strap, and T hinges, as well as the hasp, are all surface hinges.

231. To Hinge a Door. (1) When hinging a paneled door, it is the custom to place the hinges so that the upper one is just below the upper rail and the lower one just above the lower rail (Fig. 567). When hinging the lid of a box or chest, the hinges should be placed so that the distance from the hinges to the end of the box is equal to the length of the hinge.

2. Before the hinges can be attached, the door must be fitted to the frame. First plane the edge which is to be hinged, and then square the top of the door with that edge. If it is a large, paneled door, the ends of the stiles, called the "horns," are first sawed off.

3. The next step is to plane the door to width and finally saw and plane the lower edge until it fits in the frame. It is best to make a rather close fit to begin with, for it is easy to plane off more later on if necessary.

4. Now place the door in its opening so that its upper edge is tight against the frame. This may be done by driving wedges under it. Mark the position of the hinges both on the door and on the frame (Fig. 567).

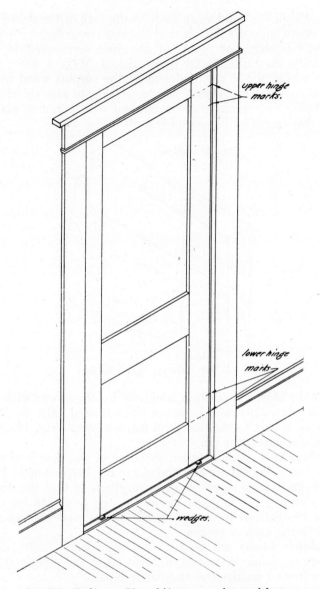

Fig. 567. Marking position of hinges on a door and frame

5. Remove the door, and square lines across its edge from the points marked on its face. Do likewise on the frame.

6. Set the butt gauge equal to the width of the leaves, not including the knuckle, which should project beyond the face of the door and frame in order to permit the door to swing freely. Mark the width on both door and frame.

7. When hinging a cabinet door, set the butt gauge to half the thick-

ness of the "knuckle," and mark lines on the face of the door and frame. On larger doors, only the thickness of the leaf is marked.

8. Chisel the outline or "gain" of the hinge very carefully, making a small V cut on the inside of the lines marked. Make a series of shallow chisel cuts within the V cut, and remove the surplus wood by chiseling carefully across the grain with the bevel side of the chisel up (Figs. 420 and 568). The recess may be finished with a router plane. Hinge gains also may be cut with a portable router (Fig. 208).

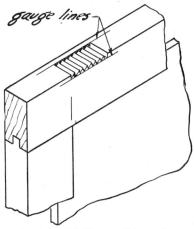

Fig. 568. Chiseling "gain" on door

9. Place the hinges in position, and bore for the screws with a bradawl or small bit (Art. 228). If a loose-pin hinge is used, take the hinge apart and screw each part to the door and frame respectively. Place the door in position, and insert the pin.

10. If there is a crack between the edge of the door and the frame, the recesses or gains cut for the hinges are not deep enough. If the edge of the door and frame come too close together, so that the door springs back when an attempt is made to close it, the gains are too deep. This defect can be rectified by removing the hinges, and placing a piece of cardboard in the gain or recess.

232. Cabinet Locks are used on drawers, doors, desks, chests, and boxes. They are made in several different types and sizes and are either of brass or iron or partly iron and partly brass.

1. The principal parts of a lock are the lock box, the bolt, and the selvage. The lock box contains the tumblers, levers, springs, bolt, and other parts of the mechanism. The bolt is an iron bar which is moved in and out of the lock box with a key. It passes through the edge of the lock which is called the selvage.

When sizes of locks are given, the distance from the selvage to the key pin or center of cylinder is always included.

2. Some locks are furnished with a metal plate, called the strike, which corresponds in size and shape to the selvage and is fastened to the frame

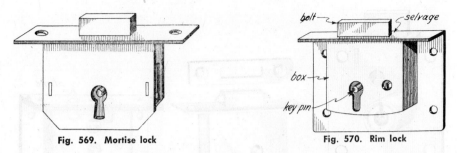

Fig. 569. Mortise lock   Fig. 570. Rim lock

of the door. It adds to the security of the lock, because it protects the wood from wear and it cannot easily be pried loose.

3. There are two kinds of cabinet locks — the mortise lock (Fig. 569) and the rim lock (Fig. 570). The mortise lock is completely set into the wood (A, Fig. 571). Some rim locks have no selvage and are screwed to the wood without cutting any recess. Others have to be recessed both for lock box and selvage (B, Fig. 571).

4. Keys are of two general kinds, barrel keys which are round and fit over a key pin, and flat keys which fit into cylinder locks (Fig. 572). Cylinder locks always are rim locks except on house doors, which have mortise locks with detachable cylinders.

5. Locks for desks, boxes, chests, and pianos are constructed to withstand an upward pull. The bolts on such locks therefore have hooklike projections, which are forced out by a spring, and engage the strike when in the locked position (Fig. 573). Some have bolts which move sideways and engage prongs on a strike which enters the lock (Fig. 574).

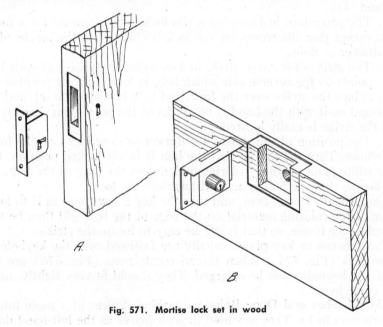

Fig. 571. Mortise lock set in wood

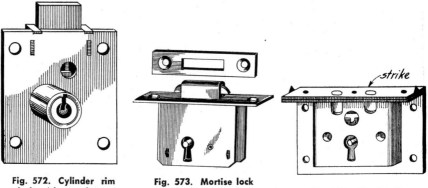

Fig. 572. Cylinder rim
lock without selvage

Fig. 573. Mortise lock
with strike for a box

Fig. 574. Chest lock

233. To Attach Locks. (1) Measure the distance from the selvage to the key pin, and lay it off on the center line or above the center line as the case may be. Bore a hole slightly larger in diameter than the barrel of the key. *Note that the key pin is not always in the center of the lock box* (Fig. 570).

2. If a mortise lock is used, bore and chisel the mortise for the lock box in the center or toward the rear edge of the wood, so that sufficient material remains in front of the lock on which to fasten the escutcheon.

3. Place the lock in the mortise, and mark around the edges of the selvage. Then remove the lock, chisel the recess for the selvage, bore for screws with a bradawl, and screw the lock in position.

4. Finish the keyhole with a keyhole saw or coping saw (Figs. 39 and 41).

5. The procedure in fastening a rim lock is the same as for a mortise lock, except that the recess for the lock is chiseled on the inside edge of the drawer or door.

6. The strikes for chest, desk, or box locks are always provided with little points on the reverse side which help in locating their position (Fig. 574). Place the strike over the lock, and lock it. Close the lid, and press or pound on it with the hand. The marks of the points can then be seen, and the strike is easily located.

7. The position of the strikes for drawer or door locks can be located as follows. Turn the key so that the bolt is in the locked position. Put a little white paint or other coloring material on the edge of the bolt. Turn the key so that the bolt is again drawn into the lock.

Close the door or drawer, and turn the key a few times as if to lock it. Some of the coloring material on the edge of the bolt will then be transferred to the frame, so that it will be easy to locate the strike.

Escutcheons or key plates usually are fastened over the keyhole with brass pins (Fig. 575). When thread escutcheons (Fig. 576) are to be used, the keyhole must be enlarged. They should fit very tightly, or they will come loose.

234. Catches and Door Bolts are locking devices of a more informal nature than locks. They are used in such places as the left-hand door of double doors, tilt-top tables, or small single or double doors which need not be locked with a key. The following are the most commonly used bolts and catches in cabinetwork.

1. *Elbow catches* (Fig. 577) may be used on left-hand cupboard or bookcase doors. The plate is simply screwed to the underside of the center shelf, and the catch to the inside of the left-hand door.

2. *Door bolts* (Fig. 578) are screwed to the inside of left-hand bookcase doors near the top and bottom of the door, so that the bolt locks into the frame around the doors. Sometimes only one bolt is used on a door. Door bolts are sometimes fitted with a steel spring, which automatically keeps the bolt in the locked position. They are usually furnished with a strike plate. A hole must be chiseled or bored in the frame for the bolt.

3. *A flush bolt* (Fig. 579) is the neatest type of door bolt. It is fastened to the edge of the left-hand door and must be set flush with the wood. Flush bolts are sold in different widths according to the thickness of the wood. The strike plate is set flush with the doorframe, and a hole is bored for the bolt.

4. *Ball catches* (Fig. 580) or friction catches consist of small brass cylinders with a steel spring bearing against a steel ball. They are used on small doors such as those on a phonograph or a radio cabinet, and are usually fitted into the upper or lower edges of the door. They are manufactured in diameters of $\frac{1}{4}$, 5/16, and $\frac{3}{8}$ in., and all that is necessary to do to attach them is to bore a hole of the proper diameter in the edge of the door. The strike, which is beveled on one edge, is set into the frame flush with the wood. The beveled side should be placed toward the front.

5. *A table catch* (Fig. 581) is in reality a small spring lock, the bolt of which is moved in or out by means of a spring and a knob. A table

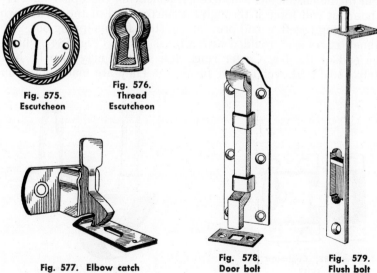

Fig. 575.
Escutcheon

Fig. 576.
Thread
Escutcheon

Fig. 577. Elbow catch

Fig. 578.
Door bolt

Fig. 579.
Flush bolt

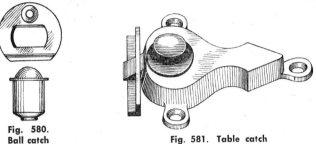

Fig. 580.
Ball catch

Fig. 581. Table catch

catch is used for locking the top of a tilt-top table in a horizontal position. It is screwed to the underside of the table top. The strike plate is fastened to the wooden block to which the top is hinged. It is set flush with the wood and a recess chiseled for the bolt (Fig. 783).

6. *A cupboard catch* (Fig. 582) is a small lock on a kitchen cabinet which is opened with a knob instead of a key. It is closed automatically by a coil spring which pushes against the bolt. A spring lock has a beveled bolt that slips easily into the strike.

235. To Attach Casters, Glides, Chair Tips, Drawer Pulls, and Knobs. (1) Casters are used on heavy pieces of furniture to make them more mobile. They are generally made with a stem and a socket. The socket has a ring of teeth at its lower extremity, while its upper end is slit for a short distance and pressed to a smaller diameter. The wheels of casters are made of steel, brass, wood, fiber, rubber, or felt (Fig. 583).

2. To attach the caster, bore a hole in the end of the leg so that the socket fits snugly, but not tight enough to split the wood when the socket is driven in place. The ring of teeth must be driven into the end wood. The stem of the caster has a little enlargement on the upper end. A tap with a hammer will force it through the narrow end of the socket, which will again spring together and prevent the stem from slipping out.

3. Some casters are provided with a brass socket (Fig. 584) which fits over the end of the leg. Caster rings and sockets may also be bought separately and fitted over legs of furniture. They are made both square

Fig. 582. Cupboard
catch

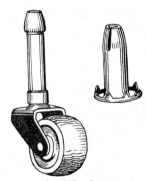

Fig. 583. Caster

Fig. 584.
Brass socket

Fig. 585. Glide

Fig. 586. Chair tip

and round, and furnished in various sizes. They are decorative and prevent the wood from splitting.

4. *Glides* are hardened, polished, cup-formed pieces of steel used instead of casters (Fig. 585). They are provided with steel points and are fastened to the legs of furniture simply by driving them into the wood with a hammer.

5. *Chair tips* (Fig. 586) are similar to glides except that they are made of soft material, such as rubber, felt, or leather. They are attached to chair legs either by screws, nails, or steel points.

6. *Drawer pulls and knobs* are made in a great variety of patterns to conform to the furniture designs of the different historical periods. They are fitted with machine screws about 3/16 in. in diameter and 1 in. long which screw into holes, bored and tapped in the pull itself. These screws have a round, slotted head with a small washer soldered to it (Figs. 587 to 589).

Fig. 587.
Furniture knob

Fig. 588. Furniture handle

7. After locating their position on a drawer or door, as the case may be, bore holes of the same diameter as the screw right through the wood. Place the pull in position, insert the screws from the inside of the door or drawer, and tighten them with a screw driver.

8. No definite rules can be given for the location of pulls and knobs, except that they are always placed on the horizontal center line of drawers, and usually above the center of a cabinet door. On a chest of drawers, one is placed directly below the other; i.e., the same distance from the ends of the drawer (Fig. 589).

236. To Fasten a Table Top to a Frame. In fastening a table top, provision should be made for the swelling or shrinkage of the wood. The following methods are in general use.

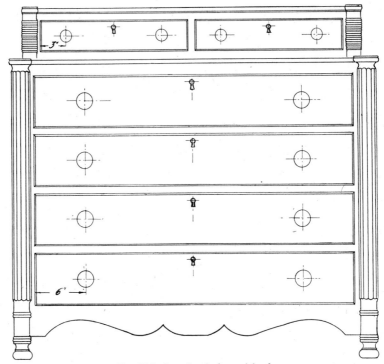

Fig. 589. Locating locks and knobs

1. Holes are bored through the rails at an angle. The boring is done from the upper edge of the rail with a gimlet or twist bit, and a recess is cut on the inside of the rail with a gouge so as to make room for the head of the screw (A, Fig. 590).

2. A hole large enough for the head of the screw may also be bored part way through the rail with an auger bit, after which the remainder is bored with a gimlet or twist bit and the screw inserted (B, Fig. 590).

3. Strips of wood, called "cleats," about ¾ to ⅞ in. square, may be screwed to both frame and top. Holes are first bored and countersunk from two adjoining sides at right angles to each other. The cleats are then screwed to the inside surface of the rails flush with or a trifle below their upper edges (C, Fig. 590).

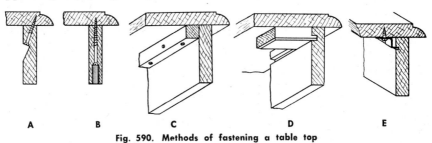

A   B   C   D   E

Fig. 590. Methods of fastening a table top

4. The top is placed face down on the bench, the frame centered on it and then fastened to it with screws driven through the holes previously bored and countersunk. Protect the finished surface of the top by placing a newspaper, a piece of cardboard, or a couple of small boards on the bench top.

5. Another method is to cut a groove on the inside of the rails before they are glued to the legs. Wooden blocks, rabbeted on the end so that they fit into the groove, are then screwed to the top at intervals (D, Fig. 590). This method permits of considerable movement of the top.

6. A modification of the wooden block is the table-top fastener, which is a small piece of iron bent at right angles. One end fits into a slit cut on the inside of the rails with a circular saw, and the other end is screwed to the top (E, Fig. 590).

REVIEW QUESTIONS

1. Nails are used for (a) ....; (b) ....; (c) ....;
   (d) ....; (e) ....
2. Nails in common use are: (a) ....; (b) ....; (c) ....;
   (d) ....; (e) ....
3. The penny system of giving sizes of nails means ....
4. Box nails hold better if they are .... or ....
5. Brads are marked with two numbers on the box, the .... and the ....
6. Cut nails are made of .... and are used for ....
   because ....
7. Which brad is the thickest, No. 16 or No. 18?
8. The length of carpet tacks is given by the word ....
9. Thin nails can be driven in hardwood if ....
10. A nail should be clinched .... the grain, because ....?.......
11. Screws are superior to nails, because ....
12. Which screw is thicker, No. 9 or No. 10?
13. A screw ¼ in. thick has a wire gauge No. ....
14. Lag screws are made of ...., have a .... head, and are used
    in .... and ....
15. The root diameter of a screw is ....
16. Make a sketch of a screw eye, a screw hook, and a cup hook.
17. To reduce friction when driving a screw, use ....
18. Twisting off means .... and is caused by ....
19. A screw driver should have .... and .... end and edges,
    and should fit ....
20. A screw will hold well in endwood if ....
21. A toggle bolt is used for .... Instead of a regular nut
    it has ....
22. An expansion bolt is used for .... Its parts are: (a) ....;
    (b) ....
23. A carriage bolt is used for .... It has a .... head and
    a .... part below it.
24. Stove bolts have .... or .... heads and a .... nut.
25. An iron bolt has a .... head and nut. It is used in ....
    and ....

26. Threads are cut on a bolt with a .... or on ....or ....
27. Name eight hinges commonly used in cabinetwork.
28. Butt hinges are of two kinds: (a) ....; (b) ....
29. The pivot hinge and the Soss hinge are both ....
30. Name six hinges commonly used in carpentry.
31. The term "surface hinge" means that ....
32. When fitting hinges to a paneled door, the upper one is placed ....
    and the lower one ....
33. When fitting hinges to a box, the distance from the end of the box to the
    hinges should be ....
34. If a door springs back when you want to close it, it is because ....
35. Cabinet locks are of two general types: (a) ....; (b) ....
36. The principal parts of a lock are: (a) ....; (b) ....;
    (c) ....; (d) ....
37. The strike makes the lock more secure, because (a) ....; (b) ....
38. A cylinder lock is always a .... lock. It opens with a .... key.
39. A drawer lock cannot be used on a box, because ....
40. The position of the strike for a chest lock is located by ....
41. The position of the strike for a door lock can be located by ....
42. Elbow catches are used on ...., ball catches on ....,
    and table catches on ....
43. A flush bolt is used on .... and set ....
44. Drawer pulls are located on .... and fastened with ....
45. Table tops are fastened to the framework with (a) ....; (b) ....;
    (c) ....; (d) ....; (e) ....

Chapter 15

WOOD TURNING

The wood-turning lathe is a link between machine and hand tools, combining the art and skill of handwork with the speed and power of the machine. Wood turning as a trade, however, has practically disappeared, because all kinds of turned work can be produced on the modern turning machine much more rapidly and accurately than is possible with the human hands.

239. History. (1) The art of wood turning is so old that detailed knowledge of its beginnings has been lost in antiquity. The most primitive lathe, called the bow lathe, is said to have been invented in Egypt and used there and in other Eastern lands long before the Christian era.

2. The bow lathe is rotated by the string of a bow wrapped around the work being turned (Fig. 595). The bow is held in one hand and the tool in the other. Strangely enough this primitive lathe is still used in parts of Asia and Africa (Fig. 596).

3. The next step in the development was the pole lathe in which a string wrapped around the work being turned was still used. One end of this string was tied to a flexible pole, bolted to the ceiling, and the other to a treadle (Fig. 597). When the treadle was pressed down to the floor, the pole would bend and the work revolve toward the turner. When the treadle was released, the pole would straighten out and rotate the work backwards. When using this lathe or the bow lathe, the wood turner was able to cut only while the work revolved toward him, which was only half the time.

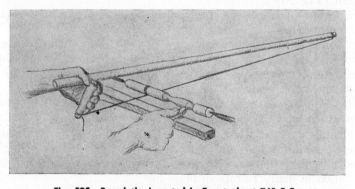

Fig. 595. Bow lathe invented in Egypt about 740 B.C.

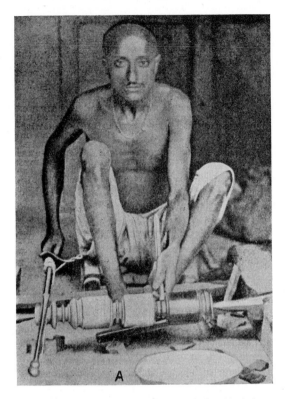

Fig. 596. A Hindu turning on bow lathe shown in
Figure 595. (Courtesy New York Museum of Science
and Industry.)

4. Later on, the treadle was connected by a crankshaft to a large wheel, which in turn was connected by a rope to a smaller wheel which rotated the lathe spindle. This same mechanical movement is used on a spinning wheel and a sewing machine, producing a continuous rotary movement (Fig. 598).

5. This type of lathe was used until about fifty years ago, when the electric motor came into general use.

6. In some localities, however, where labor was cheap, lathes were sometimes rotated by a helper turning the "great wheel." This wheel was 6 ft. in diameter, bolted to the floor and connected by belt to a cone pulley on the lathe (Fig. 599).

7. These old lathes were made entirely of wood, except for the metal spindles which held the work being turned.

8. During the sixteenth and seventeenth centuries, wood turning was practiced as a hobby by kings, queens, princes, and nobles of high rank. The costly inlaid lathes used by them, as well as examples of their work, can be found in many European museums.

240. The Wood-Turning Lathe. The modern lathe is made entirely

of iron and steel. Its principal parts are: the bed, the headstock, the tail-stock, and the tool post.

1. *The bed,* which is supported on cast-iron legs, is a substantial casting resembling two parallel I beams. The bed of smaller lathes is fastened directly to a bench, bringing it to a height of 36 in. above the floor. The upper part of the bed is called the "ways" or "shears" and has a flat, smooth surface.

2. *The headstock* is bolted to the left end of the bed and contains

Fig. 597. Pole lathe. String tied to pole and to treadle

Fig. 598. Treadle connected by crankshaft to large wheel
which is connected to small wheel with rope

Fig. 599. Great wheel lathe

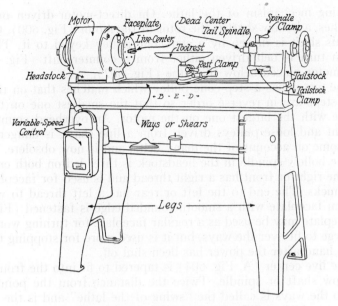

Fig. 600. Motor-head wood-turning lathe

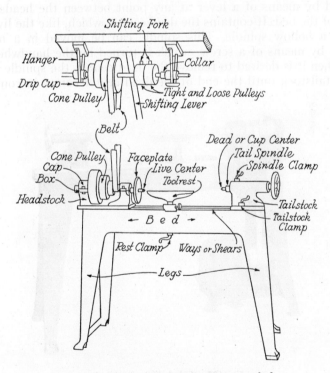

Fig. 601. Wood-turning lathe with countershaft

the driving mechanism of the lathe. On direct-motor-driven or motor-head lathes, a hollow shaft is the rotor of the motor (Fig. 600). On older types this shaft is driven by a step-cone pulley keyed to it. The cone-pulley in turn is belt driven either from a countershaft (Fig. 601) or from a motor placed below the lathe (Fig. 602).

3. The motor has a step-cone pulley which matches that on the lathe, but the steps are in reverse order so that the smallest one on the lathe is in line with the largest one on the motor. An overhead countershaft, with tight and loose pulleys driven from a line shaft, is dangerous and cumbersome on account of the many belts, and is now obsolete.

4. The hollow spindle in the headstock is threaded on both ends. The end to the right or front has a right thread and is used for faceplates and screw chucks. The end to the left or rear has a left thread to which an aluminum faceplate with a smooth rounded edge is fastened (Fig. 603). This faceplate may be used as a regular faceplate for turning work which is too large to fit over the ways, but it is used more for stopping the lathe with the hand after the power has been shut off.

5. The live center (A, Fig. 604) is tapered to fit into the front end of the hollow shaft or spindle. Twice the distance from the point of the center to the ways is called the "swing of the lathe" and is the greatest diameter to which stock can be turned.

6. *The tailstock* consists of a casting, which can be clamped to the lathe bed by means of a lever at any point between the headstock and the end of the bed. It contains the dead center, which, like the live center, fits into a hollow spindle. This spindle can be moved in a horizontal direction by means of a screw, which is turned by the handwheel at the right. When it is desired to remove the dead center, the spindle is moved into the tailstock until the end of the dead center comes in contact with

Fig. 602. Underbelted speed lathe

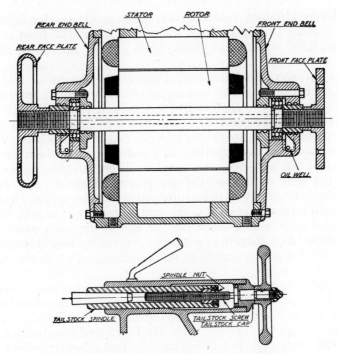

Fig. 603. Sections of motor-head stock and tailstock

the internal screw and can go no farther. Continued turning of the hand-wheel moves the spindle farther to the right, and the dead center is pushed out. The spindle may be clamped in any desired position by means of a lever (Fig. 603).

7. *The tool post,* like the tailstock, may be clamped at any point on the lathe bed. It consists of a socket which holds the T rest. The turning tools are held directly on the T rest, which can be moved up or down in the socket and fastened by means of a lever at any point.

8. A tool rest is a T-shaped casting with a short, round shaft. They are made in various lengths, some having two shafts and requiring two tool posts.

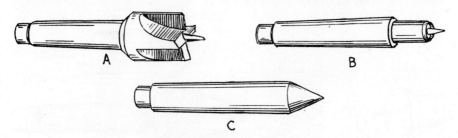

Fig. 604. Lathe centers. A, Live center;
B, cup center; C, cone center

241. Lathe Holding Tools. Several tools or devices for holding stock while it is being turned are used with every lathe. The most common of these are: lathe centers, faceplates, screw chucks, drill pads, and steady rests.

1. *Lathe centers* hold the work between the headstock and the tailstock. This is called spindle turning, because the centers are held in the spindles. The center in the headstock spindle is called the "live" center, because it rotates the stock. It has a central point and two or four steel spurs or prongs, which are driven into one end of the stock (A, Fig. 604).

2. The other end is supported on the dead center which fits into the tailstock spindle and does not revolve. There are two types of dead centers, the cone center and the cup center (B and C, Fig. 604). The cone center is tapered to a point; the cup center has a thin, circular steel edge around a thinner central point, and is less likely to split thin stock. As the dead centers do not revolve, the end of the stock which turns on them must be oiled, soaped, or waxed to prevent burning through friction. All lathe centers are tapered to fit corresponding tapers in the two hollow spindles.

3. *Faceplates* are cast-steel disks with a threaded hub which screws onto the headstock or "live" spindle. They are made in several diameters according to the size of the lathe and the diameter and weight of the stock they have to support. Several holes are bored and countersunk in them for flathead screws (B, Fig. 605). Circular disks, bowls, pulleys, etc., are fastened to faceplates for turning. Faceplate work is supported on the headstock only.

4. *Screw chucks* are small faceplates with a single screw in the center (A, Fig. 605). They are used for holding smaller work such as napkin rings, boxes, pin trays, bases for candlesticks, etc.

5. *Drill chucks* are held on a tapered center which fits into either the headstock or tailstock spindle. They have three jaws and a sleeve and can be used only for straight-shank machine drills (Fig. 606).

6. *Drill pads* are used for supporting or centering turned work while boring it in the lathe (Fig. 606). Like drill chucks, drill pads are also held on a tapered center and may be used in either spindle. The drill chuck, drill pad, and work to be bored are brought close together. The lathe is then started and the tailstock spindle is gradually advanced until the drill enters the wood to the required depth.

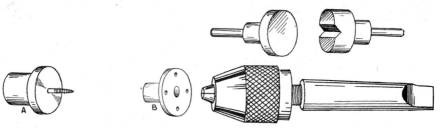

Fig. 605. A, Screw chuck; B, faceplate   Fig. 606. Drill chuck and drill pads

7. *Steady rests* are devices for supporting thin stock between centers and preventing it from vibrating. They are made in different forms as shown in Figure 607, one supporting the wood at two points and the other at three points. Steady rests may also be made entirely of wood as shown in Figure 608.

242. Wood-Turning Tools. (1) The common wood-turning tools are gouges, chisels, dividers, and calipers. Gouges and chisels are longer and thicker than similar bench tools. They are made in different widths and

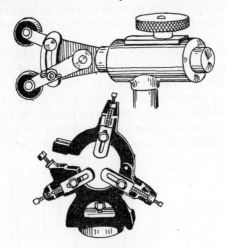

Fig. 607. Steady rests

have long, sturdy handles. They have no shoulder, because they are not driven into the wood like hand chisels (Fig. 609).

2. *Gouges* are beveled on the outside or convex side, and the length of the bevel is about twice the thickness of the tool. The cutting end of

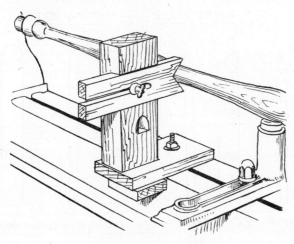

Fig. 608. Homemade steady rest

wood-turning gouges is also rounded, because square corners would catch in the wood.

3. *Skew chisels* are beveled on one or both sides, and are ground to an angle of 60 deg. with one edge of the chisels. Skew chisels, beveled on both sides, are used for cutting and smoothing. Skew chisels, ground on only one side, are scraping tools. They are either right or left, depending upon which side the bevel is ground.

4. *Diamond or spear-point* chisels also are beveled on only one side, but they have two bevels which meet in a point in the center. One of these chisels, therefore, may be said to combine the right and left skew chisels in one.

5. *Parting or cut-off tools* also have two bevels which meet in a central point, but these bevels are ground on the edges of the tool instead of the sides. The center of these chisels is thicker than the edges, so that they will not bind or overheat when cutting off parts of turned stock.

6. *Square-nose chisels* are like ordinary chisels, but have a longer and heavier blade. They are scraping tools used only on straight surfaces.

7. *Round-nose chisels* also are scraping tools, with only one bevel.

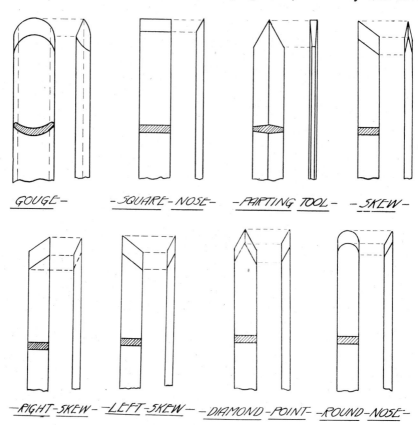

Fig. 609. Turning tools

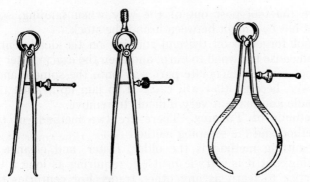

Fig. 610. Dividers and inside and outside calipers

They are like ordinary chisels except that their cutting edge is round. They are used on concave surfaces.

8. *Beading tools* are scraping tools having only one bevel. This bevel is ground to concave shapes, so that beads of various sizes may be made.

9. *Dividers* are used to step off measurements and mark circles on faceplate work (Fig. 610). Spring dividers have two sharp-pointed legs. They can be set to distance by a screw and nut working against a steel spring.

10. *Inside and outside calipers* are constructed like the dividers, but are used for measuring inside and outside diameters of turned work.

The sharpening of turning tools is fully explained in Chapter 4, Articles 134 to 140 inclusive.

243. Safety Rules. Although the lathe is not a dangerous machine to operate, accidents may happen either through carelessness or ignorance. To guard against such accidents, the following safety rules are given:

1. Fasten the stock securely between centers and to faceplates, because stock thrown from a lathe strikes with tremendous force.

2. Examine the stock for cracks and flaws, and test all glue joints before fastening stock in the lathe. Cracked or poorly glued stock may come apart when run at high speed.

3. Tighten the clamps on the tool post and tailstock, and always revolve the stock by hand to see that it has enough clearance before turning on the power.

4. Do not run the lathe at too high speed, especially before the stock is rounded off, as it may cause excessive vibration and be thrown from the lathe. After rounding, stock less than 3 in. in diameter may be run at the highest speed. Stock over 6 in. in diameter should be run at the slowest speed, and stock from 3 to 6 in. at medium speeds.

5. Clamp the tool rest as close as possible to the work, and use only sharp tools. Dull tools are always dangerous.

6. Wear no loose or ragged clothes, roll up your sleeves and tuck in your necktie, or better remove it. Loose clothing can very easily be caught by the revolving stock and cause a serious accident.

7. Move the tool post out of the way when sanding, so that your fingers will not be caught between it and the stock.

8. Do not forget to oil the end running on the dead center, because friction will cause the wood to burn, and then the exact center will be lost.

9. Do not screw a faceplate part way onto the spindle and then turn on the power, because that will cause it to jam up against the shoulder of the spindle and make it very difficult to remove.

244. Methods of Turning. There are two methods of turning, the cutting method and the scraping method.

1. The cutting method is the older, faster, and cleaner method of wood turning, but it is a trade in itself, requiring as long a time and as much practice to learn as any other trade. For centuries this method has been handed down from one generation of turners to the next and is, therefore, so well established that many teachers will not even consider the scraping method, although they will allow it on faceplate work, because it is safer.

2. The scraping method is newer and more accurate. It is quickly learned, but is not so fast, nor are the surfaces as smooth as those produced by the cutting method. More sanding, therefore, is necessary.

3. The patternmaker uses the scraping method exclusively, because his work must of necessity be very exact. Moreover, as turning is only part of his trade, he need not spend so much time learning it.

4. Since practically all commercial turning now is done entirely by turning machines, wood turning as a trade is of little importance. It, therefore, does not seem logical to spend so much time teaching it in the old traditional way, because now it is only an aid to the general woodworker or cabinetmaker and a hobby for the amateur. Moreover, as the scraping method is permitted on much faceplate work, why not use it also in spindle turning and save time, temper, and material.

SPINDLE TURNING

Spindle turning includes all turning operations on stock that is held between the live and dead centers. These are: straight and taper turning, shoulder cuts, hollows, rounds, beads, and split turning.

245. To Center and Clamp Stock in the Lathe. (1) Saw the stock to dimensions, having the ends square to the sides.

2. On square or rectangular stock, draw diagonals on both ends. The center of the piece lies in the point of intersection.

On irregularly shaped stock, the center may be found as follows: Set a pair of dividers to approximately half the thickness of the piece. Hold one of the legs of the divider against one of the edges, and scratch a line parallel to it. Repeat on the other three edges. The center is now readily determined (Fig. 611).

3. If the lumber is hard, it is well to make a saw cut on the two diagonals on one end (Fig. 612), and to bore a small hole in the center of both this and the other end (Fig. 613), so that the live and dead centers may enter the wood more readily.

4. Remove the live center from the headstock of the lathe by pushing it out with an iron rod, which can be inserted from the opposite end of the headstock. This rod is part of the regular equipment of the lathe, and is usually found hanging on a lug on one of the legs.

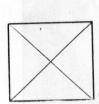 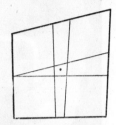

Fig. 611. Finding centers of square and irregular-shaped stock

5. Drive the live center into that end of the wood on which the diagonals were sawed, so that the prongs enter a saw cut. *Use a mallet* when driving on the center, because a steel hammer will upset (widen) the end of it so that it will not fit into the tapered spindle (Fig. 614). Do not drive the wood onto the live center while it is in the lathe, as the blows of the hammer will injure the bearings.

6. Drip machine oil on the other end of the wood, holding it in a vertical position, and allowing the oil to soak in. Soap or wax may also be used and will not discolor the wood.

7. Place the live center in the headstock spindle without removing the wood from it, and then slide the tailstock along the bed until its dead center enters the hole bored for it in the wood.

8. Clamp the tailstock in this position and turn the handwheel until the dead center presses against the wood. Then clamp the spindle to prevent it from moving backward. The cone center should not enter more

Fig. 612. Sawing on diagonals

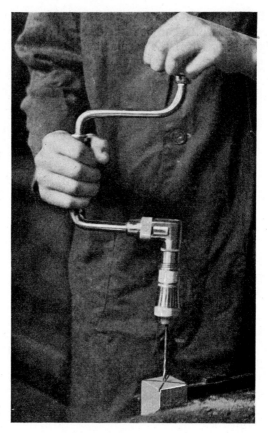

Fig. 613. Boring for centers

than 3/16 in. into the endwood otherwise it will cause excessive friction and burn the wood.

9. Adjust the tool rest so that it is about ⅛ in. away from the edge that is nearest to it when the wood is revolved. Clamp it firmly to the lathe bed. Also adjust it to the correct height. This varies somewhat with the height of the person, but is *never below the lathe centers*. It is generally from ⅛ to ¼ in. above the centers.

10. Revolve the wood by hand to make sure that it has sufficient clearance. See that all the clamps are tight and that no tools are in the way.

246. To Turn a Plain Cylinder. (1) Start the lathe so that the stock does not revolve too fast causing the lathe to vibrate, which it is very likely to do before the stock has been rounded off. Excessive speed may even cause it to fly out of the lathe and injure someone.

2. Use the gouge for the first cut. Grasp the handle near the end with the right hand, and hold the blade firmly against the T rest with the left hand, so that the palm of the hand near the wrist and the little finger are

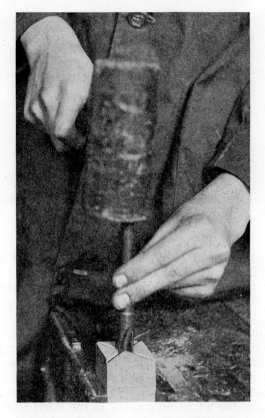

Fig. 614. Driving live center into end of stock

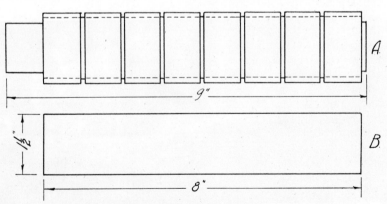

Fig. 615. Method of turning plain cylinder. (A) Rough cylinder sized with parting tool; (B) finished cylinder

Fig. 616. Cutting with gouge

in contact with the T rest (Fig. 616). Hold the handle well down and roll the gouge a little toward the right. This will throw the shavings away from you. Some turners hold the gouge in the manner illustrated in Figure 632. It is claimed that this method is faster and allows greater freedom of movement.

3. Start cutting a couple of inches from the dead center, moving the gouge away from you toward the dead center. Then start the next cut a couple of inches farther to the left, and so on until only an inch or so is left. Roll the gouge toward you, and move it toward the live center to round off the last part of the stock. Do not begin the cuts at the ends of the stock, because the gouge may catch in the wood and cause it to be thrown from the lathe. When too long a cut is taken while rounding off the corners, large chips are likely to fly off and injure the operator.

4. Move the gouge freely from one end of the piece to another until it is perfectly cylindrical and a little larger in size than actually needed.

5. Stop the lathe and move the T rest closer to the wood being turned.

Fig. 617. Cutting to size with parting tool

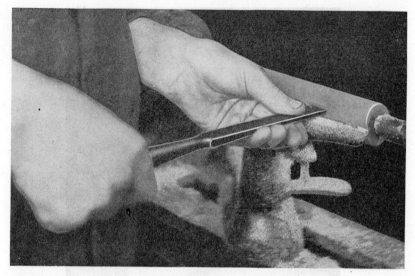

Fig. 618. Smoothing with square-nose chisel

6. Set the outside calipers to about 1/32 in. more than the finished diameter of the piece. Grasp the parting tool in the right hand and the calipers in the left (Fig. 617). Cut into the wood with the parting tool while holding the calipers in the groove being cut until they slip over the cylinder. Make several cuts about 1 in. apart with the parting tool (Fig. 617).

7. *Using the scraping method,* smooth the cylinder with a square-nose chisel as shown in Figure 618. Run the lathe at high speed, and hold the chisel flat on the tool rest with the beveled side down. Cut down to the bottom of the grooves made with the parting tool until the cylinder is smooth and of the same diameter throughout.

8. Square the end that runs on the dead center, with the parting tool or with the point or toe of a skew chisel held flat on the tool rest (Fig.

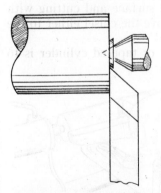

Fig. 619. Squaring end with skew chisel. Scraping method

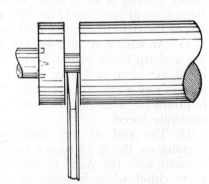

Fig. 620. Cutting to length with parting tool. Scraping method

Fig. 621. Testing for squareness with side of chisel

619). Test for squareness by placing the edge of the tool or a try square across the end (Fig. 621).

9. Finally measure the length of the cylinder from the squared end and cut down at this point with the parting tool until only ¼ in. of stock remains. This may then be cut through with the toe of the skew chisel. Hold the chisel in the right hand and catch the cylinder with the left when the wood separates (Fig. 620).

10. *Using the cutting method,* smooth the cylinder with a ¾-in. skew chisel, holding it at an angle of 60 deg. to the surface and cutting with the middle of the edge (Figs. 622 and 623). Move the chisel either to the left or the right, but never start a cut at the end.

11. An easy way to smooth a long, straight or tapered cylinder is to use a sharp block plane, holding it as shown in Figure 624. In this way a smooth, even cut is produced. Run the lathe at moderate speed.

12. The end of the stock running on the dead center is squared with the point of the skew chisel when its edge is held on the tool rest. Hold

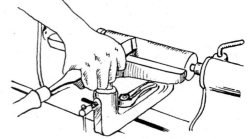

Fig. 622. Smoothing with a skew chisel

Fig. 623. Smoothing with a skew chisel

the handle of the chisel toward the right so that the bevel will be parallel to the endwood. Raising the handle forces the point or toe of the chisel into the stock (Figs. 625 and 626).

13. The stock is cut to length by first making a perpendicular cut with the toe of the skew chisel. A slanting cut is then made on the waste side of the stock meeting the perpendicular or square cut (Fig. 626). Slanting cuts may be made either with the toe or heel of the skew chisel. Continue in this way, alternating slanting and perpendicular cuts until only ¼ in. of stock remains. Finish the cut as explained in step 9.

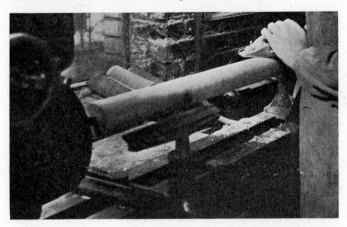

Fig. 624. Smoothing a long cylinder with a block plane on a lathe

247. To Make Shoulder Cuts. (1) Turn a plain cylinder as described in the preceding article to make the exercise shown in Figure 627.

2. Place a rule on the T rest, and lay off the dimensions from the drawing without moving the rule. Then hold a pencil point against one mark after the other, steady it on the T rest, and revolve the cylinder by hand, so that a line is marked all around its circumference at each point (Figure 628).

Fig. 625. Squaring end with skew chisel

3. *Using the scraping method,* set the calipers to 1 1/32 in., and cut down to this diameter with the parting tool on each side of the ¾-in. and ⅞-in. spaces (Fig. 617).

4. Run the lathe at high speed and, using a sharp ¾-in. chisel, cut the 1-in. spaces down to the bottom of the cuts made by the parting tool.

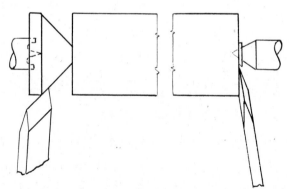

Fig. 626. Squaring one end of stock and cutting the other to length. Cutting method

5. Finish the ends of the shoulders as shown in Figure 619, and touch up the cuts just made, taking very fine shavings.

6. *Using the cutting method,* make the shoulder cuts as explained in Article 246, step 12, and as shown in Figure 626.

7. Remove the waste stock between the shoulders with a ¼-in. gouge (Fig. 629), and smooth with a ½-in. skew chisel as in Figure 623.

8. Finish the ends and cut to length as described in steps 11 and 12, Article 246.

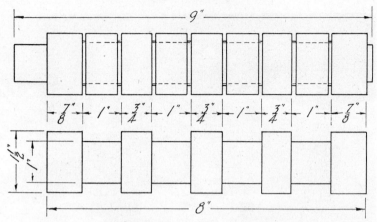

Fig. 627. Steps in making shoulder cuts

248. To Make Taper Cuts. (1) Consult the drawing (Fig. 630) and turn a plain cylinder large enough for this exercise.

2. Lay it out as described in the previous article, step 2, and mark lines all around it as in Figure 628.

3. *Using the scraping method,* cut down with the parting tool as shown in the drawing, and then turn the ends to finished dimensions with a square-nose chisel.

4. Rough out the tapered parts with a gouge, and smooth with a right and left skew chisel or with a square-nose chisel. Test the flatness of the taper cuts with a try square. There must be no hollows or bumps.

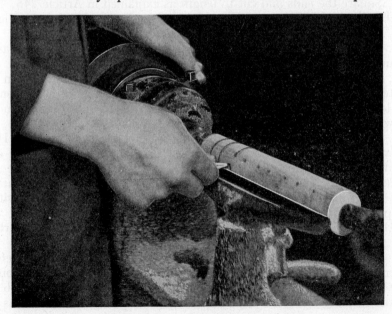

Fig. 628. Laying out dimensions with a pencil

Fig. 629. Cutting between shoulders with a gouge

5. Square the ends, and cut to length as explained in Article 246.

6. *Using the cutting method,* turn both end and taper sections to a little more than finished dimensions with a gouge. Then smooth with a skew chisel as shown in Figure 622.

7. Square the ends and cut to length as explained in Article 246.

249. To Make Concave Cuts. (1) Consult the drawing in Figure 631, and turn a cylinder of the proper size for this exercise.

2. Lay out the cylinder according to Figure 631, and mark it as in Figure 628.

3. *Using the scraping method,* cut down with the parting tool in the center of the 1-in. spaces. Set the caliper to 11/16 in., and hold them in the left hand while cutting with the parting tool held in the right hand as shown in Figure 617.

4. Use a ½-in. round-nose chisel for making the concave cuts. Hold it level and perfectly flat on the tool rest (Fig. 632), and begin the cuts a little inside the lines marked. Move the chisel from side to side and gradually work down to the bottom of the cuts made with the parting tool. The finished cuts must be semicircular in shape. Test them with a template made of cardboard or sheet metal.

5. Cut the stock to length and square the ends as explained in Article 246.

6. *Using the cutting method,* lay out and mark the cylinder as before. Then make the concave cuts with a ¼-in. gouge. Hold the gouge on its side at the beginning of the cut (Fig. 633), and start cutting with the center of the edge, gradually rolling the gouge over on its back as the cut progresses.

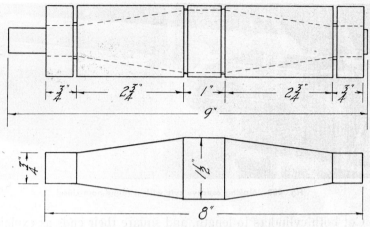

Fig. 630. Steps in making taper cuts

7. Cut from each side toward the center. In this way the cuts will be smooth, but do not attempt to cut past the center. Cut only a little at a time until the correct depth and curvature have been obtained. Test with calipers and templates.

8. Cut to length and square the ends as explained in Article 246.

250. To Make Convex Cuts. (1) Turn a plain cylinder 9 in. long and 1 9/16 in. in diameter.

2. Lay it out and mark it according to the drawing in A, **Figure 634.**

3. *Using the scraping method,* make shallow V cuts with the spear-point chisel on all the lines marked.

4. Then round off the corners with the spear-point or right and left skew chisels.

5. Cylinder *B* in Figure 634 is first cut down with the parting tool, after which the square corners are rounded off as in step 4.

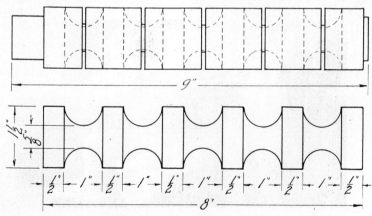

Fig. 631. Steps in making concave cuts

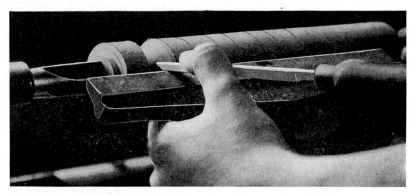

Fig. 632. Making concave cuts with a round-nose chisel

6. Cut both cylinders to length, and square their ends as explained in Article 246.

7. Beads, from ⅛ to ⅝ in., may also be made with special scraping tools called "beading tools." They are ground to the correct curve and are held level and flat on the tool rest like roundnose or any other scraping chisel.

8. *Using the cutting method,* make the V cuts on cylinder *A* with the toe or heel of the skew chisel as shown in the left view in Figure 626.

9. Round the corners with the heel of a skew chisel, starting the cut near the center of the bead and rolling the chisel to right and left (Fig. 637).

10. Cut the openings between the beads on cylinder *B* with the parting tool, and then round them as explained above.

11. Cut both cylinders to length and square their ends as explained in Article 246.

251. To Turn Legs With Square Parts. Turned legs and stretchers for chairs, tables, or stools often have square or rectangular sections, which are mortised to join the tenons on rails and stretchers. Beginners

Fig. 633. Making concave cuts with a gouge

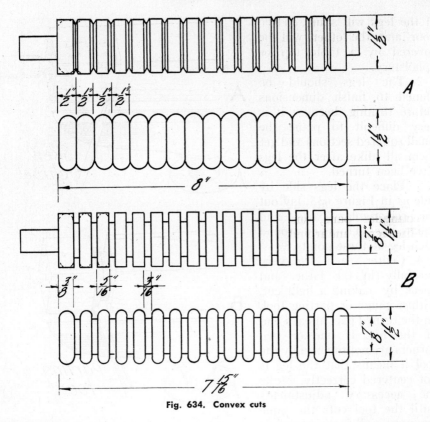

Fig. 634. Convex cuts

usually have difficulty in turning such legs without chipping off the corners of the square parts.

1. Plane the stock to finished dimensions and cut the legs to exact length, because the marks of the lathe centers will not show, as one end

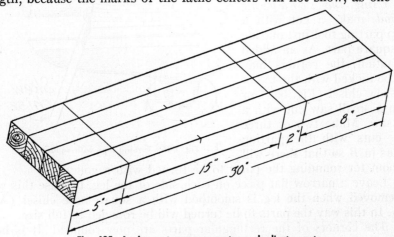

Fig. 635. Laying out measurements on duplicate parts

of the legs will stand on the floor and the other will be covered by a table top or upholstery.

2. The legs should be planed to finish dimensions before turning, because it is very difficult to plane the small squared sections and get them all alike after the legs have been turned.

3. Place the legs side by side as in Figure 635, lay out the rectangular parts, and square lines across and around each leg at these points.

4. Center each leg very carefully in the lathe, and check by making a light cut, with a gouge or parting tool, on the turned part at each end of the leg. If one or two corners are not touched by the tool it means that the leg is not centered correctly. Make the necessary adjustments until the tool cuts the same amount on all four corners, as the square parts otherwise will not be centered with the turned parts.

5. *Using the scraping method,* make a cut with a sharp parting tool just outside the square part. As an added precaution, the corners may first be nicked with the toe of the skew chisel (Fig. 636) or given a small saw cut with a backsaw. Make two or three more cuts with the parting tool as in *B* so that there will

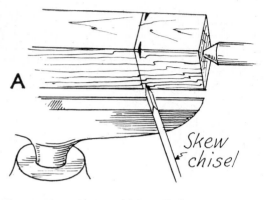

A

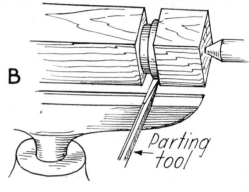

B

C

Fig. 636. Turning legs with square parts

be room for rounding the parts to be turned with a gouge.

6. Leave a narrow flat piece on each side of the leg, because this will be removed when the leg is smoothed with a square-nose chisel (Art. 246). In this way the parts to be turned will be rounded to full size.

7. The corners of the rectangular parts are now rounded. It is best

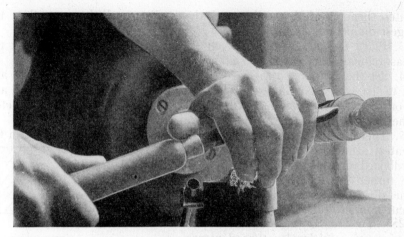

Fig. 637. Cutting beads with a skew chisel

to measure the distance of the rounding — usually from ¼ to ⅜ in. — and square lines all around the leg at these points. Use a right and left skew chisel, hold it flat on the tool rest, and move the handle back and forth.

8. Then lay out the parts to be turned, and follow the directions given in the preceding Articles.

9. *Using the cutting method,* nick the legs with the skew chisel as in *A,* Figure 636, round the parts to be turned with a gouge, and square the ends of the square parts with the skew chisel as in *C.* The square corners are rounded with a small gouge or skew chisel as in Figures 633 and 637.

252. To Turn Duplicate Parts. This is one of the most difficult things for the beginner to do, usually because he does not go about it in a logical and systematic manner.

1. The first thing to do is to make a full-size measuring stick by laying out the most important lengthwise dimensions on a thin piece of wood (A, Fig. 638). The edge of this stick corresponds to the center line of the turning. Mark also the most important diameters on the stick.

2. Cut all pieces to thickness, width, and length at the same time,

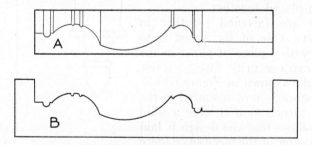

Fig. 638. (A) Full-size layout and measuring board;
(B) template, which may be cut into convenient lengths

center them carefully, and round them off to a little more than the largest diameter.

3. Place the measuring stick on the stock in the lathe, lay out the measurements, and mark lines all around at these points (Fig. 628).

4. Set the calipers to the largest diameter needed, plus 1/16 in., and cut to size with a parting tool. Then cut to the next largest diameter, and so on. Sometimes different parts of the turning have the same diameter. When that is the case, it is logical to cut them at the same time.

5. Then turn the "sized" parts of the cylinder to shape. To obtain the greatest accuracy, make a template of cardboard or sheet metal to fit over the turned parts (B, Fig. 638). It is generally easier to use a template that is cut into several smaller parts.

253. To Do Split Turning. Split turnings or semicircular turned pieces are used to decorate flat surfaces, such as the legs or panels of a cabinet. This method of decoration, which originated during the Jacobean period (1603–1688), is used extensively on modern reproductions, often in combination with moldings (Fig. 639).

1. Split work is turned between centers like any other piece of spindle turning. The stock is prepared and held together in the following way:

2. Cut 2 pieces of lumber about 4 in. longer than the finished dimensions of the split turning. Their width should be about $\frac{1}{4}$ in. more than the greatest width shown in the drawing, and their thickness should be equal to a little more than half their width.

3. Plane the faces of these two pieces, so that they will make a perfect joint when placed together.

4. They are fastened together in several ways. One of the safest is to glue them with a piece of paper in the joint. For extra security, insert a screw in each end as shown in Figure 639.

5. The stock is now mounted in the lathe, and turned as if it were a solid piece. It follows that the design is laid out in the center of the piece since there are 2 in. to spare on each end.

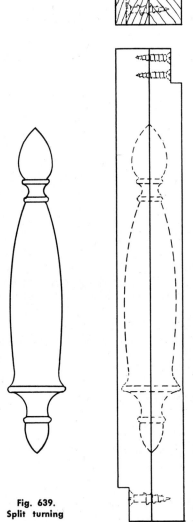

Fig. 639.
Split turning

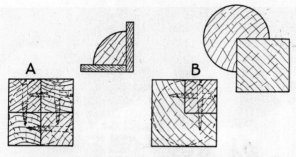

Fig. 640. Split turnings. (A) Quarters; (B) three quarters

6. Cut the two ends away with a backsaw, and not with the parting tool. Sand the ends of the turned pieces smooth by hand.

7. The turned pieces may be separated by inserting the sharp blade of a ¾-in. paring chisel in the joint at one end. A light tap will usually cause the paper to split. Scrape and sand away the remaining paper and glue.

8. Quarter and three-quarter columns are sometimes used on chests of drawers, mirror frames, and other pieces of furniture. Quarter columns are first glued up in two halves as explained in previous steps. When dry, this piece is then cut in halves at right angles to the first cut, after which the pieces are planed and glued again as in A, Figure 640. Square the glued-up stock to dimensions and turn as a solid piece.

9. The three-quarter section is made by cutting a rabbet as shown in B. Another piece is cut to fit this rabbet and is glued to it with a piece of paper in the joint.

FACEPLATE WORK

In faceplate work the stock is fastened to a faceplate or screw chuck, which is screwed to the headstock spindle and supported entirely on that.

254. To Fasten Stock to a Faceplate or Screw Chuck. As in spindle turning, it is of the greatest importance to mount stock in the lathe so that it can be operated with safety.

1. Examine stock carefully for cracks and strength of glued joints. Then, with a pair of dividers, mark a circle a little larger in diameter than the finished dimension is to be, and saw it on a band saw or with a turning saw.

2. The faceplate can be accurately centered by marking a circle on the stock, equal to its diameter, using the same center as before. If the wood is hard, holes should be marked and bored, so that the screws will not twist off when they are inserted (Art. 228). If this should happen, it would be necessary to replace the stock in most cases. About No. 12 screws should be used and soap or wax should be put on the threads.

3. Push the live center out of the spindle with an iron rod supplied for that purpose, and screw the faceplate onto the live or headstock spindle. It is best to place a leather or cardboard washer over the spindle, and to

Fig. 641. Cutting edge of disk with skew chisel

turn the faceplate on slowly, so that it will not jam against the shoulder, because then it will be hard to remove. *Never start the motor until the faceplate is fully screwed on the spindle.*

4. Screw chucks are fastened to the stock with a single central screw of the same diameter as the hole in the chuck. Fold a piece of fine sandpaper, with the abrasive side out, to place between the chuck and the wood. This is to prevent slipping, which is likely to occur since the screw chuck has only one screw.

5. The side or end of the wood to be fastened to a faceplate or screw chuck must be flat and smooth.

255. To Turn a Disk. (1) Screw the stock to the faceplate, and mount it in the lathe as described in the preceding article.

2. Adjust the T rest so that it is parallel to the face of the disk and at right angles to the lathe bed. It should be placed at a height a little below the center of the stock and only about ¼ in. away from it.

3. See that the disk revolves freely, and start the lathe at its slowest speed.

4. Remove enough of the material from the edge to make the disk circular. This will diminish the vibration caused by uneven centering. The cutting is done with the toe of a skew chisel (Fig. 641) which is held at right angles to the face of the disk. The cut should be stopped about ⅛ in. from the rear face of the disk, as the wood is liable to split if the cut is extended all the way across the edge of the disk.

5. If the face of the disk is rough, or much material has to be removed, first use a round-nose chisel holding it flat upon the T rest and at right angles to the disk. Move the chisel across the face of the disk from the edge nearest the operator to the center and back again.

6. Smooth the face of the disk with a square-nose chisel (Fig. 642), and test for flatness with a try square (Fig. 643). This is called "facing off."

Fig. 642. Smoothing face of disk with square-nose chisel

7. Mark the diameter of the disk by setting a pair of dividers to a distance equal to the radius. Place one leg on the center, and scribe the circle with the other while the stock is revolving (Fig. 644).

Another way is to set the dividers to the required diameter. Rest one leg of the dividers on the T rest, and place it in contact with the stock while it is revolving. Bring the other leg of the dividers gradually in contact with the stock (Fig. 645). If two circles are marked, shift the dividers so that the points come in contact with the stock halfway between the two circles. When only one circle is marked, the dividers are held centrally. This method is more exact, and especially useful for smaller diameters and when the center is cut away. It is very quickly mastered.

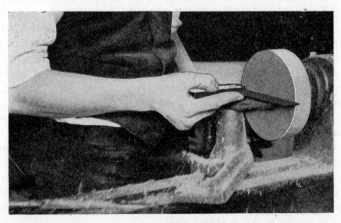

Fig. 643. Testing face of disk for flatness with try-square

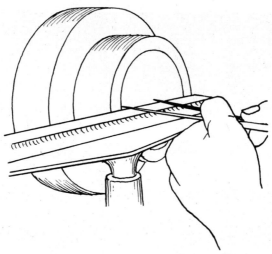

Fig. 644. Marking circle with the dividers set to the radius

8. Reduce the disk to the required diameter as explained in step 6.

Then clamp the T rest parallel to the lathe bed and to the edge of the disk, and with the square-nose chisel remove the thin piece of material left on the rear edge of the disk.

9. Test for squareness by holding the stock of a try square against the face of the disk and the blade over its edge.

10. Convex and concave shapes are worked out very easily with the round-nose chisel, held flat on the tool rest and used as in spindle turning (Arts. 249 and 250).

11. A hole to fit a turned tenon may very easily be cut with the toe of a skew chisel held perpendicular to the face of the disk (Fig. 646). The center of the hole may be cut away either with the skew chisel or round-nose chisel.

256. To Do Chuck Turning. A chuck is an appliance in which work may be held securely while it is being turned in a lathe. Chucks are made in several different types and of different materials, as steel, brass, or wood. The type to be described in the following consists of a turned disk of wood fastened to a faceplate or a screw chuck. The wood turner makes these chucks easily and quickly as he needs them for the work he is doing. They are used for holding such turned objects as lamp bases, trays, bowls, boxes, rings, etc.

A lamp base, such as is needed for the lamp illustrated in Figures 773 and 774 is made as follows:

1. Get out the stock for the base, plane one side, cut it round, and screw it to the faceplate as explained in Article 255, steps 1 to 3.

2. Reduce it to the thickness and diameter required. Then cut a shallow recess in its face about 1/16 in. deep and extending within an inch of its outer edge. This is the lower surface of the base, and the depression is cut to make it stand well.

Fig. 645. Marking diameter with dividers

3. Bore a ¼-in. or a ⅜-in. hole from the side of the base to its center, as shown at A, Figure 647. This hole is for the electric wires. Sand the edge and lower surface of the base, and remove it from the faceplate.

4. Turn a disk from a piece of softwood at least 1 in. larger in diameter than the base, and not less than 1½ in. in thickness. This is to be the "chuck."

5. Caliper the diameter of the lamp base carefully, and mark a circle of this diameter on the disk with a pair of dividers (Fig. 644).

6. Cut a recess in the disk within the circle marked. This recess should be about 3/16 in. deep. The lamp base should fit into it very tightly as shown at B, Figure 647. If the recess is a little too large, place a piece of paper over it, and force the base into it. If the thickness of the paper is not sufficient to hold the base firmly in the recess, face the disk off again and cut another recess.

7. Drive the base into the recess, so that its lower surface bears against the bottom of the recess. This operation is called "chucking." It is the only way in which the base can be accurately centered and turned from the opposite side.

8. If the base is chucked correctly, it will run true without any danger of coming loose. The turning may now be finished according to the draw-

Fig. 646. Cutting hole with skew chisel

ing, after which the hole is bored to fit the tenon for the upright. (Fig. 646).

In this case, the chuck was made by cutting a recess into it. This is called *outside chucking,* because the outside edge of the lamp base was held in the chuck. In other cases, chucks are made by turning a shoulder on the disk, on which the object to be turned is held or chucked.

9. *Plug chucking* means to turn a cylinder and drive it into a hole bored for it in a wooden disk or chuck. Turn a tenon on the cylinder as shown in Figure 648 while it is held between centers.

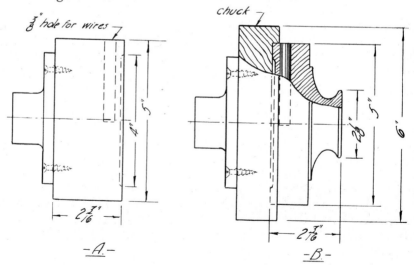

Fig. 647. Lamp base. A, Base turned to size; recess cut and hole bored; B, base chucked and turned; hole for tenon of upright remains to be bored

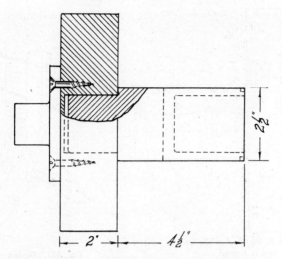

Fig. 648. Plug chucking. Note that tenon is undercut
to make a perfect fit against faceplate

10. Then cut a hole for the tenon in the wooden disk using a round-nose and a skew chisel as explained in Article 255. It should be a very close fit, so that the tenon will have to be driven in with a mallet.

11. A box, as shown in Figure 649, may now be turned on the end of the cylinder. Deepen the hole with a round-nose chisel and smooth its sides with a skew chisel. As the hole gets deeper, the end of the tool rest may be turned into it to give better support to the turning tools.

12. Turn a rabbet for the lid on the edge of the box as shown by the dotted lines, then stain and finish it and cut it off with a parting tool.

13. A shoulder is now turned on the end of the chucked cylinder, over which the open end of the box fits (Fig. 649), while a shallow recess is

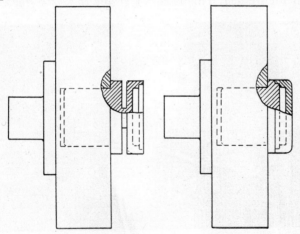

Fig. 650. Turning and chucking lid of box

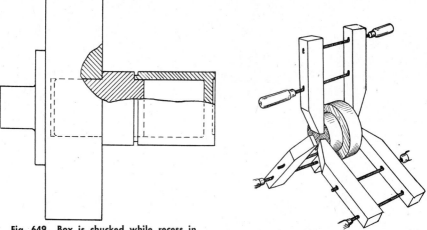

Fig. 649. Box is chucked while recess in
end is turned

Fig. 651. Gluing to waste stock

turned in its bottom, so that it will stand well. This is called *inside chucking*, because the inner side of the box is held on the chuck.

14. The lid is turned and chucked as shown in Figure 650. First turn a recess to fit the rabbet on the top edge of the box. Try the fit frequently as the turning progresses, then hollow out the lid further and finally chuck and finish it.

15. When turning objects as trays, plates, and boxes, which cannot be screwed to a faceplate or screw chuck without marring a finished surface, the stock may be glued to a disk turned on a faceplate. Spread glue on the disk, then glue a piece of heavy paper to it, and mark the diameter of the stock to be turned with a pencil. Finally, spread glue on one side of the stock, center it on the paper, and clamp it with three or more hand screws as in Figure 651. This is called *gluing to waste stock*.

Fig. 652. Sanding leg on spindle

16. When the turning has been completed, the object may be removed by driving a sharp chisel or a plane iron into the joint. This will cause the paper to split, so that the turned object can easily be separated from the disk. Scrape off glue and paper and sand smooth by hand.

257. To Sand in the Lathe on a Spindle. Where a sanding machine is not available, spindles of different diameters may be turned, covered with sandpaper, and used very effectively in sanding concave surfaces.

1. Turn the spindle according to directions given in Article 246. It should be somewhat smaller in diameter than the diameter of the curve to be sanded, generally from ¼ to ½ in., to allow for the thickness of the sandpaper and facility in working.

2. Fold a sheet of No. 1½ sandpaper around the cylinder, and cut away the surplus so that the ends of the sandpaper just meet when it is wrapped tightly around the cylinder.

3. Apply glue to the cylinder, wrap the sandpaper around it, and hold it in place by winding a string, or better, a piece of bandage around it. Set it away to dry (see also Art. 119, Figs. 225 and 226).

4. Place the cylinder in the lathe, applying sufficient oil to the end running on the dead center, and remove the tool rest. Curves, such as those on the legs of the tilt-top table, Figure 784, are easily sanded by holding the pieces perpendicularly to the face of the cylinder, Figure 652, and moving them rapidly back and forth. If held too long in one place, ridges and hollows will result.

Fig. 653. Sanding end of leg to fit against turned column

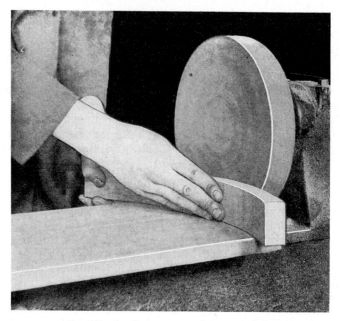

Fig. 654. Sanding convex surface on a disk

5. When it is desired to sand a curve on the 'end wood of a leg to be doweled to a turned column, the leg to be sanded is steadied on the tool rest (Figure 653). Move the leg from side to side to avoid burning the sandpaper and the wood.

258. To Sand in the Lathe on a Disk. A wheel or disk sander is useful for all convex surfaces. It is not recommended to sand flat surfaces on this "homemade" sander as the sides of the wheel very easily dig into the surface. It may be useful in sanding the ends of the legs of a table or stool, which does not stand evenly on all four legs.

1. From a 2-in. plank, preferably softwood, cut out a circular disk, or wheel, of as large a diameter as the lathe will swing. Cut it as nearly round as possible with a handsaw or turning saw.

2. Screw a faceplate securely to the disk, and as nearly in the center as possible.

3. Turn the disk as explained in Article 255.

4. Apply glue to the disk, and glue the sandpaper in place. If the disk is larger in diameter than a sheet of sandpaper, place two pieces edge to edge.

5. Clamp the disk to a flat surface until the glue is dry. Trim the edges with a dull chisel or plane iron.

6. When the sanding wheel is to be used, the tool post should be removed from the lathe bed and a board clamped to it instead. This board should be thicker than the distance between the lathe bed and the edge of the wheel (Fig. 654).

259. To Finish and Polish Turned Work. It is a good deal easier to finish and polish work that is revolving in a lathe than it is to finish and polish flat surfaces of a piece of furniture.

1. A good polish can only be built up on a surface that is well sanded and free from any blemishes and defects. When sanding in the lathe, move the tool post out of the way so that the fingers will not be caught between it and the work.

2. Begin sanding with No. ½ sandpaper. For flat and rounded surfaces, use a quarter sheet folded once or twice. Move it quickly back and forth along the surface so as not to leave scratches. If moved slowly or held in one spot, a series of fine rings will show on the surface. These rings are difficult to remove, but if left on the surface they will show much more when the polish is applied.

3. When sanding hollows, fold a quarter sheet into the desired shape and move it quickly from side to side. Beads are sanded with narrow strips of sandpaper held between thumb and forefingers of both hands.

4. Be careful not to round any sharp edges. Continue sanding with No. 2/0 sandpaper until the work is very smooth and free from scratches. It is then a good plan to wet the work with a brush dipped in clear water. Let it dry for an hour or two and then sand it again with No. 3/0 sandpaper.

5. The work is now ready for the stain, which should be allowed to dry a couple of hours. Be careful to apply it evenly and, if necessary, wipe the work with a piece of cotton waste to absorb any excess.

6. Rub the stained surface lightly with a piece of No. 3/0 steel wool, while the work is revolving slowly. Then apply a coat of thin shellac with a brush, and let it dry for two hours.

7. Rub this coat lightly with the steel wool, and apply the polish with a clean linen rag. The rag should be folded into a pad about 2 in. wide and 10 in. long. Thin shellac is applied to the middle of the rag with a brush, and a few drops of paraffin oil are placed on the work.

8. Run the lathe at its slowest speed, hold the ends of the rag with

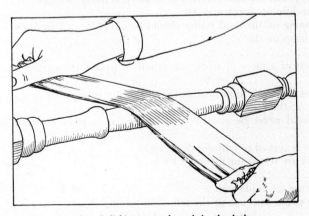

Fig. 655. Polishing turned work in the lathe

both hands, and move the rag slowly back and forth over the work with a light pressure. Keep moving the pad constantly, otherwise the shellac may pile up and form rings and ridges (Fig. 655).

9. If this should happen, apply a little denatured alcohol to the rag and a few more drops of paraffin oil to the work, because this helps to distribute the shellac more evenly.

10. When a good polish has been obtained, let the work dry overnight and apply a second coat the next day. If the pad is kept in a closed can or bottle it will not become hard and stiff, but remain soft and pliant.

REVIEW QUESTIONS

1. The trade of wood turning is disappearing, because ....
2. The bow lathe and the pole lathe were both rotated by ....
3. What is understood by the great wheel?
4. The principal parts of a lathe are: (*a*) ....; (*b*) ....;
   (*c*) ....; (*d*) ....
5. The "shears" of a lathe is ....
6. The live spindle has .... on the front end and ....
   on the rear end.
7. The "swing" of a lathe is ....
8. The faceplate on the left end of the spindle is used mostly for ....
9. The hollow spindle in the headstock ....; the one in
   the tailstock moves ....
10. The lathe centers are: (*a*) ....; (*b*) ....; (*c*) ....
11. A screw chuck differs from a faceplate by ....
12. A cup center should be used on .... stock, because ....
13. Drill chucks are fastened to .... which fits ....
    or ....
14. When boring in the lathe, the .... is advanced until ....
15. Steady rests are used for ....
16. Turning tools having two bevels are: (*a*) ....; (*b*) ....;
    (*c*) ....
17. Turning tools having round ends are: (*a*) ....; (*b*) ....
18. Stock that is run too fast before it is rounded is likely to cause ....
19. A loose necktie or sleeve may be ....
20. Stock running on the dead center should be .... because ....
21. A loose clamp on the .... or the .... may cause the
    stock to ....
22. The centers of a piece of stock that is out of square are marked on the endwood
    with .... set to ....
23. The end of the stock to be held on the live center is prepared by ....
    ....; the other end is ....
24. A cut should never be started from the end of a piece of stock being turned,
    because ....
25. A cylinder is turned to uniform diameter by ....
26. Taper cuts are tested for flatness with a .... They must have
    neither .... nor ....
27. Concave cuts are made with a .... or a ....
28. Beads are made with one of the following turning chisels:
    (*a*) ....; (*b*) ....; (*c*) .... (*d*) ....

29. A wood turner uses only the .... of the .... when making beads.
30. Split turnings are held together with .... and ....
They are separated by ....
31. Split turnings may be used in such furniture as (a) ....; (b) ....;
(c) ....
32. A faceplate can be accurately centered on a disk by ....
33. A faceplate may jam against the shoulder of the live spindle when ....
34. The stock may be prevented from slipping on a screw chuck by ....
35. The diameter is marked with a pair of dividers on a disk by ....
or by ....
36. "Facing off" means ....
37. A hole or recess is turned in a disk with a .... and a ....
38. The difference between inside and outside chucking is ....
39. Gluing to waste stock means ....
40. Paraffin oil is used in wood finishing to ....
41. A polishing pad is kept in good condition by ....
42. Plug chucking means ....
43. The edge of a turned disk is squared with the face by using a ....
chisel held ....
44. A washer on the live spindle may prevent ....
45. Sanding cylinders for use in the lathe may be made by (a) ....;
(b) ....; (c) ....

Chapter 16

SURFACE DECORATION

The most common ways of enriching or decorating a wood surface are by inlaying, veneering, carving, and painting.

While the majority of these processes require the highest type of skill and artistic ability, it is nevertheless possible to select some which, while comparatively simple to execute, are of sufficient artistic merit to greatly enhance the beauty as well as the intrinsic value of pieces of furniture such as those described in Chapter 20.

Great care must be taken in decorating an object. This rule is of especial importance to beginners, who, in their eagerness and enthusiasm over the new work, often overdecorate the object, or select a design or type of decoration that is unsuitable for the work in hand.

It may be said in general that surface decoration should be simple and appropriate, and should be used sparingly. The beginner should not rely entirely on his own taste, but should be guided by a study of good designs. These are easily found in museums, exhibits, books, and art magazines. In them, numerous examples of both classic and modern decoration may be studied and the proper selection made.

262. General Suggestions for Decorations. (1) Furniture, such as tables, chairs, or cabinets for the kitchen, made of soft or inexpensive woods, should not be decorated by inlaying or carving. It would be more appropriate to paint these pieces. A border or edge painted in a darker or contrasting, harmonious color would be a suitable form of decoration. If more color is desired, a decalcomania transfer may be added.

2. Inlaying, veneering, carving, or reeding are best employed to decorate or enhance the beauty of pieces on which a good deal of labor has been expended, such as small decorative tables, cabinets, lamps, etc.

Inlaying should be done only on close-grained woods, such as maple, birch, walnut, mahogany, etc. A thin line of 1/16-in. satinwood is often appropriate as a border line on the front of a drawer, or on straight, tapered legs. Inlaid border lines are also used along the edges of table tops of different shapes, on cabinet doors, mirror frames, serving trays, and similar pieces. Sometimes the corners of an inlaid top or door are made more prominent by the design of the border line itself or by inlaying special corner insets (Fig. 659). Occasionally an inset is placed in the center of a top, door, or tray having an inlaid border line (Fig. 770).

The contrast in color between the inlay and the surface should not be

302

too glaring, but it should be sufficiently well defined to make the inlay stand out clearly.

3. The purpose of veneering is to enhance the beauty of the wood surface. A fine line of inlay is often combined with the veneers to form or accentuate a border. Insets are rarely used with matched veneers, because such veneers are decorative enough.

4. In general, it is better not to use carving and inlaying on the same piece of furniture. Carving may be done on both close- and open-grain woods. Simple forms of carving, such as are illustrated in Figures 686 and 687 are sufficient.

5. Spiral reeding and straight reeding should not be used together on the same turned column, except when the turned parts thus decorated differ greatly in length and shape. For example, straight reeds may be carved on a long tapering part of a column, while spiral reeds may be carved on a short ball-shaped part of the same column.

6. Overlays, veined, and pierced work should generally follow the outline of the surface to be decorated. The minor parts of the design of this type of decoration, however, may differ greatly from the contour of the surface to which it is applied. The colors of two-toned work should not be strongly contrasting, but should rather be a light tone and a dark tone of the same color.

7. When using moldings, it is better to err in making them too small, rather than too large. Moldings should be smaller when made of fine-grain woods, such as mahogany or maple, and larger when made of coarse-grain woods, such as oak and ash.

INLAYING

Inlaying is often regarded by the amateur craftsman as a difficult process, quite beyond his powers, and only within the capability of the expert or specialist. This attitude of mind is always due to the fact that the person in question has never seen how inlaying is done and, therefore does not realize how comparatively simple and easy the process really is.

In general, inlaying may be explained as the process of cutting a shallow recess in one member into which another member of a different color or material is fitted and glued.

Material for inlay is made commercially in two forms: (1) lines or

Fig. 659. Typical commercial designs of lines and insets

bands of varying widths, and (2) insets in numerous sizes, shapes, and designs (Fig. 659). Lines are generally used along the edges of a surface, as a border or frame, while insets are used in the center of a surface or sometimes in corners. While it is possible to make up lines of a simple pattern, it is rather difficult to make suitable insets. From a commercial point of view, it does not pay, as such material can be bought very cheaply from firms making a specialty of this work. Lines are made in pieces one yard long, from 1/28 to 1/16 in. thick, and vary in price according to width and design. Insets are sold by the piece, and also vary greatly in price according to their size and design. They are made of many small pieces of wood of different colors, carefully cut and glued together on a piece of brown paper. The beautiful shading, so character-istic of these pieces, is executed by placing them on edge in a shallow iron saucer filled with moist sand. When placed over a fire, the sand at the bottom of the saucer dries, and becomes so hot that the pieces are scorched on their lower edges.

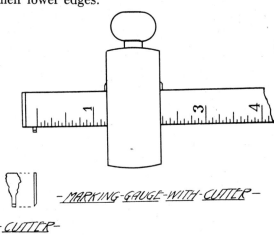

–MARKING-GAUGE-WITH-CUTTER–

–CUTTER–

Fig. 660. Tool for cutting grooves for narrow bands of inlay

263. To Inlay Lines or Bands. (1) Make a tool for cutting the grooves by breaking a piece off an old hack-saw blade and grinding it on an emery wheel to the exact width of the line to be inlaid.

2. A bevel is ground on one side, after which it is sharpened just like a cabinet scraper (Art. 131).

3. Remove the spur or point from a marking gauge, and insert the piece of steel instead, so that its sharpened edge projects about 1/16 in. or less, depending upon the thickness of the band to be inlaid (Fig. 660).

4. Make a trial cut on a piece of waste wood to see if the groove is of the right width and depth.

The marking gauge is held and operated in the usual manner; i.e., away from the operator (Fig. 661). Consequently, the beveled piece of steel is placed so that it cuts like a cabinet scraper, with the flat side toward the front.

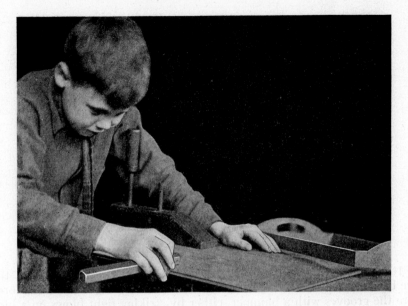

Fig. 661. Cutting grooves with marking gauge

5. The inlay should fit so snugly that it must be forced into the groove (step 10). Therefore, if the groove is too wide, a little should be ground off the sides of the cutter until it cuts a groove of the exact width.

The above method is recommended especially for narrow lines. The cutter will cut both with and across the grain on hard, close-grain woods, as maple, birch, mahogany, walnut, etc., the smoothness of the cut depending upon the sharpness of the cutter. The slight roughness appearing at the edges of grooves cut across the grain is removed when the inlaid surface is scraped and sanded, as directed in step 11 following.

6. For wider lines it is better to use a scratch stock (Fig. 662). A scratch stock is a homemade tool consisting of two pieces of close-grained hardwood, from ⅜ to ½ in. thick, bolted together with stove bolts. A piece of veneer may be glued between the pieces in the handle, but that is not necessary or even convenient if cutters have to be changed frequently.

7. The cutter is made from a piece of broken saw blade filed or ground to shape on an emery wheel. It has square edges and is sharpened like a handscraper (Art. 132). The scratch stock is a useful tool for making small moldings, beads, flutes, grooves, etc.

8. Regulate any little unevenness in the corners with a sharp chisel, cut the lines to length, and miter them in the corners. This is best done with a very sharp chisel or dovetail saw.

9. Plane a piece of wood to about 2 or 3 in. wide and 12 in. long. Glue and nail two strips of hardwood to its upper surface and make two miter cuts as shown in Figure 663.

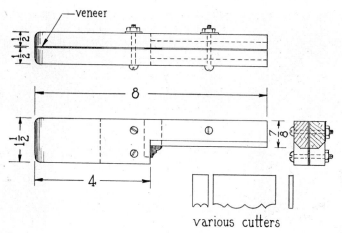

Fig. 662. Scratch stock

10. When the inlay lines have been cut to length and mitered, they are brushed with thin, hot, animal glue, or cold resin glue, and are forced into the grooves with a hammer, either by striking light blows on a block of wood laid over the inlay, or by running the hammer over the lines while exerting pressure on the head of the hammer. This must be done carefully so that the inlay will not be injured.

11. After drying about ten hours, the inlaid piece may be scraped with a very sharp cabinet scraper until all glue has been cleaned off and the lines are absolutely level with the surface. It is then ready for sanding and finishing.

Bands of inlay absorb some moisture from the glue which causes them to swell. As they cannot expand sideways in the narrow grooves, they swell in an upward direction. When the water evaporates, they again shrink to their original thickness. It is, therefore, important to allow

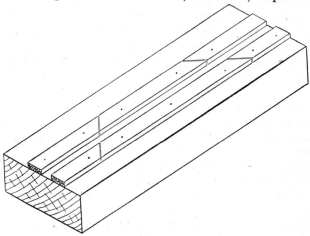

Fig. 663. Miter block for line inlay

Fig. 664. Cutting grooves with router machine

sufficient time before scraping them level with the surface. They will continue to shrink after a too early scraping, thus forming an unsightly hollow.

Grooves for line inlay can be cut very easily with a router machine (Fig. 664). This machine is furnished with a guide for both straight or curved work. The machine is fitted with a bit of the proper diameter and adjusted to the desired depth of cut. The guide is fastened at the correct distance and held against the edge of the piece while the groove is being cut.

264. To Inlay Insets. (1) Insets sold by manufacturers of marquetry are about 1/28 in. in thickness. They are glued to a piece of brown wrapping paper and are set in the center of a piece of veneer in order to protect the edges. Cut away this surplus veneer with a sharp pocket-knife by slicing it into narrow strips. After all of the strips have been carefully broken away, it will be found that bits of paper project all around the edges of the inset. This surplus paper is best removed by running a fine file, as for instance a saw file, lightly over the rear edge of the inset, which is the side to which the paper is glued.

2. When the edges have been cleaned, the inset is placed face down on the surface at the place where it is to be inlaid.

3. If the inset is elliptical, for example, and it is to be inlaid in the center of a tray or table, two center lines crossing each other at right angles are laid out both on the tray and on the inset. The inset is then placed face down so that the center lines coincide and its outline is traced on the surface with a sharp, hard pencil. As the inset may not be absolutely symmetrical, it is also well to mark it so that it will always be placed in the same position.

4. If the inset is diamond shaped, the straight lines forming the outline may be cut with a chisel, but if it is elliptical or circular, the outline, in the absence of special tools, can be cut with a sharp pocket-knife or gouges of the proper curvature.

5. The wood within the outline is cut to a depth of about 1/28 in. with a router plane. Set the plane so that it cuts only a thin shaving until the desired depth, equal to the thickness of the inset, has been reached.

6. Fit the inset into the recess just cut. If it does not go in all the way around, mark the places to be cut with a sharp knife and remove the projections little by little until the inset fits into the recess.

7. Recesses for insets are cut very easily with a portable router. Do not cut quite up to the pencil line, but finish the outline of the recess with a gouge of the proper curvature.

8. Glue the inset in place *face down,* so that the brown paper faces up. Apply hot animal glue to the recess, press the inlay into it, and force out the surplus glue by rubbing a ¾-in. chisel over it for a few minutes until the glue has set and the inset is firmly embedded in the recess. Place a piece of cardboard over it, and clamp a board across the top overnight.

Fig. 665. Portable belt sander

9. After allowing about 10 hours for drying, the inset and surrounding surface are scraped with a cabinet scraper and are sanded smooth. This will remove the brown paper so that the colors and shading of the different pieces of wood, of which the inset is composed, appear in all their beauty. The paper can be sanded off very easily if a portable sander is available (Fig. 665).

If an inset is glued in place with the papered side down, a good bond is not formed between it and the wood into which it is inlaid, because the paper is liable to split, causing the inset or parts of it to become loose.

265. To Cut Straight Reeds. The beauty of a turned column, such as illustrated in Figure 666, may be greatly enhanced by reeding. A reed, in this sense, may be defined as a semicircular molding or bead; in architecture, it is known under the name "astragal." A reed is really very easily carved by hand, and the time and patience needed for its execution is fully repaid by the added beauty and intrinsic value of the piece of furniture thus decorated.

1. The first step in the process of reeding is to make a box having neither top nor bottom, but only the four sides which may be nailed together. The size of this box should be such that the piece to be reeded will fit easily within its four sides (Fig. 668).

2. The piece to be reeded is held in this box with a screw driven through each end of it into the holes left by the lathe centers.

3. Lay out vertical center lines on each end, and bore a 3/16-in. hole

Fig. 666. Beautiful example of reeding
done by hand

Fig. 667. Laying off reeds from paper strip

for the screw in each of these lines, so that the part to be reeded will be nearly level with the top edges of the box.

4. Determine the number of reeds to be cut. Wrap a strip of paper around the thickest part of the column. Cut it so that the ends just meet, and divide it into the desired number of parts.

5. Wrap the paper around the column again, and lay off the divisions (Fig. 667).

6. Place the column so that one of these marks is approximately equidistant from both sides of the box. Set a marking gauge with the block against one of the sides and the point on the mark, and gauge a line throughout the length to be reeded (Fig. 668). It is best to bring the point of the marking gauge all the way out, so that it can reach the smaller diameters of the column. If there is much difference in the diameters of the part to be reeded, a piece of wood, shaped to its outline, must be nailed to the side of the box so that the marking gauge can ride on that (Fig. 669).

7. Repeat at all the other marks of division, being careful to hold the block of the marking gauge against the same side of the box.

8. Wedge the column firmly against the sides of the box, and chisel a V cut on one of the gauge lines. A carver's veining tool or skew chisel, or an ordinary $\frac{1}{2}$-in. paring chisel having beveled sides, may be used, for this work (Fig. 670). Be careful to see how the grain runs, taking small cuts and reversing the direction of the cut whenever necessary.

9. When the V cuts have been made sufficiently deep, the sharp edges are rounded, thus forming the beads or reeds.

10. These are further smoothed with scrapers and sandpaper.

Fig. 668. Gauging reeds from division marks

11. Flutes may be laid out and cut in the same way, but it is more difficult to get them smooth and even.

Flutes on straight work may be cut with a scratch stock (Fig. 662).

12. Reeds and flutes are easily cut with a portable shaper. The piece to be reeded is placed between the lathe centers. A board is fastened to the lathe bed, and the shaper is screwed into the holder which is moved along this board (Fig. 671). The cutter is set to the level of the lathe

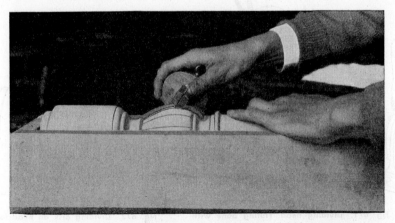

Fig. 669. Gauging division lines. Note block nailed to far side of box

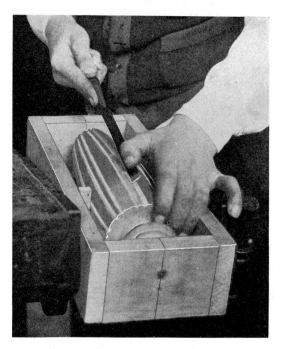

Fig. 670. Chiseling "V" cuts

centers and held against the stock being reeded or fluted. A cogwheel attachment is fastened to the live spindle for the purpose of dividing the turned stock into the desired number of reeds equally spaced. Some lathes are equipped with a permanent dividing disk on the headstock (Fig. 672).

Fig. 671. Dividing head. Fluting done with portable shaper

Fig. 672. Dividing disk on headstock

266. To Cut Spiral Reeds. (1) Place the column to be reeded in the lathe. Wrap a strip of paper around it at each extremity of the part to be reeded, and divide the two strips into the same number of equal parts. If the diameters of the column are different, it follows that the divisions on one strip of paper will be larger than on the other.

2. Determine the pitch the reeds are to have. This is done according to the desire of the workman. The reed may go once around the column or only halfway. In either case, a straightedge is cut from a piece of cardboard or other flexible material, and is wrapped around the column so that each end of the cardboard touches one of the division points marked at each extremity of the column (Fig. 673).

Fig. 673. Laying out spiral reeds

3. Draw a pencil line along the edge of the cardboard as it winds around the column. Move the cardboard to the next pair of division points, and mark a line along its edge as previously done. Continue around the column in this way until all the reeds have been marked.

4. Chisel a V cut along these lines, as explained in Article 265, round off the sharp corners, and smooth the reeds with scraper and sandpaper.

It will be found that the shaping of spiral reeds is easier than the straight ones, because the cutting is done at an angle to the direction in which the grain runs. There is, therefore, less chance of the chisel following the grain rather than the line marked.

267. To Carve a Single Spiral on a Turned Cylinder. (1) Turn the cylinder to the required diameter, and determine the number of turns the spiral is to make. It is customary to make the length of each turn approximately equal to the diameter of the cylinder.

2. Divide the length of the cylinder into that number of equal parts, and mark a heavy line at these points while it is revolving in the lathe.

3. Divide each of these major parts into four equal parts, and mark lighter circles at these points, A, Figure 674.

4. Wrap a strip of paper around the cylinder and divide it into four equal parts. Mark these divisions on the cylinder, move the T rest close

to it, and draw longitudinal lines along it at these points as in *a, b, c, d,*
A, Figure 674.

5. Draw the spiral line, beginning at the left end of the cylinder on
one of the longitudinal lines, for example *a.* Continue toward the right to
where the next line *b* intersects the first circle, and so on. When the first
heavy circle is reached, the spiral should have made one complete turn
around the cylinder. Proceed in like manner until the end of the cylinder
has been reached. Do not let the spiral line begin or end too abruptly,
but make it more parallel to the turned beads at both ends.

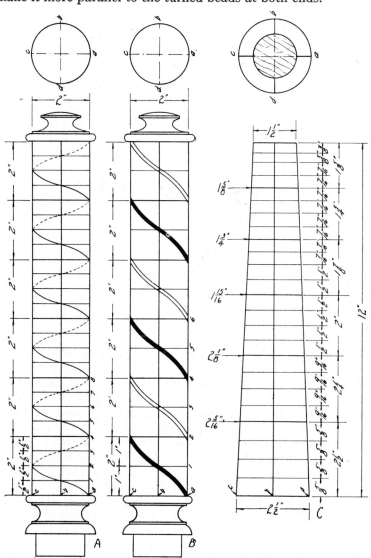

Fig. 674. Layout of single, double, and tapered spirals

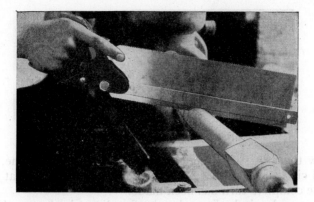

Fig. 675. Making saw cut along spiral line

6. The carving is done as follows: With a backsaw, make a shallow cut about ½ in. deep, starting and stopping the cut about ½ in. from each end. Use a backsaw with a metal guide as in Figure 675, or clamp one of wood to an ordinary backsaw. It is best to make this saw cut while the turning is held between centers in the lathe.

7. Now clamp the leg on the bench top while making broad V cuts all along the spiral with a ¾-in. chisel (Fig. 676). Finally shape the spiral with rasp, files, and sandpaper.

These operations, which are quite easy to do, are shown in Figures 677 and 678.

268. To Carve a Double Spiral on a Turned Cylinder. (1) When a double spiral is to be carved, proceed as explained in Article 267, steps 1 to 4, but divide each of the major divisions into two equal parts only (B, Fig. 674).

Fig. 676. Chiseling V cut for spiral

Fig. 677. Shaping spiral with rasp

2. Draw the first spiral, indicated by the heavy black line, from *a* to line *b* and circle 1, then to *c* and circle 2, and so on, until at line *a* and circle 4 one complete turn has been made.

3. The second spiral, shown by the fine lines, begins on the opposite side of the cylinder at line *c*, continues to line *d* and circle 1, and from there goes to line *a* and circle 2, and so on. For the sake of clearness, these spiral lines have been shown on only one side of the cylinder.

4. Figure 679 shows two double spirals. The one in the center, resembling two pieces of rope twisted together, is carved exactly as explained in Article 267, step 6.

5. The hollow double spiral at the right in Figure 679 is laid out as shown at B, in Figure 674. The spiral lines in this case form the ridge, and are 3/16 in. wide. They may be laid out from a strip of heavy paper 3/16 in. wide wrapped around the cylinder.

6. The sawing should be done on a line marked between the spiral lines starting at line *a* and circle 1, continuing to line *b* and circle 2, and so on. This line has not been shown in the drawing as it might prove to be confusing.

7. The spirals are worked out with chisel, rasp, file, and sandpaper. Spirals should not begin or end too abruptly.

Fig. 678. Finishing spiral with sandpaper. Note ends of spiral have been turned

269. To Lay Out Tapered Spirals. (1) Wrap a strip of paper around the cylinder, divide it into four equal parts and draw four longitudinal lines on the cylinder (Art. 267, step 4).

2. Measure the diameter at the largest end of the tapered cylinder, and lay off this distance along one of the horizontal lines.

Fig. 679. Single and double spirals

3. Then measure the diameter at this point, and lay off this distance along the cylinder. Continue in this way until the small end of the cylinder has been reached.

4. Adjust the various lengths so that they diminish proportionally, and so that the sum of their lengths equals the total length of the tapered cylinder.

5. These major divisions are again divided into two or four parts according to whether a single or a double spiral is to be carved.

Spiral turning, which is of eastern origin, was introduced in Europe in the seventeenth century by Portuguese explorers. It is done commercially on special lathes and routers.

SIMPLE CARVING

Wood carving, even in its simplest forms, adds much to the beauty and distinction of a piece of furniture. As this art cannot be learned very readily from written instructions only, the easiest way for the beginner is probably to try to imitate some simple border or ornament such as those illustrated in Figures 686 and 687. This, in most cases, will be

Fig. 680. Floor-lamp base showing carvings of beads
and acanthus leaf

found surprisingly easy, especially if an actual carving can be had
for a model.

In selecting a carved ornament for a piece of cabinetwork, the student
should consult books on historical ornament in order to have the carving
of a form and type that is in keeping with the period of the piece of
furniture which he is constructing.

TOOLS

The beginner needs only a few carving tools, such as a ½-in. skew
chisel, two or three straight gouges of medium curvature, ⅛, ¼, and ⅜
in., a veining tool, and a parting or V tool (Fig. 67).

270. To Cut Beads. Beads, such as those shown on the legs of the
table in Figure 681 and the stretcher in Figure 682 are made with a
scratch stock, shown in Figure 662, and described in Article 263.

271. To Cut Chamfers and Hollows. Stopped chamfers do not
extend all the way along the edge of a board, and, therefore, cannot be
planed except on a portion in the center. They may be chiseled with a
paring chisel. Cut the ends first, holding the bevel of the chisel down
(Fig. 683), but do not chisel quite down to the lines. Finish the part
between the ends, holding the chisel diagonally and the beveled side up
(Fig. 684). Smooth with block plane scraper and sandpaper.

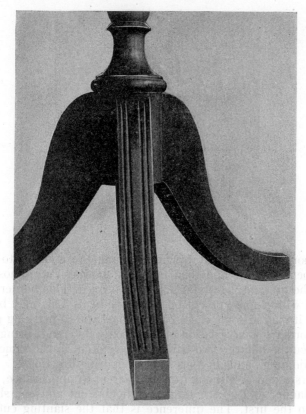

Fig. 681. Beaded table leg

Stopped chamfers may be planed on the jointer by tilting the fence to 45 deg. and lowering both tables the same distance as shown in Figure 684a.

Hollows are chamfers which have been curved with a gouge. First plane the chamfer, and then chisel the hollow in the center with a gouge of the proper diameter and curvature (Fig. 685). The sharp edges of the chamfer determine the width of the hollow. Chamfers and hollows also may be made with a scratch stock.

272. To Carve Borders. Other examples of carving made with the gouge only are illustrated in Figure 686 at *a, b, c,* and *d.*

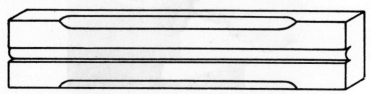

Fig. 682. Beaded and stop-chamfered stretcher

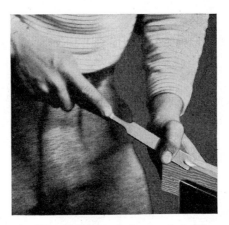

Fig. 683. Chiseling end of stopped chamfer

1. The border at *a* is cut by first driving the gouge into the wood almost perpendicularly, and then taking a slanting cut, almost horizontally, into the first cut, so that a hollow is formed. This border is further embellished with a fine line cut on each side of it. This may be cut with a V tool, or it may in some cases be scratched with a marking gauge.

2. The border *b* is a variation of *a*, the only difference being the direction of the cut. While the two bands in *a* were cut in the same direction, each two adjoining bands in *b* are cut in opposite directions.

3. Borders *c* and *d*, although quite different in appearance, are cut in the same manner as *b;* i.e., one perpendicular cut and one slanting cut running into the first. The difference is that the slanting cuts in these borders are much steeper than in *b*.

4. The *strapwork* shown at *b*, Figure 687, is a very popular and quite simple form of wood carving. In this example, the outline has been cut with a V tool, after which the band between these outlines has been hollowed with a gouge.

Fig. 684. Finishing a chamfer

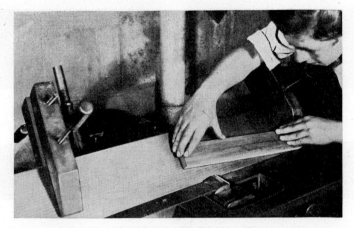

Fig. 684a. Planing stopped chamfer. Hand screws clamped to
fence as stop blocks

It is more common in strapwork to leave the bands in relief and cut
down the background to a depth of about ⅛ in. (Fig. 688). The usual
procedure is to cut the outline of the bands with a flat chisel held perpendicularly. A mallet is used to drive the chisel into the wood. Be careful not to undercut the bands because the edges are liable to crumble and
break. Then make slanting cuts meeting the perpendicular cuts, gradually
working toward the center of the background.

Fig. 685. Cutting hollow on edge with
bent-shank gouge

The router machine described in Article 115 is a very useful tool for
cutting away the background.

5. A very effective and easy form of carving, made by a combination
of perpendicular and slanting cuts as explained above, is shown at *a*,
Figure 687.

6. The lower border at *c*, Figure 686, shows outline carving done with
a V tool. While this appears the most simple and easiest of the types described, it takes quite a good deal of practice to be able to cut these fine
lines so that they are of a uniform width and closely follow the curves
or straight lines of the design.

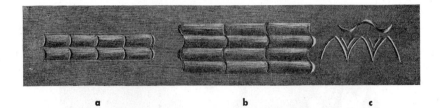

Fig. 686. Simple carved borders

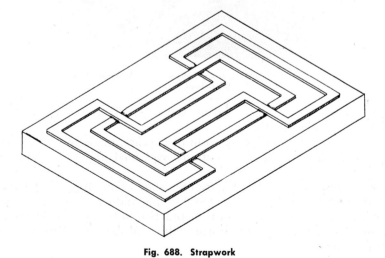

a   b

Fig. 687. Simple carving

Fig. 688. Strapwork

7. Carvings, such as the acanthus leaves illustrated in Figures 680 and 689, are not difficult to make for the beginner, especially if he has a model from which to work. It is recommended first to outline the rib running through the center of the leaf, then shape the latter roughly, and finally cut and shape the small individual leaves.

MOLDINGS

The appropriate use of moldings adds much to the beauty and character both of cabinetwork and interior woodwork. Like carving, it is the play of light and shadow over the uneven surface which attracts the eye to a molding. Moldings are therefore used to accentuate certain parts of a piece of furniture such as a cornice, a base, or a panel (Fig. 690).

Moldings are either plain or carved. They are made in a great variety of shapes, and are known by many names of Greek, French, Latin, and English origin. Some of the most common moldings are: the band, the sunk or raised fillet, the round shapes such as quarter, half round, and three-quarter round, the bead or astragal, the

Fig. 689. Acanthus leaf

hollow shapes or cove moldings made in several degrees of curvature, and the combination round and hollow moldings called "cyma" moldings (Fig. 691).

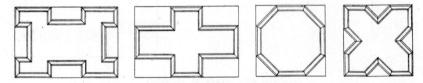

Fig. 690. Panels decorated with moldings

273. To Make Moldings. Moldings are usually cut on the shaper or planed by hand with special molding planes or with a universal plane. Small moldings may be made entirely with the scratch stock (Fig. 662).

They also can be worked out roughly on a circular saw and smoothed with chisels, gouges, or scrapers. The method of procedure in the latter case is as follows:

1. Square the stock from which the molding is to be made, and lay out its profile on one end of the stock.

2. Make a number of saw cuts on the circular saw in the manner

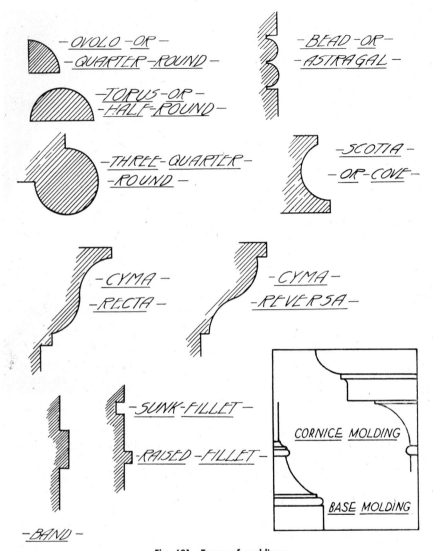

Fig. 691. Types of moldings

suggested in Figure 692. All square and flat surfaces of the molding can be cut exactly in this way. All curved surfaces can be cut only approximately to shape.

3. The curved surfaces are now smoothed with sharp chisels and gouges, after which they are scraped with molding scrapers, whose edges are filed to conform to the shape of the molding.

4. The final smoothing is done with sandpaper folded over small pieces of wood, which are shaped to fit different sections of the molding. These pieces of wood, called "rubbers," should be at least 4 in. long.

Directions for mitering and applying moldings are given in Chapter
10 on miter joints.

274. To Shape the Edges of Table Tops. In order
to make a table or cabinet more attractive and interesting, the edges of the top may be shaped or molded
in different ways.

1. The edges shown in A, B, and C, Figure 693, are
all produced in the following manner: Cut a shallow
rabbet, about 1/16 in. deep and from ¾ to 1 in. wide,
on the face of the top as shown in D, Figure 693.
If a circular saw is available, this may be very easily
done by making a single cut 1/16 in. deep. The
rabbet otherwise may be planed with a rabbet plane
(Art. 167).

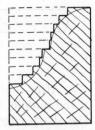

Fig. 692. Sawing
molding by mak-
ing a series of
parallel cuts

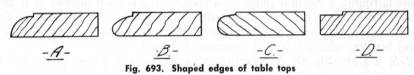

-A-   -B-   -C-   -D-

Fig. 693. Shaped edges of table tops

2. The edge is now planed to the desired shape with a block plane.
Clamp a piece of thin stock on the edge of the rabbet in order to prevent
the plane from cutting into it. Test the edge frequently with a template
made of cardboard or sheet metal while it is being planed.

3. A round top may be rabbeted as at D, on the circular saw by first
making a form or cradle for it in which it can be rotated as in Figure
694. The form is clamped to the saw table, and the saw is started and
brought up through it to the correct height.

Fig. 694. Cutting shallow rabbet on edge of circular table top
to be rounded. Saw guard cannot be used

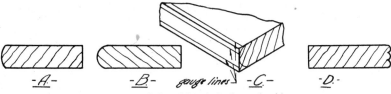

Fig. 695. Rounded and beaded edges of table tops

4. After rounding the rabbeted edge, fold a quarter sheet of sandpaper in the middle, hold it in the palm of the hand, and sand until smooth. The sharp edge of the rabbet may be sanded by folding the sandpaper over a hand scraper.

5. The edges shown at A and B, Figure 695, are simply rounded with a jack plane according to lines marked with a pencil (C, Fig. 695). If the table is round, a circular plane or a spokeshave is used instead of a jack plane. These edges are smoothed with a file scraper and sandpaper. The beaded edge, D, Figure 695, is made with a scratch stock (Fig. 662) or a hand beader, which is a tool resembling a spokeshave.

275. To Do Simple Veneering. (1) To veneer a surface means to glue a thin sheet, usually of another kind of wood, to it. This is done for two reasons, first, to strengthen the wood and, second, to make its surface more beautiful.

2. Wood is many times stronger when it is built up of several layers glued together at right angles to each other, than when it is in one solid piece. Plywood is glued up in that way from several layers crossing each other, called "laminations." The modern waterproof glues make such fabricated wood practically indestructible (see Article 339).

3. Veneer consists of thin sheets of wood, usually only 1/28 in. thick, which are sliced from a solid log on special machines. Depending upon its use, some veneer is plain and cut from common woods, and some is highly figured and cut from rare and costly woods.

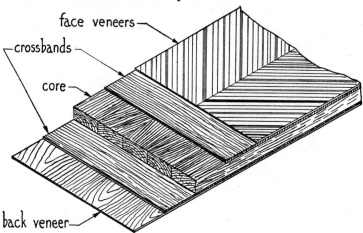

Fig. 696. Simple veneered construction

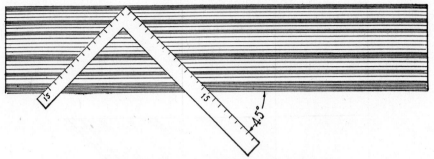

Fig. 697. Laying out 45-deg. angle on striped veneer

4. The latter wood could not be used if cut into solid boards, because highly figured wood splits and warps more than straight-grained wood. It is, therefore, necessary to make a good foundation of plain, straight-grained boards on which to glue veneers. Such a foundation is called a "core."

5. The core for a table top should be glued up like an ordinary table top, but of narrow boards only from 2 to 3 in. wide. When dry, this core is planed flat and smooth on one side, then gauged on edges and ends and planed on the other side until it is smooth and of uniform thickness throughout.

6. Two pieces of plain, straight-grained veneer, called the "cross-bands," are glued at right angles to the core, one on each side (Fig. 696). Use a cold-water glue, such as resin or casein glue, apply it to both sides of the core, and clamp the pieces in a veneer press. If the work is small enough, it may be clamped with hand screws between two boards.

Note that much veneering is still being done in the old way with animal glue, which requires a hot press or heated sheet-metal plates.

7. The work is now ready for the two outside pieces of veneers. The one to be glued to the bottom of the table top is called the "back veneer" and has plain grain. The other, to be glued to the top or face, is called the "face veneer" and is usually of a better grade of veneer, selected for its beauty, color, and grain. It is often cut to form various geometrical patterns. This is called "matching."

8. One of the most common forms of matching is the "diamond match." To make this match, select a piece of striped veneer and cut it at an angle of 45 deg. to its side (Fig. 697). This may be done by placing a steel square on the veneer so that the same number on the tongue and blade is over the edge. The angle will then be 45 deg. Use a veneer saw (Fig. 698) or a strong, sharp knife for cutting the veneer.

9. Place the piece of veneer, just cut, on the center lines which should be marked on the face of the top (Fig. 699). Turn the sheet of veneer over as in Figure 700, and cut the second piece of veneer. Then cut the third and fourth pieces as

Fig. 698. Veneer saw

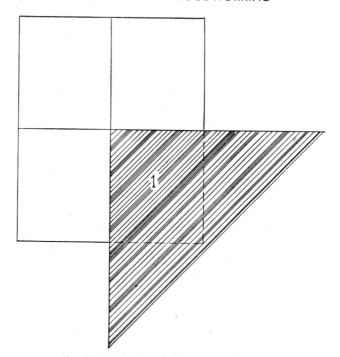

Fig. 699. First piece of diamond match in place

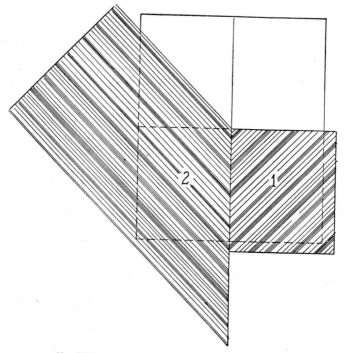

Fig. 700. Second piece of diamond match in place

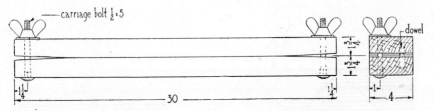

Fig. 700a. Clamp for holding veneers while jointing

shown in Figure 701. Another method of cutting a diamond match is shown in Figure 702.

10. It is now necessary to plane the sawed edges of the veneer, so that they will fit perfectly together. This is done by clamping them in a homemade clamp made of hardwood such as birch or maple. Note that the inside surfaces of the clamp are slightly rounded in order to hold the veneer tightly (Fig. 700a).

Fig. 701. Diamond match completed

11. Plane the edges to be glued along one of the center lines, then nail two of them (1 and 2) to a board, using veneer pins or fine brads. Drive them on a slant so that the two veneer edges will be brought as closely together as possible (Fig. 703). Reverse Nos. 2 and 4 and join to Nos. 1 and 3. If the veneer is too narrow for the pieces needed, waste pieces may be joined to the edge with veneer tape as shown in the lower drawing. While in this position, glue a piece of veneer tape or ordinary gummed paper over the joint. Plane and tape the other two veneers (3 and 4) in the same way.

12. The two taped pieces of veneer are then placed face to face and their edges are planed and taped. Be sure to plane these long edges

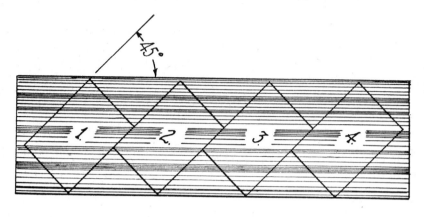

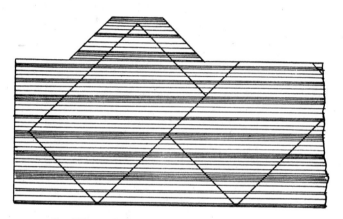

Fig. 702. Method of cutting Diamond Match

Fig. 703. Taping veneers

Fig. 704. Veneered stock in press. As the stock in this case was a little larger than the press, the projecting parts were clamped with C clamps

square to the taped edges, and be careful not to chip them in the center. Tape the veneers on the face side only, because a piece of paper in a glued joint will not make a good bond.

13. Before gluing, the center lines should be squared over the edges in order to center the diamond match correctly. Each two joined edges

Fig. 705. Cutting veneer across the grain for a border

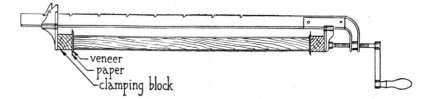

veneer
paper
clamping block

Fig. 706. Veneering edges

must be directly above each center line. Put plenty of glue on the face side of the cross-banded core, but none on the veneer. Place the veneer in position and nail it with veneer pins (headless) or fine brads. Cut the heads of the brads off ¼ in. above the surface, place a couple of sheets of newspaper over the veneer, and then a piece of fir plywood, named the "caul," which is pressed down over the projecting brads.

14. Glue the back veneer at right angles to the crossbands, and then put the whole assembly in the veneer press and tighten it as much as possible. If the veneered surface is a little larger than the platen of the press, a few C clamps may be clamped along the edge as in Figure 704.

15. The veneered top should be left several hours in the press until perfectly dry. It is then squared in the same way as solid wood and the veneer tape removed by moistening it with water and gently scraping it off.

16. If it is desired to veneer the edges of the table top, cut strips of wood, a little wider than the thickness of the top, across the grain as in Figure 705. Tape them together, side by side, and glue them to the edges as in Figure 706.

Note that there are many variations of the diamond match and endless ways of combining veneers into beautiful and harmonious designs. For further information on this subject, consult the author's book *Forty Pieces of Fine Furniture*.

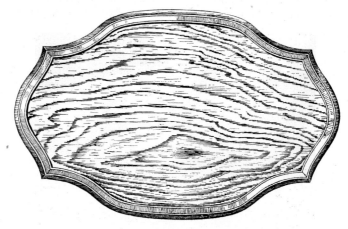

Fig. 707. Overlay

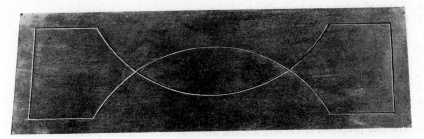

Fig. 708. Veined panel

276. To Decorate by Overlays, Frets, or Veining. The chief object of these types of decoration is to relieve the monotony of a surface by a suitable design applied to it or outlined on it in two different shades of a color.

1. Overlays, as the name implies, are pieces of thin wood applied on top of a surface so as to form a raised part (Fig. 707). They should be made of selected grades of veneer with beautifully figured grain, and may be built up with plywood to various thicknesses. They are generally stained a lighter tone than the surface they decorate.

2. Frets are pierced overlays used especially as a decoration on panels. They are often stained darker than the panel to which they are glued. Both panel and fret should be finished before gluing. Glue should be applied very sparingly to the back of the fret, so that it will not be squeezed out on the panel.

Grilles are frets or latticework set in an open frame, as in doors of bookcases. They are sawed out of plywood.

3. Veining consists of a thin line of pleasing patterns, carved with a veining tool or a machine router, to decorate a plain surface (Fig. 708). As a method of decoration, it is almost identical with overlays.

In some cases, the part within the line is stained a different shade from the part without the line, called "two toning," and in others the line itself is colored to make it stand out more clearly.

4. In the latter case, stain and fill the wood as described in Chapter 18, and clean the filler out of the line with a pointed stick.

5. Apply a sealing coat of shellac or lacquer, and sand smooth.

6. Apply the vein line color over the sealing coat with a fine-pointed artist's brush.

REVIEW QUESTIONS

1. A wood surface may be decorated by (a) ....; (b) ....; (c) ....; (d) ....
2. Woods suitable for inlaying are .... (name 6)
3. Commercial inlaying material is made up into .... and ....
4. Grooves for inlaying are made with a .... or a ....
5. Which side should be up when gluing an inset into a table top and why?
6. Line inlay should not be scraped until the glue is dry, because ....
7. A turned column may be divided into a number of equal spaces by ....

8. A turned column to be reeded is placed in a .... with no ....
9. Lines for reeding are marked on a turned column with a .... held ....
10. If the diameters of the part to be reeded vary greatly, it is necessary to .... while marking the reeds.
11. Spiral reeds are laid out by ....
12. Some lathes have a .... for dividing turned work into equal spaces.
13. When laying out a single spiral, divide it lengthwise into ....
14. The difference between laying out a single and a double spiral is ....
15. The tool processes in carving a spiral are: (*a*) ....; (*b*) ....; (*c*) ....
16. A scratch stock is made of .... and used for ....
17. The cutter in a scratch stock is sharpened like ....
18. A round table top may be rabbeted on the circular saw by ....
19. The core for a table top is made ....
20. Crossbands are .... glued to ....
21. The diamond match is ....
22. The back veneer is glued .... to the crossbands, but .... the core.
23. A 45-deg. angle is laid out ....
24. When the edges of a table top are veneered, the grain generally runs ....
25. Overlays are .... Frets are .... Grilles are ....

Chapter 17

UPHOLSTERY

279. History. The art of upholstery dates back to antiquity in Egypt and the Orient. In France, it reached a high degree of development during the reign of Louis XIV (1643–1715). In the same period of time, only loose cushions or pads were used in England, but when the monarchy was restored under Charles II (1660–1685), real upholstered furniture and fine woven fabrics made their appearance. The revocation of the Edict of Nantes in 1685 was a great factor in this development, because the French protestants, called "Huguenots," many of whom were skilled craftsmen, emigrated in large numbers to England to avoid religious persecution. The Edict of Nantes was a guaranty of religious freedom to French Protestants.

Upholstery, like wood finishing, wood turning, and wood carving, is one of the trades that is closely related to cabinetmaking, and in some measure dependent upon the latter. It is, therefore, fitting that this book should give some attention at least to the most elementary processes of this art, a knowledge of which will be found useful and valuable in the making of chairs, stools, and similar articles of furniture.

280. To Make a Plain Pad Seat. A pad seat is the simplest form of upholstery and, as the name implies, merely consists in making a pad or cushion on a wooden base (Fig. 711).

1. If the pad is to cover the entire board, except for a 1-in. margin along the edges, a line is marked accordingly all around the board.

2. Use tow, moss, or hair for the stuffing; pick it carefully so that it is free from lumps, and spread half of it evenly over the seat to about ½ in. from the line marked.

3. It is important that the stuffing does not slide on the wooden base. It may be held in place either by tacking it to the base or by coating the base with glue before spreading it.

4. Distribute the rest of the stuffing evenly over the first layer, and stretch and tack a piece of muslin over it. Fold the muslin over on itself, and begin tacking it from the center of the four edges, gradually working toward the corners.

5. Place a piece of cotton wadding over the muslin, and then tack the covering in place.

6. Begin tacking from the centers of the front, back, and sides, driving the tacks only partly home. This is called "slip tacking."

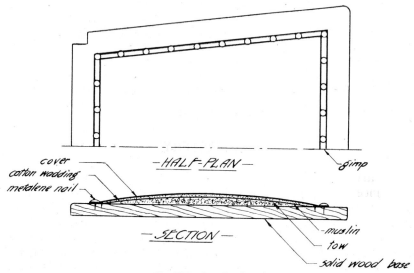

Fig. 711. Details of pad seat

7. Restretch the cover by stroking it from side to side and from front to back. Pull out a few of the tacks at a time, and retack the cover firmly.

8. Make a gimp or narrow band of the same material as that of the covering. Gimps also may be bought ready made. Tack the gimp in place, so that it is even with the line marked. Use metalene nails on leather or imitation leather, and gimp tacks on a cloth covering. Space the tacks from 2 to 4 in. apart.

9. The gimp is mitered in the corners by folding a pleat on it.

Tow is made from the dried stems of flax plants, which go through various picking and refining processes. Tow is sold to the trade in different grades of fineness. Muslin, wadding, and imitation leather are all products of the cotton plant. Muslin is a thin cloth which is sold either bleached or unbleached. Wadding or cotton felt is a by-product of the ginning process. Imitation or artificial leather consists of a strong woven cloth, which is dyed to the color of the finished product. It is then covered with nitrocellulose, which is a liquid also made of cotton. This forms a very strong and durable material used for many other purposes besides upholstery, as, for instance, suitcases, bookbindings, novelties, and automobile tops.

Moss is a plant which grows on the branches and trunks of trees. It grows abundantly in swampy regions in Louisiana, Florida, and South America.

Fresh moss is piled in small heaps kept moist with water. In the course of two or three months, the green covering rots away leaving only the black hairlike fiber. This is then dried, ginned, and baled. Moss is sold in different grades, according to the length of the drying time and the number of ginnings it has had.

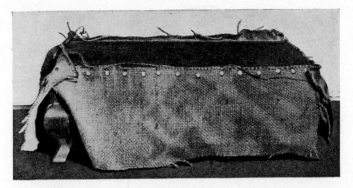

Fig. 712. Burlap for roll edge tacked to sides of seat

Hair used in the upholstery trade is cut from the tails and manes of horses and from cattle and hogs. Most of it comes from South America, Texas, Montana, and Canada. It is sorted, sterilized, and permanently curled in a chemical bath.

281. To Make a Pad Seat With a Roll Edge. This type of seat differs from a plain pad seat in that the covering extends over its outer edges. A roll of stuffing must be made to cover the sharp wooden edges in order to prevent them from cutting through the cover. A roll edge is formed as follows:

1. Tack a piece of burlap, about 3 to 4 in. wide, close to the outer edges of the seat so that the burlap projects beyond the seat (Fig. 712). Sometimes a fold about ¼ in. wide is made on the edge of the burlap so that the tacks will hold better.

2. Use fine tow, hair, or moss for the stuffing. Place it along the edge and fold the burlap over it. Make the roll as hard and as even in size and shape as possible, and then tack the burlap in place (Fig. 713). If the burlap is cut straight, the lateral threads of the material will act as a

Fig. 713. Roll edge formed

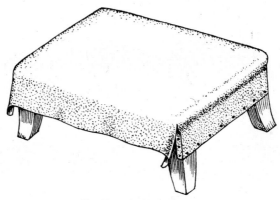

Fig. 714. Making pleats

guide in forming the roll. The size of the roll varies with different conditions. For ordinary work, such as a seat on a footstool, a roll about 1 in. in diameter is suitable.

3. Proceed with the upholstery as explained in Article 280, steps 2 to 4.

4. Sliptack the muslin to the sides of the seat, or in the case of a footstool, to the rails near their upper or lower edges. Restretch the muslin as explained in Article 280, step 7, until it is tight and smooth. Then tack it firmly in place folding the edge over on itself.

5. Place a piece of wadding over the muslin, and tack the covering and the gimp along the lower edges of the rails.

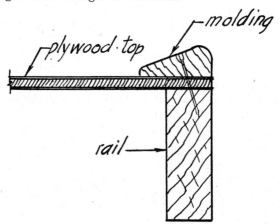

Fig. 715. Wood molding taking place of roll edge

6. When the covering extends over the sides of the seat and is tacked to the lower edge of the rails as in the footstool, Figure 714, the corners must be folded or pleated in a certain way.

7. Stretch the covering well, and tack it along the lower edges of the rails to within 2 in. of the corners.

8. Fold the cover from the sides with the short rails over the front and rear corners, and tack it in place.

9. Cut away the surplus material at the corners, fold a pleat on the front part of the covering, and fasten it with one tack so that it is even with the corner. Pleats on chairs are always laid to the rear.

10. The effect of a roll edge may be produced very simply by making a molding as shown in Figure 715, mitering it in the corners and nailing it along the edges.

Burlap is a coarse cloth, woven from the bast of the jute plant (Art. 318) which grows in India. It is used for a great many purposes, such as upholstery, draperies, bags for sugar, potatoes, and other products, as a base for linoleum, etc. Burlap is made in different qualities or weights. The pieces are generally 40 in. wide and 100 yds. long.

282. To Upholster a Slip Seat. A slip seat fits tightly between the rails of a chair, bench, or stool. The seat, which may be upholstered or woven over a wooden frame (Art. 283), generally fits into a rabbet cut on the inside edges of the rails. It may also be supported and fastened to blocks or cleats screwed to the rails.

1. The frame of the seat is made of four pieces of wood $\frac{3}{4}$ to $\frac{7}{8}$ in. thick and about $2\frac{1}{2}$ to 3 in. wide. They may be joined by end-lap joints (Art. 180), dowel joints (Art. 175), or slip joints (Art. 191). Slip joints are the strongest and, therefore, preferred.

2. Join the pieces to conform to the shape of the seat as square, rectangular, or trapezoid. Allow from 1/16 to $\frac{1}{8}$ in. for the covering on each of the outside edges of the frame, depending upon the thickness of the material. In other words, if the seat, for example, measures 12 by 18 in. within the rabbets, the finished outside dimensions of the frame should be $11\frac{7}{8}$ by $17\frac{7}{8}$ in. if 1/16 in. is allowed, and $11\frac{3}{4}$ by $17\frac{3}{4}$ in. if $\frac{1}{8}$ in. is allowed.

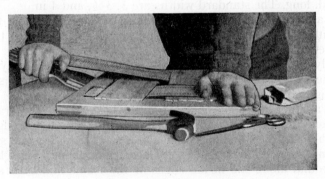

Fig. 716. Stretching webbing

3. After the frame has been glued, it should be smoothed with a plane. A chamfer, about 3/16 in. wide, should also be planed on the upper outside edges of the frame.

4. Begin the upholstery by nailing strips of webbing to the upper faces of the frame. For a chair-seat frame, two or three strips of webbing are used each way. Fold the webbing over about $1\frac{1}{2}$ in. from the end so that the carpet tacks pass through two layers of webbing. Tack one end

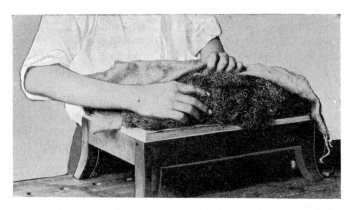

Fig. 717. Picking stuffing and placing it on frame. Notice burlap
tacked over webbing

of a piece of webbing in the center of one of the rails and about 1 in. from its outer edge. Stretch the webbing over the opposite rail with the webbing stretcher (Fig. 716), and drive in three or four 10-oz. tacks. Release the stretcher, and cut the webbing with a pair of scissors about 1½ in. outside the tacks. Bend this end back over the tacks and fasten with a few more tacks. Fasten the other pieces of webbing in the same manner.

Pieces of webbing crossing each other should be interlaced for greater strength.

Like burlap, webbing is also made from jute fibers. Webbing is sold in rolls 72 yd. long. The standard widths are 3, 3½, and 4 in.

5. Cut a piece of burlap to about the size of the frame. Fold the edges over about ¾ in. all around, stretch and tack it to the face of the frame so that the webbing is covered. Use 4-oz. tacks.

6. Apply a layer of fine tow, or moss, about 2 in. thick, evenly over the face of the seat (Fig. 717). Pick it carefully with the fingers so that it becomes light and fluffy without any hard lumps.

7. Cut another piece of burlap a little larger than the frame, and stretch it over the layer of stuffing. Tack it temporarily to the edges of the frame without driving the tacks home. Now sew the burlap and stuffing to the webbing, using a long upholsterer's needle and twine (Fig. 718). First sew all around along the inside edges of the frame and then along the center. Have the stitches about 3 in. long come on top of the burlap, and pull them tight after completing the sewing. The stuffing and burlap are now held firmly, and the tacks temporarily holding the latter should be removed from the edge of the frame.

Thin three-ply veneer may be used instead of webbing. The processes in applying and sewing stuffing and burlap are the same. The upholsterer's needle is generally strong enough to go through thin three-ply veneer, but if the veneer should be too heavy for the needle, a few small holes may be quickly bored.

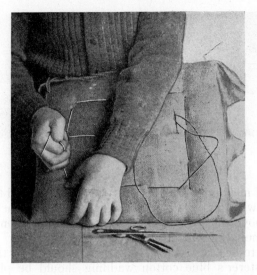

Fig. 718. Sewing stuffing to webbing

8. To form the edge of the seat, add some moss along the edge, shape it into a roll, pull the burlap over it, and tack the latter to the chamfered edge of the frame. Shape the edge of the seat so that it overhangs the edge of the frame a little and is of the same height as the part that was sewed to the webbing. When tacking the burlap to the frame, fold its edge toward the inside so that the outside is perfectly smooth.

9. Finish the corners last. If they have been cut to fit against the corner of a chair leg (Fig. 719), as is often the case, the edge must, of course, conform to that shape. The sharp peen of an upholsterer's hammer is very helpful in forming such corners.

10. The shape of the edge is now improved and made sharper by manipulating the stuffing with the regulator (Fig. 720). It is then sewed with a curved needle, so that the stitches, each about ½ in. long, lie on top and below the edge, but do not pass over it (Fig. 721). The thread passes over the edge only in corners that fit around a square leg or post.

This is done so as to make a sharper corner.

A curved needle is used instead of a straight one, because it goes in deeper and therefore pulls more material toward the edge.

11. A thin layer of moss or hair is next spread over the seat, so that it is made slightly higher in the center, sloping gently toward the edges (Fig.

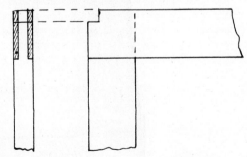

Fig. 719. Rear corner of chair-seat frame

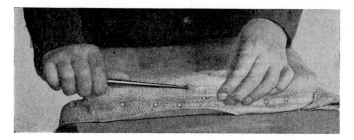

Fig. 720. Shaping edge with regulator

722). A piece of muslin is stretched over this and fastened temporarily by slip-tacking or with large pins or skewers which are stuck into the upholstery just above the wooden frame. The muslin is then tacked to the edge of the frame, after which the pins are removed.

If the seat is to be covered with silk, damask, or other thin material, a sheet of upholsterer's blue cotton wadding should be placed over the muslin to prevent the hair from sticking through the covering fabric.

12. The covering is tacked to the underside of the frame.

13. A piece of black cambric tacked to the underside of the frame will prevent dust from the upholstery material from falling to the floor.

Cambric is a cloth woven either of linen or cotton threads. Upholsterers use a cambric made of cotton. It is made only in two colors, white and black.

Fig. 721. Sewing edge with curved needle

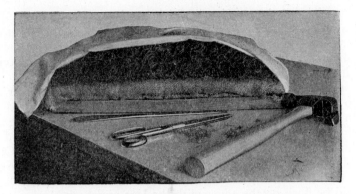

Fig. 722. Stretching and tacking muslin to edge

When a slip seat is made flush with the rails of a chair, the sewed edge may be omitted.

283. To Weave a Fiber Seat. Although rush weaving and caning has nothing to do with upholstery in the strict sense of the word, these processes are, nevertheless, used for the same purpose — the covering of a chair seat — and are, therefore, treated in the present chapter.

Woven seats for chairs, stools, and settees have been popular in this country since the first New England settlements. These seats were called "rush seats" or "flag seats," and were woven from a grasslike plant growing to a height of from 2 to 4 ft. The soft, pliant stems of these plants were dried and then twisted together to form the ropelike strands of the rush weave.

Rush seats are still made in the same manner, but it requires some skill to keep the strands properly twisted and of a uniform thickness. A

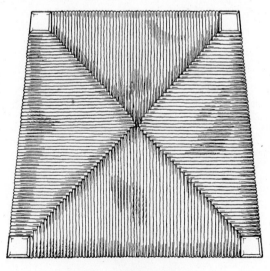

Fig. 723. Rush-woven slip seat

newer material called "art fiber," which consists of paper twisted into a rope of uniform thickness, makes a strong and good-looking seat, and is much easier to work with. This fiber is made in various thicknesses. A strand about 3/16 in. or less in diameter is suitable for the weaving described in the following.

Fiber may be woven over the rails of a chair or stool, or over a loose frame to fit inside the rails of a chair. This loose frame is called a "slip seat." In any case, the outside sharp edges of the wood should be slightly rounded so as not to cut the fiber. On a fixed seat, the legs should extend as much above the rails as the thickness of the fiber (Fig. 724). On a slip seat, a block of the same thickness as the fiber should be glued to the top of the frame in each corner (Figs. 723 and 725). In both cases, the weaving should be flush on the edges with the legs or corner blocks. The rails should, therefore, set back from the corners for a distance equal to the thickness of the fiber. The weaving is done as follows:

1. Cut a few yards from the roll of fiber and tack one end of this to the underside of the rail numbered 1 (Fig. 724).

2. Bring the length of fiber back and up over 1, under 2, back over 2, under 3, over 3, under 4, over 4, under 2, over 2, under 1, over 1, under 4, over 4, under 3, over 3, under 1, and so on until the seat is completed.

3. Keep each succeeding strand as close to the previous one as possible and be careful to pull them as tightly as you can. ·

4. This weave forms two diagonal lines which cross in the center on a square seat. Take care to get these lines straight. If necessary, hammer the fiber in place by driving on a block of wood held against any strand which is out of line.

5. Join a new length of fiber to the one with which you are weaving by

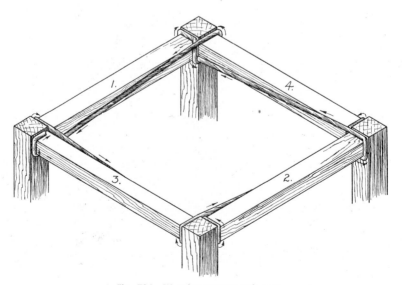

Fig. 724. Weaving square rush seat

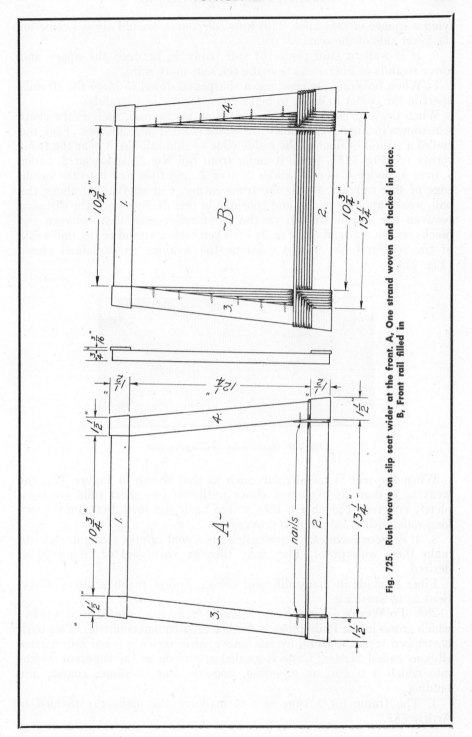

Fig. 725. Rush weave on slip seat wider at the front. A, One strand woven and tacked in place. B, Front rail filled in

tying a square or reef knot. This knot, of course, should always come on the lower side of the seat.

6. It is well to stuff pieces of soft paper in between the upper and lower strands of fiber so as to make the seat more solid.

7. When finishing the seat, use a sharpened dowel to force the strands apart in the center in order to make room for the last strands.

When the seat is wider at the front than at the rear, such as the chair seat shown in Figure 723, this extra width is filled in as follows: Tack the end of a strand of fiber to the inside edge of side rail No. 3 near the front corner (A, Fig. 725). Bring it under front rail No. 2, back over 2, under 3, over 3, under 4, over 4, under 2, over 2, and then nail it to the inside edge of side rail No. 4 near the front corner. Cut off the end above the nail, weave another strand and continue in this manner until the distance between the woven strands on the front rail equals that between the blocks on the rear rail (B, Fig. 725). Then tack a strand to the underside of the rear rail No. 1 and continue the weaving as explained above (Fig. 724).

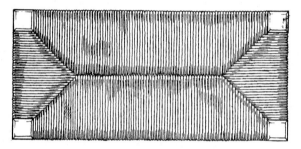

Fig. 726. Rectangular rush-woven seat

When the seat is rectangular, such as that shown in Figure 726, the weaving is done as explained above until the two short rails are completely covered. The fiber is then woven back and forth between the two long rails until these are also covered.

8. It is recommended to give rush seats a coat of glue sizing in order to make them waterproof. They may then be varnished or lacquered as desired.

Fiber is made in many different colors. Follow manufacturers' directions as to finishing.

284. To Weave a Cane Seat. Cane is made from the bark of a palm, which grows in the Philippines and other East Indian countries. This bark is stripped from the trunk by machinery, after which it is cut into narrow ribbons called "cane." Cane is graded according to the different widths into which it is cut, as superfine, fine-fine, fine, medium, coarse, and binding.

1. The frame for a cane seat is made in the manner explained in Article 282.

2. The holes for the cane are bored about ⅝ in. from the inside edges of the frame. For fine cane, the holes should be 5/32 in. in diameter and spaced ½ in. center to center. For medium cane, the holes should be 3/16 in. in diameter and spaced ⅝ in. center to center.

3. Mark a pencil line all around the frame ⅝ in. from its inside edges. Mark the center point of each member of the frame on this line, and lay out the centers of the holes from these points.

4. Notice that there are four holes more in the front rail than in the rear rail (Fig. 727). To overcome this difficulty, start the first strand of cane in the center hole in one of the sides, and bring it down through the second hole in the front rail. Then draw it up through the third hole in the front rail, and down through the corner hole in the rear rail, and so on, until a row of parallel strands is stretched between the front and rear rails (Fig. 727).

5. Now weave a similar row of strands between the two side rails. This row of strands will cross the first row at right angles (Fig. 727).

6. When a strand is used up, its end is looped around the weave running between the holes on the underside of the seat. A new strand is fastened in a similar way. A couple of round, wooden pegs, fitting into the holes of the frame, will serve to hold the cane during the weaving process.

7. After completing the weaving of the single strand between the sides, repeat the weaving between the front and rear rails, drawing the cane

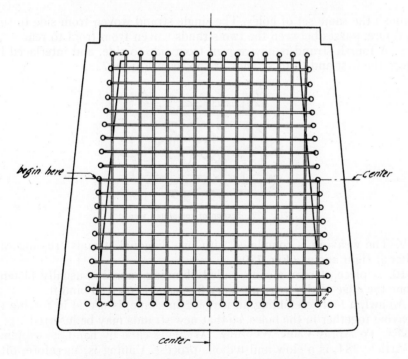

Fig. 727. Caning a chair seat; two single strands woven

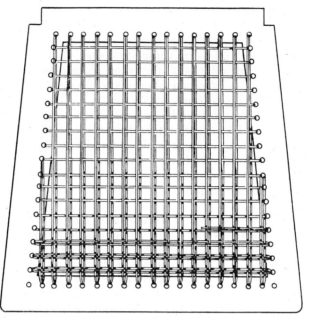

Fig. 728. Caning a chair seat; fourth strand being interlaced
between first and third strands

through the same set of holes. The single strand woven from side to side,
therefore, passes between the two strands woven from front to rear.

8. A fourth strand is now woven from side to side, and interlaced between the first and third strands as shown in Figure 728.

Fig. 729. Section of completed weave

9. The weaving is completed with two diagonal strands crossing each
other at right angles (Fig. 729).

10. A piece of coarse cane, called "binding cane," is usually fastened
along the edge of the weaving. Very fine cane is used to bind it.

An awl, a tool resembling an ice pick in shape, is useful in forcing the
weaving together in the holes, so that new strands may be inserted.

285. To Apply Cane Webbing. Weaving cane by hand, as explained
in Article 284, is a slow and tedious process. Caning is, therefore, often
done with machine-woven cane, called "cane webbing."

Cane webbing is manufactured in widths of 10, 12, 14, 16, and 18 in., and is sold by the yard. Open-woven cane resembles the weaving done by hand. Close-woven cane is the kind commonly used on seats of street and railroad cars. Cane webbing is quickly and easily applied, and it looks just as well as hand-woven cane.

1. Cut a groove ¼ in. wide by ⅜ in. deep along the inside edges of the seat frame to be caned. The distance from the edges to the groove should be about ⅝ in. If the grooves are straight, they may be cut on the circular saw, but if they are curved, they must be cut on a router or boring machine, using a router bit.

2. Cut the cane sheets, so that they are at least 1½ in. larger than the

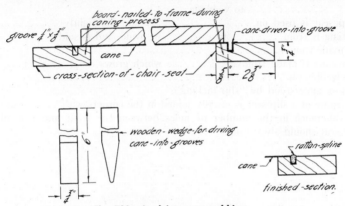

Fig. 730. Applying cane webbing

distance between the outside edges of the grooves. This will allow ¾ in. of cane on each side for driving into the grooves.

3. Soak the sheet of cane in water for at least one-half hour, and in the meantime prepare a board which will fit over the inside edges of the frame without covering any part of the grooves.

4. Run hot glue into the grooves, and place the wet sheet of cane over the frame, so that it projects equally over the grooves on all four sides. Place the board over the cane, and fasten it with a fine brad to each of the rails (Fig. 730).

5. Drive the cane into the grooves with a wooden wedge, shaped like a ¾-in. cold chisel, but with a rounded point (Fig. 730).

6. Run more glue into the grooves and drive the splines in halfway.

Splines made of rattan are used especially on curved grooves. On straight grooves, wooden splines may also be used.

7. Cut away the projecting ends of the cane before driving the splines in all the way. This may be done by running a sharp knife or chisel along the outside edges of the spline.

8. Drive the splines in all the way, using a small block of wood to protect them from being marred by the blows of the hammer.

9. When the cane dries, it will contract, thus making the seat very tight.

REVIEW QUESTIONS

1. The art of upholstering was brought to England by .... in the .... century.
2. A pad seat is ....
3. Tow is ....; muslin is ....; wadding is ....
4. Burlap is a .... made from .... which grows in ....
5. Moss grows on .... and is prepared by ....
   Hair is .... and is prepared by ....
6. A roll edge is made by ....
7. A roll-edge effect may be produced by ....
8. The stuffing may be kept from slipping on a wooden base by ....
   It is .... to webbing.
9. A slip seat is used on .... and fits tightly ....
10. Webbing is from .... to .... in. wide, and is sold in .... long.
    It is made from ....
11. Chair cane is made from .... which grows in ....
12. Cane webbing is ....
13. What is understood by "slip tacking"?
14. The frame of a slip seat is usually joined in the corners with .... joints.
15. The difference in the number of holes between the front and rear of a caned chair seat should always be ....

Chapter 18

WOOD FINISHING

Wood finishing is the last step in the completion of a piece of furniture, and a very important one. It was formerly a part of the cabinetmakers' trade, but now requires so much skill and knowledge that it has developed into a distinct trade. During the past decade or two, a great many discoveries, both chemical and mechanical, have made this trade one of the most important specialties in the furniture industry.

While nowadays the professional cabinetmaker seldom "finishes" a piece of work himself, yet it is important that he should know something about finishing methods. To the student and nonprofessional woodworker, this subject should be of particular interest.

Modern methods of finishing are too numerous and complex to be treated in this volume. Only the simplest and most common will, therefore, be described in the following.

Wood finishes are either transparent or opaque. The finishing processes of the first type, with which we are principally concerned, fall into three main divisions: staining, filling, and polishing.

Opaque finishes are produced by paints, colored lacquers, or metallic leaf or powders.

288. To Prepare the Surface. While the different parts of a piece of furniture should be prepared for finishing during the process of construction, especially those that are inaccessible after gluing, it is, nevertheless, of the utmost importance to give the piece a thorough inspection when all the toolwork has been completed, so that any little damage or defect may be repaired. Check the following points:

1. See that every trace of glue is removed from around the joints, because stain does not penetrate through glue. Any speck of glue, therefore, leaves a light mark on the stained surface. Use the blade of a cabinet scraper or a chisel, with the edge bent over, to remove glue from corners that are not easily accessible.

2. Inspect the surfaces thoroughly for any dent or bruise. A dent in the wood often may be removed by the application of a small pad of cotton waste soaked in hot water. Leave the pad on the bruise for a few minutes, and repeat. The water will fill the cells in the wood near the surface and cause them to swell, thus bringing the bruise to the level of the surrounding surface.

3. A quicker way of taking out dents is to use steam. This may be done by placing a small pad of wet cotton waste over the dent, and then

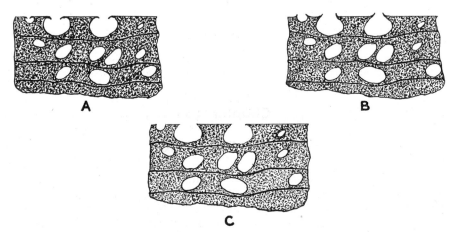

Fig. 733. Magnified cross section through wood. Upper edge planed. A, pores cut through and fine edges bent down by plane or scraper. B, edges of pores bent upward after staining with water stain. C, projecting edges cut away with fine sandpaper

applying a hot soldering iron to it. The steam generated will enter the pores and cause them to swell more rapidly than if only water had been applied. If a soldering iron is not available, an ordinary flatiron, placed on several layers of wet paper, will serve the purpose.

4. Look for any marks left by the cabinet scraper or any scratches caused by sanding across the grain. Nothing shows up more prominently and is more unsightly when the finish is applied than scratches across the grain. It is usually necessary to use a scraper to remove them entirely, and then resand the surface.

See that there are no spots of oil or grease on the surface, because they will prevent the stain from penetrating. They should be removed by rubbing with naphtha or benzine.

6. Any holes, cracks, or other defects should be filled with crack filler, which is also known as wood cement or stick shellac. It is sold in sticks of different colors, and is composed largely of shellac and resin. It is melted into the hole to be filled like sealing wax, or by holding a heated iron against it until the drops melting off fill the crevice to above the level of the surface. Work it in with the hot iron. It hardens in a moment, and should then be cut down almost to the level of the surface with a very sharp chisel or scraper. Finish with sandpaper until the surface is perfectly level and smooth.

7. Give the piece of furniture to be stained a final but thorough sanding, using No. 2/0 sandpaper (see Art. 121, Abrasives). Hold the work toward the light, and see that no imperfections remain on the surfaces. If water stain is to be used, wet the work before this final sanding, because water raises the grain of the wood and makes the surface rough.

8. Wood is composed of millions of little cells, the great majority of which run lengthwise. When the surface is planed, a great many of these cells are cut through and their fine, hairlike edges are bent down by the pressure of the tool (A, Fig. 733).

9. When water is applied to the surface, the hairlike edges of the cells bend upward by capillary attraction, and this makes the surface rough to the touch (B, Fig. 733).

10. When dry, the surface is given its final sanding with No. 2/0 or 3/0 sandpaper. The object of the sanding is to cut the hairs off and make the surface smooth. Use a piece of new, sharp sandpaper and rub very lightly at first. Then fold the paper around a sanding cork and, using both hands, apply plenty of pressure (Fig. 734).

11. When the hairs are cut off, the wood looks like C in Figure 733 under a microscope. When water is again applied a second time, less hairs will bend up and the surface will therefore not be so rough.

Too much care cannot be given to this final preparation and inspection for, contrary to the popular belief, imperfections in the surface are not covered by the finish. Rather, they appear as if magnified. An extra hour spent in preparing the surface for staining is, therefore, well spent, and often saves many hours of tedious refinishing.

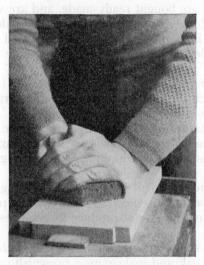

Fig. 734. Sanding with sandpaper wrapped around sanding cork

Fig. 735. Container for oil-soaked rags

STAINS

The purpose of staining usually is to produce a rich and mellow color on freshly-cut although seasoned wood. Oftentimes certain species of wood are stained to imitate others more costly, provided their grain and texture are similar. Many species of wood, for example, are stained to imitate mahogany or black walnut. Furniture stained with this end in view is labeled by the honest manufacturer as "mahogany finish" or "walnut finish," as the case may be. In any case, stains are always transparent and do not obscure the grain of the wood.

Stains are classified according to the material of which they are made. The following are the most common:

289. Water stains are made by dissolving powdered aniline colors in *hot* water. They are clear, penetrate deeply, and do not fade. As they are also inexpensive, they are widely used at the present time, especially on high-grade work. The only disadvantage in using water stains is that they raise the grain of the wood. This is overcome by sponging the wood with water, and sanding it again after drying. The stain should be applied cold, brushed dry, not wiped, and allowed to dry for about six hours.

290. Spirit stains also are made from aniline colors, but the solvent used is alcohol. They dry so rapidly that it is difficult to cover a large surface without showing laps or streaks, except with an air brush. They are used chiefly for shading and for refinishing old work, because they penetrate more readily than water or oil stains. They are liable to fade when exposed to the light.

291. Oil stains are made by dissolving oil aniline colors in turpentine, benzine, or benzol. Asphaltum and naphtha also are among the ingredients of these stains. They usually are bought ready-made, and are very easy to apply because they take a longer time to dry. They may fade or change color when exposed to the light. Oil stains should be wiped dry with a clean cloth as soon as they begin to show streaks and become flat. Allow 24 hours for drying.

Aniline and benzine are coal-tar products; naphtha is distilled from petroleum; asphalt is a mineral pitch found around oil wells, and turpentine is an oil produced from the sap of long-leaf pines.

NOTE: On account of the fire hazard, oil-soaked rags should be deposited immediately in a special metal container with a self-closing lid (Fig. 735). Under certain conditions, oily waste and rags may even ignite by spontaneous combustion.

292. Acid stains or stains due to chemical action were used a great deal in former years, but are very seldom used commercially at the present time. They are dangerous to use, and do not produce as good results as the more modern water stains.

Some of the most common acid stains are as follows: *Bichromate of potassium* dissolved in water gives oak and mahogany a brownish color. Oak and mahogany contain tannic acid which reacts with the bichromate of potassium.

Permanganate of potash dissolved in hot water also produces brown shades of color on oak. A strong solution of *ammonia* allowed to evaporate in a small closed room or box produces a rich brown color on oak called "fumed oak."

Quicklime dissolved in water gives a rich reddish color to mahogany, and is of value for this purpose, because it does not affect the color of inlays. It is applied with a brush. When dry, the surface looks like it had been whitewashed. It should be wiped off with burlap or cotton waste. A coat of boiled linseed oil, thinned with turpentine, will remove the last traces of the lime. This should invariably be applied before the wood filler.

293. General Directions for Staining. (1) Brush with the grain, using a flat brush, and apply the stain rapidly and evenly.

2. Finish all inside surfaces before staining the outside surfaces.

3. Stain all removable parts, as drawers or doors, separately.

4. Brush along the entire length of a surface to prevent laps. When the surface has been covered, brush any water-soluble stain back and forth over it until it gradually dries. If any laps or other unevenness is then discovered, it can be corrected by rubbing the surface vigorously with a wet rag. This will lighten the color, but it will also make it uniform, especially if it is done soon after the stain has dried.

5. After dipping the brush, begin on the unfinished part, and brush toward the finished part.

6. Regular stain should be applied to sapwood parts, and allowed to dry before the general staining. This is because sapwood is generally lighter than heartwood, and needs a second coat to make the staining uniform.

7. To prevent endwood from getting too dark, it may be brushed with water immediately before staining. Staining it while it is wet lightens the color.

8. Sand lightly with No. 3/0 sandpaper after the stain is thoroughly dry.

294. To Apply Wood Filler. Wood filler is used for filling the pores of open-grain woods like oak, chestnut, ash, walnut, mahogany, etc., so as to produce a perfectly level and smooth surface.

It is manufactured in paste form, and consists of silex ground in japan, linseed oil (Art. 298), and turpentine. The natural color of filler is a light cream, but any color may be obtained by the addition of colors ground in oil or japan.

Wood filler is thinned with turpentine, benzine, or naphtha according to manufacturers' directions.

Silex or silica is a white powder consisting of quartz and sand.

Japan is a drying agent made from various gums, shellac, linseed oil, metallic oxides, and turpentine.

Filler is usually applied after the stain and in a corresponding color. Sometimes, however, filler is used as a stain, especially on dark woods, by coloring it a little darker than the wood. Two-tone effects can be produced by using a lighter and a darker shade of filler.

1. Take a small quantity of paste filler from the can, add a little solvent, and stir the mixture with a wooden stick, shaped like a paddle, until it has become a homogeneous mass. On oak, 1 lb. covers about 30 sq. ft. Add small quantities of turpentine at a time, and mix well until the filler has the consistency of thick cream or soup. The coarser the grain of the wood to be filled, the thicker the filler should be.

2. Brush it on with a fairly stiff bristle brush, so that it is worked well into all the pores.

3. When the filler, which was first applied, begins to look flat, stop putting on more filler and begin wiping off with some material that does

not lie flat on the surface. Coconut hair, sea moss, fine excelsior, burlap, or cotton waste are all useful for this purpose. Wipe first across the grain so as not to lift part of the filler out of the pores. Finish by wiping lightly with the grain, using a clean soft cloth or cotton waste until a clear, smooth surface is produced. If the filler is hard to wipe off, moisten the wiping cloth slightly with the solvent.

4. Stir the filler well before resuming the brushing-on process, because the heavier parts of it will settle to the bottom of the can, leaving only the solvent on top.

5. Remove surplus filler as before, using a pointed wooden stick to clean out corners, recesses, and other irregular surfaces. So far as possible, all surfaces should be filled in a horizontal position, as this gives the best results.

6. If the filler is lifted out of the pores while it is being wiped off the surface, add a little japan drier to the mixture.

7. Usually 1 coat of filler is sufficient. Allow 24 hours for drying. Close-grained woods, such as maple or birch, are generally given a coat of shellac instead of filler.

8. An extremely thin coat of shellac, called a "wash coat" is sometimes applied before filling. It is sanded when dry, after which the filler is applied as just described. This treatment prevents a filler smudge on the surface which sometimes results from the filler solvents and color penetrating the wood. If the coat of shellac is too thick, it will glaze the open pores and prevent the filler from sticking in the pores.

295. Production and Manufacture of Shellac. Shellac is produced by an insect called *Tachardia Lacca* (the lac bug, Fig. 736), which is native to the southern part of India. This insect lives on the sap of a few species of acacia trees which are now cultivated in plantations. After being host to a colony of lac bugs, a tree needs several years of rest and care to recuperate.

The lac bug sucks up the sap through a needlelike elongated mouth, which it inserts under the tender bark of young twigs. Through the bug's digestive processes, the sap is changed into shellac which is exuded through numerous pores in its skin. Pretty soon the insect, which is about the size of an apple seed, is covered with shellac. As more shellac is exuded, it runs together with that produced by the hundreds of other insects sitting on the same twig (Fig. 737). Finally the twig and all the insects are completely encased in shellac, but before that happens the females lay thousands of eggs.

When the larvae are hatched from the eggs, they first live off the dead bodies of their parents. Later on they bore their way through the shellac. When this is about to happen, the native workmen break the shellac-covered twigs off and hang them on another tree which is strong and healthy enough to support another colony of lac bugs. Once the lac bugs have inserted their needlelike mouth into a tree, they never move until they die.

When the new generation of lac bugs have begun their life cycle, the

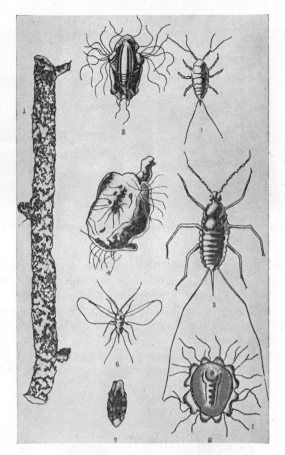

Fig. 736. Lac bug in various stages

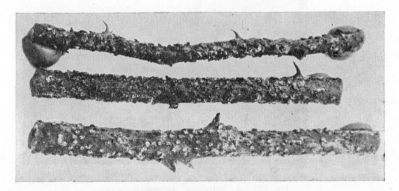

Fig. 737. Sticklac showing encrustations on twigs

Fig. 738. Seed-lac in cheesecloth bag being heated and melted
over fire

shellac-covered twigs, from which they came, are collected and broken up into small pieces, either by hand or by machinery. The crushed shellac is washed in a large, circular vessel filled with water. Bits of wood and remnants of the dead insects float to the top and are skimmed off, after which the shellac pellets are spread out and dried in the sun. Shellac in this stage is called "seed-lac."

The seed-lac is put into a cheesecloth bag several feet long, but only about 2 in. in diameter. Two men hold the bag in front of an open fire.

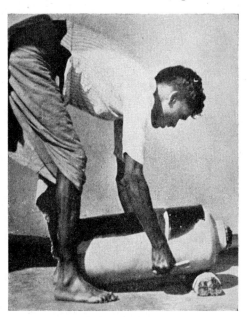

Fig. 739. A "Bhilwaya" spreading molten
seed-lac over large porcelain cylinder

Fig. 740. The sheet of lac taken from the cylinder is stretched four times its size

The heat melts the shellac, which drops down upon a marble slab while the men are twisting or wringing the bag (Fig. 738). Another man then picks up the sticky molten mass and lays it on a large porcelain cylinder filled with hot water (Fig. 739), thereby producing a sheet of lac about ¼ in. thick and 2 ft. square. He then takes this sheet and, holding its four corners with his hands and toes, while standing in front of the fire, stretches it to four times its size or about 4 ft. square (Fig. 740). The temperature is so high that it would burn the hands and feet of anyone not trained to do this work. These sheets are then laid on the floor and later are broken into small pieces, cooled, and packed. Shellac of the lightest color is the finest. Garnet lac and button lac is shellac of darker color and inferior quality.

Shellac is dissolved in alcohol only. It is sold according to the number of pounds of shellac which are dissolved in one gallon of alcohol. A 4-lb. cut, for example, means that four pounds of shellac have been dissolved in one gallon of alcohol. The natural color of shellac is orange. White shellac is bleached orange shellac.

296. To Apply Shellac. (1) Prepare the first coat by adding from 25 to 50 per cent of alcohol to a 4-lb.-cut stock solution.

2. As shellac dries very rapidly, it is difficult to brush it on evenly. Use a rubberset brush with medium-size bristles. Start from the top of a piece of furniture working downward. Be careful not to let the shellac

run on the edges. Pick up such runs immediately with an almost dry brush. The brush strokes always should be with the grain, and doors and drawers should be removed and shellacked separately.

3. Allow from 2 to 4 hours for drying, and then rub down with No. 3/0 steel wool, or very fine sandpaper. Steel wool is preferable, because the sandpaper "gums up."

4. If a shellac finish is desired, apply two or three coats more, and rub down between coats with No. 3/0 steel wool. Each succeeding coat should contain a little more shellac in proportion to the alcohol, but each coat should still be thin enough to brush on evenly. Rub down the last coat in the same way, and apply wax (Art. 297).

5. A common mistake is to use shellac too thick and to keep brushing it over the work several times. If used too thick, it will not fill the small pores of the wood, and if brushed over the work too many times it will pile up in uneven layers, which must be scraped off.

6. For a finer, smoother finish, rub the last coat with No. 6/0 water-proof sandpaper and crude oil, using a felt rubbing pad. Rub only a small area at a time, and be careful not to rub through the finish, especially along the edges. Clean off the oily surface by rubbing it with sawdust, because this absorbs the oil.

7. Make a polishing pad by folding a piece of coarse linen cloth over a handful of cotton waste on which very thin shellac has been poured. Rub the surface along the grain, making quick, parallel strokes from edge to edge. A few drops of paraffin oil applied to the surface will help to spread the shellac evenly. Never allow the pad to rest a fraction of a second on the surface, because it will stick to it and spoil the finish.

8. If a duller finish is desired, rub this surface gently with No. 3/0 steel wool. A rubbing paste may also be made by mixing FF powdered pumice stone with vaseline, thinned with paraffin oil to the consistency of thick paint. This paste may be used with the steel wool or with a felt rubbing pad.

297. To Apply Wax. Wax is composed chiefly of beeswax, paraffin, carnauba wax, and turpentine. Carnauba wax is the best and hardest kind of wax, and is extracted from the leaves of a tree native to South America.

Some waxes are manufactured in paste form, but more modern waxes are manufactured in liquid form.

1. Before a surface is ready for waxing, it must be filled and given a sealing coat of shellac, varnish, or lacquer. If a sealing coat is not given, the wax penetrates into the wood, leaving a dull, uneven finish.

2. Apply the wax, either paste or liquid, with a soft cloth. Do not put too much on at a time, as it is likely to make the surface greasy and consequently difficult to polish.

3. Allow the wax to dry for about 20 minutes, and then rub briskly with a soft cloth. Finish rubbing with the grain.

4. A second coat may be applied after an interval of 1 or 2 hours.

5. A wax finish is easy to produce, but is not durable. Any liquid spilled on a waxed surface makes a dull spot. In most cases, however, this will disappear if rubbed vigorously with a soft cloth.

298. To Apply Linseed Oil. Linseed oil is produced by subjecting flaxseed to pressure. The raw oil is very fatty, and dries slowly. Raw oil is used in outside paint. Boiled linseed oil is produced by boiling the raw oil with certain chemicals. Many of the fatty substances which retard the drying qualities of the oil are removed by this process. As boiled linseed oil, therefore, dries faster than raw linseed oil, it is used principally on inside work. Linseed oil dries by oxidation; i.e., contact with the air.

1. Boiled linseed oil, thinned with from 2 to 3 parts of turpentine, is applied with a brush or rag directly over the wood filler. The best results are obtained by letting the filler dry 48 hours. Put plenty of oil on the surface, and allow it to soak into the wood for about half an hour.

2. Rub hard and vigorously with a dry, clean cloth, being careful to rub each part of the work absolutely dry. If this is not done, the surface becomes sticky and must be cleaned with turpentine.

3. Allow 24 hours between coats. At least 3 or 4 coats are necessary. This treatment produces a soft sheen, and brings out the color and grain in the wood. It is an old type of finish, very durable and easy to apply, but not used commercially. Another coat of oil may be applied at any time or as often as furniture polish would ordinarily be applied.

NOTE: Be careful about the disposal of rags that have been used with linseed oil, because spontaneous combustion is likely to occur.

299. To Apply Lacquer. Lacquer is one of the newer products of the finishing industry. It is composed of many chemicals, some of the most important being nitrated cotton, banana oil, alcohol, naphtha, shellac, or varnish gums.

Banana oil is a complex chemical substance, technically known as amyl acetate. It has many advantages, such as drying quickly, withstanding heat or cold, and not cracking easily. It is difficult to apply, however, and cannot be used over oil stain, varnish, or paint, because it contains some of the ingredients used in varnish and paint remover, and, consequently, dissolves these undercoats. A sealing coat of thin shellac must be brushed over ordinary wood filler if lacquer is to be used, because it dissolves these undercoats, giving the finish a muddy appearance.

Lacquer is a hard and durable finish, but very difficult to apply because it dries so fast. The best method of application is by a spraying machine or air brush, but if this is not available it may be applied by hand as follows:

1. Use the lacquer as it comes out of the can, unless it is too thick to flow freely. Brush it on with a soft fitch or camel's hair brush. Do not brush over the same place twice. Work rapidly, and follow the directions given for applying shellac in Article 296.

Lacquer should be thinned only with special thinners sold by the manufacturers of the lacquer. These thinners *should not be interchanged,* but should be used only with the brand of lacquer for which they are made.

2. It is not necessary to sand between coats except to remove imperfections, as each coat of lacquer makes a perfect bond with the preceding one. Two or three coats should be sufficient. Allow from 4 to 6 hours for the last coat to dry.

3. A lacquered surface may be rubbed down with steel wool, but more quickly with No. 6/0 waterproof sandpaper. Rub with the grain, using plenty of water under the sandpaper. This paper cuts very fast and little pressure should, therefore, be used.

4. Wipe off the surface with a sponge and a chamois skin, and inspect it frequently.

5. When the gloss has been removed, the rubbing should be continued with FF pumice stone and clear rubbing oil. A pinch of pumice stone is sprinkled on the surface, and the felt rubbing pad is dipped in the oil. Begin with a gentle pressure until the pumice and oil have been well distributed over the surface. Be careful about the edges, as beginners are very likely to rub through the finish on the edges. Rubbing oil should be used only on the last coat of lacquer.

300. To Apply Varnish. Varnish consists of copal gums dissolved in linseed oil. It is thinned by adding turpentine. Varnish is made in many grades and for different types of work. A good rubbing varnish suitable for cabinetwork should be transparent, dry hard, and be able to resist heat.

Varnish produces a beautiful finish, and is used on the highest grade of cabinetwork. The disadvantages in using this finish, however, are that it generally cracks and becomes dull and very ugly with age, and that a special, dustproof finishing room is necessary.

Copal gums are fossilized resin deposits from pine trees long since dead. They are found buried in the ground in certain parts of Africa, New Zealand, East and West Indies, and South America.

There are several kinds of varnish. Some are used for exterior work, such as spar varnishes which dry quickly and are not rubbed. Some varnish is made for interior woodwork, and others for furniture. Furniture varnishes are also called "cabinet-rubbing varnishes" and dry slowly.

1. Varnishing must be done in a dust-free room. One cannot be too particular in removing dust from one's clothing, before entering the room, sprinkle water on the floor, and brush off the article of furniture to be varnished. A rag moistened with turpentine is the best thing with which to remove the last vestige of dust from the surface to be varnished.

2. Varnishing should be done at a temperature of about 80 deg. The varnish should be used as it comes from the can. Never shake the can or wipe a brush on its side as this causes air bubbles to form. One single air bubble may spoil a finished surface. Thinning may cause it to lose its luster. It may be heated by placing the can in a pan of hot water to make it flow more freely. It may be applied directly over the filler if the first coat is thinned with turpentine. Some finishers prefer a sealing coat of thin shellac.

3. Unlike shellac and lacquer, varnish is easy to apply, because it dries slowly. Care should be taken, however, to spread it evenly so as to prevent piling up, runs, and sags. Finish with long, light, feathery strokes with the grain.

4. Allow from 24 to 48 hours or more for drying, and sand in between

coats. This is necessary in order to get a good bond between coats. Varnish does not adhere to a glossy surface. If waterproof sandpaper is used, the dust produced by rubbing with ordinary sandpaper or steel wool is avoided. Allow 2 hours before applying the next coat, if water is used in rubbing (see directions given in Art. 299).

5. A satin finish is produced with FF powdered pumice stone and rubbing oil, as described in Article 296, step 6.

6. A higher polish is produced by adding rottenstone to the pumice, or by rubbing with only rottenstone and oil.

7. Clean the rubbed surface, and finish by rubbing it with polishing oil.

8. The surface is given a final cleaning by rubbing very lightly with a linen cloth wrapped around a small piece of waste moistened with alcohol. Rub quickly, and never let the ball rest on the surface as the alcohol will burn through the finish. This process is called "spiriting off."

A varnish remover can be made by mixing technical tri-sodium phosphate with water in the proportions of 3 lbs. to 1 gallon.

TO PAINT FURNITURE AND INTERIOR WOODWORK

The process of applying inside paint may be divided into the following general steps: preparation of the surface for the priming coat; application of the priming coat; filling of holes and other imperfections in the surface; application of second and third undercoats, and application of the finishing coats.

301. Preparation of the Surface. (1) The surface must be perfectly smooth, well sanded, and free from grease or glue spots (Art. 288).

2. Softwoods, like basswood or whitewood, should be given a coat of thin shellac before the priming coat is applied. The shellac will prevent the wood from absorbing the oil in the paint too rapidly. It will also stiffen and bind the very fine fibers of such woods together, so as to eliminate all fuzziness and produce a perfectly smooth surface when sanded. Sand lightly with No. 2/0 sandpaper before applying the priming coat.

3. Pitchy woods, such as yellow pine, should also be given a coat of thin shellac in order to prevent the pitch from penetrating, or bleeding through, and discoloring the various coats of paint. Sand the coat of shellac as explained in step 2.

4. Porous woods, such as chestnut, oak, and ash, should be given a coat of paste wood filler before the priming coat is applied (Art. 294).

5. Hard, close-grain woods, such as birch or maple, need no further preparation beyond smoothing and sanding. The priming coat may be applied directly to such woods.

302. Application of the Priming Coat. The chief ingredients of inside paints are white lead or zinc white, boiled linseed oil, and turpentine. To a priming coat is generally added French yellow ocher, a claylike substance, ground in oil, because it covers the surface better.

Primers, paints, and undercoats can be bought ready mixed, and will prove very satisfactory. If it is desired to mix the primer from the raw materials, the following procedure is recommended:

1. Mix some yellow ocher together with the needed quantity of white zinc. The amount of ocher to be mixed with the white zinc depends upon the darkness of the finished color. If the finished color is to be white, no ocher should be used.

2. Add about a tablespoonful of boiled linseed oil to each quart of zinc white, and work it thoroughly together. Then add about one gill of turps and $\frac{1}{4}$ gill of japan drier to each quart of zinc white, and mix thoroughly. If this mixture is too thick, add boiled linseed oil to it until it has the consistency of cream.

It is very important to take time to mix the ingredients thoroughly because the quality of the paint, and therefore the finished product, depends upon how well this preliminary work is done.

Zinc white and white lead are both metallic compounds derived respectively from zinc and lead. As white lead is poisonous, it is recommended to use zinc white in its place.

3. Apply the primer and let it dry from 12 to 24 hours; then sand lightly with No. 0 sandpaper until all brush marks have been obliterated and a smooth surface is produced.

303. Filling Holes and Other Imperfections in the Surface.   After the priming coat has been applied, any imperfections in the surface will be more noticeable (see last paragraph in Art. 288). These should be filled with a good putty or with Danish whiting mixed with some thin glue. The latter type of putty will dry very hard in a few hours, and will not crack nor shrink if properly mixed. It should be applied with a putty knife and, when dry, sanded with No. 2/0 sandpaper. Nail holes may be filled by using the fingers instead of the putty knife.

Whiting is white, powdered chalk, which is also used as a pigment. Several preparations of this kind are on the market.

304. Applications of the Second and Third Undercoats.   Prepare the second coat from the original mixture of zinc white and ocher, but thin only with turpentine, adding a little at a time. Apply this coat, and allow it to dry from 12 to 24 hours before sanding.

For the third coat, which is often unnecessary, use pure zinc white. Add the desired color pigment ground in oil and 1 tablespoonful of turps to each quart of zinc white. Stir the mixture thoroughly. Then add a little japan drier and enough turps to give it the right consistency. Apply as before, and allow 24 hours for drying. Sand lightly with No. 2/0 sandpaper.

Ready-mixed paints and undercoats of a good grade will also give satisfactory results. They should be applied according to the directions given by the manufacturer.

305. Application of the Finishing Coats.   The finishing coat generally consists of enamel, which is a colored varnish. Enamel is more transparent than paint, and does not cover the wood so well. For this reason, paint is used for the undercoats, the last of which should be of the same color as the enamel. Enamel, like paint, may be bought to finish either flat or glossy.

1. The first finishing coat should consist of equal parts of enamel and paint used for the last undercoat. Let this dry for 36 hours. Then sand with No. 3/0 sandpaper, and wipe the surface with a piece of moist chamois skin so as to remove every particle of dust.

2. The last coat should be pure enamel just as it comes from the can. Like varnish it should be applied in a dustproof room, at a temperature of from 70 to 80 deg. (Art. 300).

3. Good enamels dry slowly. It is, therefore, best to let the work stand 4 days before rubbing it down with pumice stone and water.

306. Summary. A perfect finish can only be produced on a perfect surface. Therefore sand thoroughly and look for the following defects: glue and grease stains, dents or bruises, holes or cracks, scratches from tools or sandpaper.

Stains are of the following kinds: water, oil, spirit, and stains due to chemical action as bichromate of potash, lime, ammonia, and permanganate of potash. Brush the work with water and sand before applying any stain soluble in water.

Filler comes either in paste or liquid form. It is used to fill the pores of open-grained woods as oak, chestnut, ash, mahogany, and walnut. Shellac is used as a sealing coat over paste wood filler. It is also used as a filler on woods with small pores as maple, birch, gum, and cherry.

Transparent Finishes discussed are shellac, wax, linseed oil, lacquer, and varnish.

307. Summary of Advantages and Disadvantages of the Finishing Coats Described. *The shellac finish* is beautiful, hard, and durable, but it is somewhat difficult to apply by hand methods. No dustproof finishing room is necessary.

The lacquer finish is very transparent, lustrous, and beautiful. It is also hard and durable, and does not mar easily. It is rather difficult to brush on, but improvements in manufacturing processes are constantly being made to overcome this difficulty. As it dries quickly, no special dustproof finishing room is needed. This is a distinct advantage over varnishing.

The varnish finish is also clear and beautiful, but it is very easily marred, cracks, and becomes dull and ugly with age. It is easy to apply, but great care must be taken to keep the work free from dust. It is used commercially on all fine furniture, pianos, radio cabinets, etc.

The wax finish is very easy to apply, and very easy to repair. It is not durable, however. Finger marks show plainly, and any liquid spilled on it makes a dull spot. It is recommended for beginners on account of the ease with which it is applied.

The oil finish is not so brilliant as the shellac, lacquer, or varnish, but it is very durable and gives furniture a certain charm and quiet dignity, characteristic of antique pieces. Oil finishing was used a great deal on the earlier antiques. It is not used commercially, but is to be recommended for students and amateur woodworkers.

Opaque Finishes are paint, metallic leaf and powders, and colored lacquers.

REVIEW QUESTIONS

1. When inspecting a surface look for the following defects: (name 5)
2. A dent in a surface may be repaired by ....
3. When a water stain is to be used, the surface should first .... because ....
4. Common types of stain are: (*a*) ....; (*b*) ....; (*c*) ....; (*d*) ....
5. What are the advantages and disadvantages of water stain?
6. Paste wood filler is made of (*a*) ....; (*b*) ....; (*c*) ....
7. Wood filler is thinned with (*a*) ....; (*b*) ....; (*c*) ....
8. Explain briefly how shellac is produced.
9. The manufacturing processes of shellac are: (*a*) ....; (*b*) .... (*c*) ....; (*d*) ....
10. A 5-lb. cut means ....
11. Two common mistakes in using shellac are ....
12. Linseed oil is made from ....
13. Rags used with linseed oil should be .... because ....
14. When using lacquer, a .... over the filler, because ....
15. Copal gums are .... They are used in the manufacture of ....
16. An inlaid mahogany surface should be stained with .... because ....
17. A varnish can should never be shaken, because ....
18. Painting may be divided into the following principal operations: (name 5)
19. Inside paints are made of (*a*) ....; (*b*) ....; (*c*) ....
20. Oil may be removed from a surface with ....
21. Enamel is a ....
22. Ocher is .... It is used in the priming coat, because ....
23. Softwoods are .... before the priming coat.
24. Wood filler that has hardened on a surface may be removed by ....
25. The advantages of lacquer over varnish are ....

This giant Ponderosa Pine in Collins Almanor Forest fell five minutes after sawing began. The white paint on the bark designates it as a tree to be cut

(Photo by Rognon Studio, Westwood, Calif. Courtesy American Forest Products Industries, Washington, D. C.)

Chapter 19

WOOD

It seems but natural and reasonable that the woodworker should have at least an elementary knowledge and understanding of "wood," the principal material with which he works.

Such information will make him more intelligent by increasing his knowledge of the world about him, and it will give him certain scientific facts, that are as useful and necessary both to the art of design and to the mechanics of wood construction.

310. Botanical Division of Trees. Botanically speaking, trees may be divided into three general groups:

1. The naked seeds, also known by the less accurate names of conifers or cone-bearing trees, evergreens, needle-leaved, and softwoods. Examples of this group are: pines, cedars, and redwoods.

2. The two-seed leaves, more commonly known as broad-leaved trees, deciduous trees and hardwoods which shed their leaves annually. Examples of this group are: oak, mahogany, maple, and gum.

3. The one-seed leaf, such as the palms, yuccas, and bamboos.

It is in the first two groups of trees, the naked seeds and the broad-leaved trees, that we are chiefly interested, because these groups furnish all the lumber used for building construction, furniture, paper, and manufacture in general. The third group, the palms and bamboos, has little value for the woodworker, and is seldom used by him.

311. Life Function of Trees. A tree consists of three main parts, the roots, the trunk, and the crown. Water and minerals in solution are taken up by the roots and conducted through the trunk to the crown, where they are changed into food material in the thousands of leaves. The crown is, therefore, the most important part of a growing tree. The manufacture of food in the leaves takes place in the following manner: Water and minerals from the soil in solution are conducted from the roots of the cells in the leaves. Carbonic acid gas (CO_2), taken from the air, is also breathed in by these cells. Under the influence of sunlight, which penetrates the green (chlorophyll) cells of the leaves, these inorganic substances enter into various chemical combinations and form an organic substance, sugar ($C_6H_{12}O_6$). Part of this sugar is turned into starch and stored for future use. When it is needed, the starch is again changed into sugar, which is the food of the tree. Sugar, in combination with other chemical compounds, produces cellulose, the principal material of which the cell walls are made, and fatty oils which are contained in seeds and bulbs.

One thousand square feet of leaf surface will manufacture 1 lb. of starch in 5 hours.

During these digestive processes, oxygen (O) and water vapor are given off to the air. This is an important factor in cooling off the atmosphere on warm summer days. The oxygen is used by man and beast for breathing, and is consumed by all kinds of fuels in burning. The water vapor is placed in circulation by the air currents, and moved from place to place.

The daily evaporation of water vapor from trees planted on the banks of lakes or rivers is extremely large. An oak tree, for example, may give off as much as 2000 lb. or 240 gal. of water vapor in 24 hours.

312. Man's Dependence on Plants. Green plants use, therefore, only inorganic materials for their food supply and energy. Man and animals, on the other hand, use organic materials and are dependent on plants for oxygen for breathing; for different kinds of food containing vitamines, sugars, starches, fats, and proteins; for clothing material such as cotton and linen; for lumber, paper, medicines, rubber, alcohol, turpentine, and numerous other products. Moreover, because animals feed on plants, man also obtains such materials as milk, eggs, meat, wool, silk, leather, etc., indirectly from plants.

313. Conservation of Lumber. Since plants, and in particular, trees are so vital to the life of man, it is of the greatest importance to conserve our forests and protect the trees against dangers from fires, decay, destructive and wasteful methods of lumbering, etc. Enormous quantities of lumber have been wasted through neglect and carelessness in the past, but much is being done at present to eliminate such waste and conserve the supply of lumber.

Deforested areas are being replanted, more careful methods of lumbering are being enforced, less lumber is being wasted by modern methods of sawing, and new methods of preservation and utilization of lumber are being perfected through research. The government has established such a research laboratory in the Forest Products Laboratory at Madison, Wis.

In order to understand and appreciate the problems involved in the intelligent and economical usage of wood, it is necessary to give some attention to the study of the structure of wood and to the cutting, seasoning, and use of the commercial product — lumber.

STRUCTURE OF WOOD

Of the three classes of trees we have mentioned, the conifers and broad-leaved trees are quite similar in structure, while the palms are entirely different. Only the first two classes will be considered in this discussion.

314. Cell Formation. Examining a cross section of wood under a microscope (Fig. 743), the wood will be found to consist of innumerable small cells growing in a vertical direction. Some of these cells are small and some large. The larger cells have thin walls, and grow rapidly during the spring. The smaller cells have thick walls, and grow less rapidly during the summer.

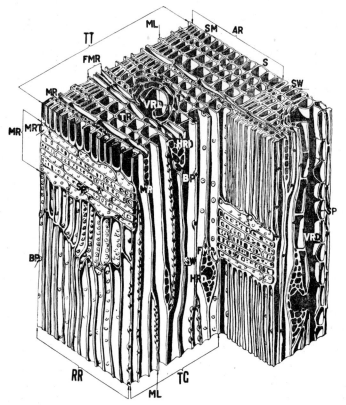

Fig. 743. Microscopic section of a softwood. TR, Cells carrying water; S, spring
wood; SM, summer wood; AR, one annual ring; MR, medullary rays

315. Annual Rings. Looking at a cross section of a tree (Fig. 744)
with the naked eye only, the small thick-walled cells, or summer wood,
appear as thin concentric circles, and the thin-walled cells, or spring
wood, as wider circles or rings alternating with the first ones. One year's
growth, or one "annual ring," as it is called, consists of one narrow and
one adjoining wide ring. In this way, by counting the rings, anyone is
able to tell the age of a tree. Sometimes a hand lens is required to see
the rings.

316. Heartwood and Sapwood. The inner core of a tree trunk is
called the "heartwood" and the outside part the "sapwood." The center
of the heartwood is a white, soft substance called the "pith." The sapwood is usually of a lighter color than the heartwood. The sapwood con-
ducts the water, called "sap," from the roots to the crown. As the tree
grows older, and new outside layers of wood are added, the inside part of
the sapwood gradually turns into heartwood. The cells then clog up and
no longer serve to conduct the sap to the leaves. Through infiltration of
chemical substances into the cells, the heartwood turns a darker color.

317. Cambium. Between the sapwood and the bark is a greenish slippery, slimy layer called the "cambium." The cell formation takes place in the cambium. When a cambium cell grows to maturity, it divides into two parts, one of which always remains cambium. The other part forms either wood or bark; most frequently wood.

318. Bark. Outside the cambium lies the bark. It consists of a thick outer part, called the "cortex," and a thin inner part, called the "bast." Both the cortex and the bast are important commercial products. The cortex furnishes such materials as cork, tannic acid, medicines, etc. Bast is used in the weaving of mats, cloth, rope, etc.

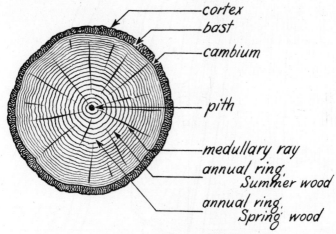

cortex
bast
cambium
pith
medullary ray
annual ring,
Summer wood
annual ring,
Spring wood

Fig. 744. Cross section of a tree

319. Medullary Rays. On some woods, notably oak, some bright lines crossing the annual rings will be seen to radiate from the center. These lines, when seen under the microscope, will be found to consist of a horizontal series of cells. The function of these cells, which are called "medullary rays," is to store and distribute food material horizontally. These cells appear in all species of wood, but are not visible to the naked eye in all instances.

When a tree trunk is cut lengthwise through the center, a section called a "radial section" is formed, as shown in Figure 745. In this section the annual rings appear as a series of parallel lines, and if the medullary rays are prominent, they appear in various patterns and lines crossing the annual rings. When a tree trunk is cut lengthwise, but not through its center, a section called a "tangential section" is formed, because all lengthwise cuts from a solid trunk, that do not go through the center of the trunk, are tangent to some annual ring.

In the tangential section, Figure 745, the annual rings, which are the grain of the wood, appear in pleasing patterns, especially in the center of the section. Near the edges, the annual rings are more straight, having the appearance of a radial section.

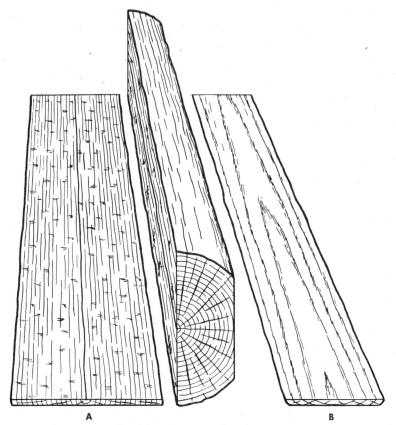

Fig. 745. Boards cut from log. A, Quarter-sawed or radial section;
B, plain-sawed or tangential section

320. Porous Woods. The chief difference between the structure of conifers and broad-leaved trees is that the first are simpler in structure and nonporous, and the second more complex in structure and porous.

The cells in nonporous woods are so small that they cannot be seen without the aid of a magnifying glass. The pores in porous woods, on the other hand, are large sap-conducting vessels consisting of several cells joined together. These pores usually can be distinguished with the naked eye (Fig. 746). In some woods, as in oak, chestnut, and ash, the pores appear mostly in the spring wood; in others, as in mahogany, beech, or maple, they seem to be distributed through both the spring and summer wood. The first of these groups is called "ring-porous wood" and the second "diffused-porous wood."

Paste wood filler is used only on porous woods, which in the lumber trade are called "hardwoods" (Art. 294).

321. Weight of Wood. From the foregoing, it should be clear that wood is not a solid mass, but a combination of very complex cell structures. Wood is generally thought to be lighter than water, because, under normal conditions, it floats on water. That this is due to air contained in the cells can be demonstrated by a very simple experiment.

Fill three glasses with water. Drop a little sawdust in the first, some very thin shavings in the second, and a small block of wood in the third. The sawdust sinks almost immediately, the thin shavings sink within a few minutes, but the block continues to float.

The explanation is simple. Sawdust consists of such small particles of wood, that the cells are partly destroyed and open. Therefore, they fill up with water immediately. The cells of the thin shavings also fill up readily, because they are practically all on the surfaces. But the interior cells of the block cannot be reached, and, therefore, it continues to float. If a freshly cut log is placed in water, it will sink in a comparatively short time, because so many of its cells are filled with sap, a condition known as "water logged." A seasoned log, on the other hand, will float for months or years, before enough of its cells can be filled to make it sink.

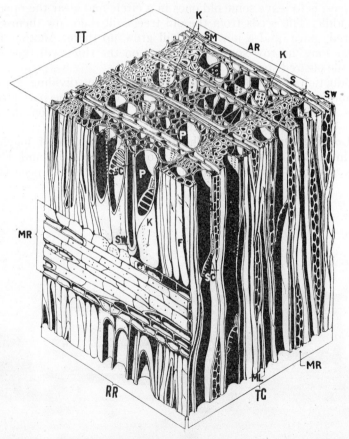

Fig. 746. Microscopic section of hardwood. P, Pores; S, spring wood; SM, summer wood; AR, one annual ring; MR, medullary rays; TT, cross section; RR, radial section; TG, tangential section

The wood substance found in both heavy and light woods is heavier than water. Different authorities state that it is from 1.5 to 1.6 times as heavy as water. Heavy woods are more compact and contain more wood substance per cubic inch than do light woods. Some tropical woods are so dense that they do not float on water, even after seasoning.

322. Reproduction of Trees.   Trees reproduce themselves by seeds and by sprouting. Some seeds are heavy, as those of the chestnut, oak, and hickory, and, therefore, fall close to the parent tree. Other seeds are light and wing-shaped, as those of the birch, pine, maple, and poplar. These may be carried long distances from the parent tree by the wind.

Nearly all the broad-leaved trees possess the power to reproduce themselves by growing new shoots from old roots, known as "sprouting." With one exception, that of the California redwood, the conifers lack the power to reproduce themselves by sprouting.

The knowledge of the method of reproduction of the various species is used by the forester in providing for new growth. One method, when felling trees, is to leave some old ones in a circle and clear the open space in the middle. The seeds from the old trees will then sow themselves in the cleared space, and a new crop will grow up there. Another method is to clear long, narrow spaces. The trees on the sides will then furnish seeds in the cleared spaces.

Reproduction by sprouts is used in forestry by dividing a piece of forest land into a number of equal parts and cutting one part at certain intervals. When the last section has been cut, the sprouts from the section first cut should have grown to maturity.

323. Logging Operations.   The traditional methods of logging and the life in lumber camps are generally so well understood and described in books of fiction and motion pictures that little attention need be given

Fig. 747. Loading logs on cars in the woods

Fig. 748. Logs taken from pond into sawmill on jack ladder

to this subject. Trees are felled in summer as well as in winter without effect on their properties if the logs are properly cared for after cutting.

Before starting the actual logging operations on a tract of forest land, roads are built through the forest, and wooden buildings, known as the "camp," for housing the lumber crew, machinery, tools, supplies, etc., are constructed. Trees to be felled on government tracts are first marked, but with a few exceptions this is not done on privately owned tracts.

The actual felling of a tree is done as follows: Two men, the sawyers, chop a deep V-shaped cut, with axes, on the side of the tree toward which it is to fall. They then saw through the tree trunk from the opposite side, using a crosscut saw with a long flexible blade and two removable handles (see end of log, Fig. 751). After the saw enters the trunk, iron wedges are driven in behind the blade to prevent the weight of the tree from "pinching" it. As the sawing progresses, more wedges are driven until finally the tree falls.

The branches are now cut off close to the trunk, after which the trunk is cut into logs of standard commercial lengths. These logs are dragged out to the sides of the road, where they are piled, measured, and stamped on both ends with the owner's name. They are then loaded on sleds or railroad cars and transported to the sawmill by rail. Formerly, logging operations were done entirely by hand methods, and horses or mules were used as draft animals. In recent years, power saws, derricks, tractors, and other modern machinery have come more and more into use (Fig. 747).

324. Sawing the Logs. At the sawmill, in order to prevent checking and decay, the logs are generally kept in a pond until wanted for sawing. From the pond, they are brought into the mill by means of an endless chain, called the "jack ladder," which grips them with steel prongs (Fig. 748).

The type of saw most commonly used in the modern sawmill is a very large band saw, with blades 50 ft. in length and 12 in. or more in width. These saws are run at speeds up to 10,000 ft. per minute, and often have teeth cut on both edges (Fig. 749). This enables the sawyer to cut boards or planks from a log both on the forward and backward movement of the carriage, which runs on rails and to which the log is clamped (Figs. 750 and 751). Besides these big band saws, the sawmill is equipped with many other machines and appliances for sawing and handling the logs. This machinery, however, is so specialized and complicated that a description would be neither profitable nor of general interest to the woodworker.

325. Plain- and Quarter-Sawing. A log is sawed in one of two ways, either "plain-sawed," or "quarter-sawed." Plain-sawing means the sawing up of the entire log in a series of parallel cuts (Fig. 745). In other words, all the boards sawed in this way, except the middle ones, will be tangential sections of the log, because they are tangent to the annual rings.

When a log is quarter-sawed, its position on the carriage is changed several times (Fig. 752), so that the saw cuts are always made at right angles, or nearly so, to the annual rings. Quarter-sawed boards are, therefore, radial sections of the log.

Fig. 749. Interior of filing room. Double-cutting band saws, 16 in. wide

Fig. 750. Sawing logs into boards

Fig. 751. Douglas-fir log on saw carriage

Quarter-sawed boards are more expensive than plain-sawed boards, because the waste by this method of sawing is greater. They have an advantage over common-sawed boards, however, in that they warp and shrink less. In some woods having prominent medullary rays, such as oak, quarter-sawed boards are also more beautiful in appearance. The best pine flooring is quarter-sawed, because on plain-sawed boards the annual rings often come loose, or "shell out."

326. Seasoning of Wood. After the logs have been sawed, the boards, planks, or timbers are seasoned or dried. This is one of the most important and difficult processes in the manufacture of lumber, because the excellence of the finished product, be it a large building or a small piece of furniture, is directly dependent upon the skill and care given to the drying of the lumber entering into its construction.

Briefly, the purpose of seasoning is to remove the moisture from the

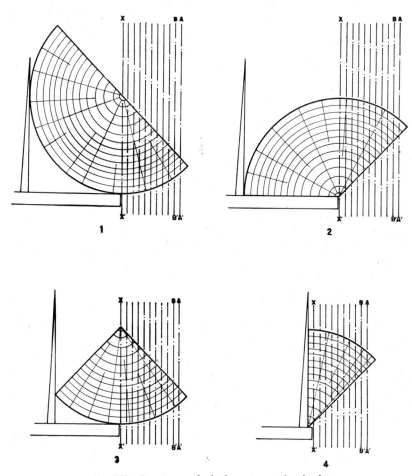

Fig. 752. Common method of quarter-sawing lumber

Fig. 753. Lumber piled for air drying

innumerable cells of which the wood is composed. Each of these cells may be thought of as a small vessel with porous sides and bottom. Water or "sap" occurs in wood in two forms, "free" and "imbibed." Free water is the amount each little vessel or cell contains, and imbibed water is the part absorbed by the porous walls of the cell. Most living trees contain free water in the cells of both sapwood and heartwood, but more in the former.

When the wood dries, the free water first evaporates from the cells. This is called the "fiber-saturation point." Drying beyond this point extracts the imbibed water from the cell walls and causes them to shrink. This loss of moisture makes the wood harder, stronger, stiffer, and lighter in weight. The drying or seasoning of lumber is usually done in one of two ways or in a combination of the two.

327. Air seasoning is the oldest method. It consists of piling the boards or planks carefully in the open air. A small open space is left between their edges, and small sticks, ⅞ by 2 in., planed on both sides, are placed crosswise between each layer of boards. Air can, therefore, circulate freely around each board. The boards are also protected against sun, dampness from the ground, and rain (Fig. 753).

This method is good, but slow. Seasoning also may be accomplished scientifically. Practically all manufacturers are now using the kiln-drying method, which is more rapid, and permits drying to a lower moisture content.

328. Kiln Seasoning. A kiln is an oven in which lumber is dried or seasoned. Every important sawmill and woodworking factory is equipped with one or more of these kilns (Figs. 754 and 755). The purpose of kiln drying, which is a very complex process, is to produce a rapid evaporation of the moisture contained in "green wood." This evaporation depends upon three factors: heat, humidity, and circulation. The control and application of these factors in the correct proportion is the main problem in kiln operation, and spells success or failure for the finished product.

329. Moisture Content. The usual method followed in kiln drying is to determine the moisture content of the boards to be dried just before entering the kiln and at various stages of the drying process. This is done as follows: A cross section of a board 3/4 in. long is cut at least 2 ft. from the end of the board. This is necessary because the wood dries faster at the ends. A section cut from the end of a board would, therefore, not be a true sample of the moisture content in the middle of the board. This sample is carefully weighed on a sensitive scale, after which it is baked in a small electric oven until it no longer loses weight. The difference between the two weights is then divided by the oven-dry weight, and reduced to per cent by multiplying by 100. For example, if the original weight is 195 units, and the weight after drying is 150 units, the difference in weight is 45 units. This 45, divided by 150 and multiplied by 100, gives a result of 30 per cent. During the drying process, the moisture content is calculated in a similar manner by cutting and weighing samples from the kiln.

The final moisture content varies somewhat with the purpose for which the lumber is to be used. For furniture, it should be from 5 to 7 per cent; for outdoor material about 12 per cent.

Thoroughly air-seasoned wood averages from 12 to 18 per cent in moisture content, depending on local climatic conditions. High-grade

Fig. 754. Lumber kilns

Fig. 755. Charge of lumber in kiln

lumber is usually air-dried for some months, before the process is completed in the kiln. The moisture content of lumber varies with changes in the relative humidity of the surrounding atmosphere.

Air-dried lumber also will absorb moisture from the air until a state of equilibrium is reached. Kiln-dried lumber will again absorb some moisture from the air, and air-dried lumber will lose more moisture if stored under heated conditions. Paint or varnish finishes do not prevent changes in moisture content, but they considerably delay the rate at which the changes take place.

330. Types of Kilns. Kilns are of two general types, known as the compartment or "box" kiln and the progressive or "continuous" kiln. In the first type, the material to be dried, called a "charge," remains in the same place during the drying period. In the second type, the charge enters at one end, and is moved through different compartments of vary-

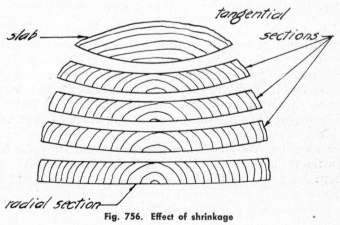

Fig. 756. Effect of shrinkage

Fig. 757. Drying defects. Upper piece shows collapse; two lower pieces show honeycombing

ing heat and moisture content, until it leaves the other end completely dried.

The time consumed in kiln drying varies with the kind and thickness of the lumber and its moisture content before drying. A 1-in. board dries four times as fast as a 4-in. plank, but twenty times as fast as 10-in. timber. The drying time of 1-in. boards varies from 14 days to 4 or 5 weeks.

331. Shrinkage of Wood. When the fiber-saturation point has been reached in the drying process, the wood begins to shrink. As explained above, this means that all the free water has evaporated, and that the imbibed water in the cell walls is beginning to evaporate. This causes a reduction in the thickness of the cell walls, and the thicker the walls are, the more they shrink. Summer wood, therefore, shrinks more than spring wood, and heavy wood more than light wood.

Wood shrinks in three directions: (1) tangentially, or along the circumference; (2) radially, or along the diameter, and (3) lengthwise. The lengthwise shrinkage is so small that ordinarily it may be disregarded. The tangential shrinkage, on the other hand, is from one and one half to three times greater than the radial shrinkage. A glance at Figure 756 will make this matter clearer. The board sawed through the center is practically straight, because it is sawed at right angles to the annual rings, or quarter-sawed. These annual rings are short and, therefore, cannot pull in a circular direction. On the other boards, however, the annual rings are longer on one side than on the other. The pull is, therefore, greater on one side, the outside, than on the other, or heart side, and the boards bend as shown, away from the heart of the timber.

332. Drying Defects. It follows that the shrinkage of millions of little cells causes tremendous stresses in lumber which is drying. If not properly relieved, by adding moisture, the wood will split or crack in various ways. Some of the most common drying defects are "honeycombing" and "casehardening" (Fig. 757).

"Honeycombing" means a series of checks or cracks either on the surface or in the center of the board. "Casehardening" means the drying of the outside layers of cells before the inside ones have had an opportunity to do so. The surface of a board, however, cannot shrink properly until after the center has shrunk, thus causing this surface to become set when expanded. Then, when the inside layers of cells become dry and are ready to shrink the wood becomes stressed.

The lumber dealer divides all species of wood into two general classes, softwoods and hardwoods.

MANUFACTURED LUMBER

Softwoods, or conifers, are used mainly in building construction, while hardwoods, or broad-leaved trees, are used mainly in furniture construction.

333. Standard Lengths and Thicknesses of Lumber. Softwoods are generally cut to even lengths as 10, 12, 14, 16, and 18 ft., while hardwoods are furnished in random widths and lengths. Boards are from $\frac{1}{2}$ to $1\frac{1}{2}$ in. thickness, planks from $1\frac{1}{2}$ to 4 in., and timbers are more than 4 in. thick.

334. Allowance for Planing. The above thicknesses refer to rough lumber only; i.e., lumber as it comes from the saw. For material less than $1\frac{1}{2}$ in. in thickness, 1/16 in. is allowed for each planed surface. For material more than $1\frac{1}{2}$ in. in thickness, $\frac{1}{8}$ in. is usually allowed for each planed or "dressed" surface. A 1-in. board, dressed on both sides, is therefore only $\frac{7}{8}$ in. thick, and a 2-in. plank, dressed on both sides, is only $1\frac{3}{4}$ in. thick.

335. Board Measure. This loss in thickness, however, is not counted when the boards are sold. The purchaser of dressed boards pays for the

shavings removed by the planer. Lumber is sold by the board foot. Each
board foot is the equivalent of a piece of lumber measuring 1 in. in thickness, 1 ft. in width, and 1 ft. in length. To calculate board feet, multiply
the thickness and the width of the board in inches by its length in feet,
and divide the product by 12. The easiest method of doing board measure is to use cancellation. The dimensions of lumber are always written
in this order: thickness, width, length. On the cheaper grades of lumber,
$\frac{1}{2}$ in. is disregarded. A board less than 1 in. thick is counted as 1 in. A
board thicker than 1 in. is figured to the nearest larger quarter inch in
thickness. Thus, $1\frac{1}{8}$ in. is calculated as $1\frac{1}{4}$ in., $1\frac{3}{8}$ in. as $1\frac{1}{2}$ in., etc.

1 piece $\frac{7}{8}''$ x 3''   x 10'-0'' $= 1 \times \frac{3}{12} \times 10 = 2.5$ board feet.

1 piece $\frac{3}{4}''$ x 6''   x 17$\frac{1}{2}''$ $= 1 \times \frac{6}{12} \times \frac{18}{12} = .75$ board feet.

1 piece $1\frac{3}{4}''$ x 6$\frac{1}{4}''$ x 12'-0'' $= 2 \times \frac{6}{12} \times 12 = 12$ board feet.

2 pieces $1\frac{3}{8}''$ x 7$\frac{1}{2}''$ x 10'-6'' $= 2 \times \frac{3}{2} \times \frac{8}{12} \times \frac{21}{2} = 21$ board feet.

Types of Manufactured Lumber. Besides plain boards, planks, and
timbers, lumber for the building and furniture trades is manufactured
into matched, grooved, and beaded boards, shingles, laths, moldings,
veneers, plywood, overlays, etc.

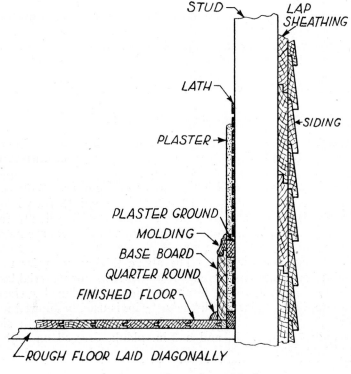

Fig. 758. Types of manufactured lumber

336. Matched. Grooved, and Beaded Boards. Some of the most common of these are as follows: *Lap sheathing* are wide boards, rabbeted or grooved on the edges, and used to cover the framework of wooden buildings (Fig. 758). *V-shaped and beaded sheathing* are narrower boards of a better grade used for partitions, wainscot, etc. (Fig. 759). *Siding* consists of matched and shaped boards covering the sides of frame buildings and nailed to the sheathing (Fig. 758). *Flooring* is of two kinds, rough and finished (Fig. 758).

Fig. 759. Beaded and V-shaped sheathing

337. Moldings are made in a great variety of shapes and for different purposes as base moldings, picture moldings, cornice moldings, etc. (Fig. 758).

338. Veneers are very thin sheets of wood, usually cut from rare woods. They are glued to more common woods, either for the sake of appearance, or durability of construction, or both.

Veneers are cut by three distinct methods: sawing, slicing, and rotary cutting. Sawed veneers are cut just as common-sawed boards are cut from a log. Special saws and carriages permitting of very fine adjustments are used for this purpose. Sawed veneers are thicker than sliced or rotary-cut veneers.

Sliced veneers are cut on a machine having a very large fixed knife, against which the log to be cut is pushed. Each time the log is pushed over the knife, a thin sheet from 1/28 to 1/20 in. in thickness, or thinner, is cut (Fig. 760). As many of the sheets cut from one log have practically identical patterns, beautiful effects are obtained by combining or matching such veneers (Art. 275).

Fig. 760. Veneer slicer

The more expensive veneers are cut by the slicing method. A part of a log is selected for its beautiful grain. It is then squared and steamed or boiled for many hours before it can be sliced.

Rotary-cut veneers are cut from a round log on a very large, specially constructed lathe. The log is turned between centers, while a long knife is pushed against it. The action of the knife may be likened to peeling. As the knife has a side movement toward the center, corresponding to the rate at which the log is revolved between centers, one continuous slice or peeling of uniform thickness is cut from the log (Fig. 761).

The rotary method of cutting veneers is more economical, but does not produce as beautiful grain figure as the slicing method, except on bird's-eye maple. It is used a great deal in the manufacture of plywood. Logs used for this purpose also are boiled or steamed for a long time before they are put in the lathe.

339. Plywood is a comparatively new product of the woodworking industry. As its name suggests, it usually consists of an odd number of layers or plies of wood glued together so that the grain of alternate pieces runs at right angles. Plywood is manufactured in different thicknesses, sizes, numbers of plies, and grades of lumber. Three-ply panels are ¼ or ⅜ in. thick, and of various widths and lengths. Panels consist simply of a core, usually of inferior or defective wood, to each side of which a sheet of veneer has been glued, the grain of the core being at right angles to the grain of the veneers.

Five-ply panels consist of a core, to the face and back of which a sheet of common veneer is glued with the grain running at right angles to that of the core (Fig. 762). These sheets, next to the core, are called "cross-

Fig. 761. Rotary veneer cutter

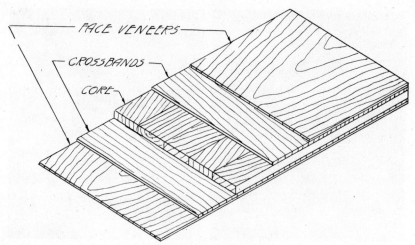

Fig. 762. Five-ply board

bands." A sheet of thin veneer, usually of a higher grade, is then glued to each of the crossbands. These outside veneers are called the "faces." The grain of the face veneers runs at right angles to the crossbands, but in the same direction as the grain of the core.

340. Uses of Plywood. Tops, panels, doors, and drawer fronts of some of the very fine furniture produced at present are made of five-ply material to prevent warping and shrinking under different climatic conditions. Both the core and crossbands are frequently made of the same kind of lumber as the face veneers.

Plywood also is used for partitions, panels, bottoms of drawers, overlays, etc. The cheaper grades are used extensively in packing-box construction, because they are thinner and stronger than the solid wood ordinarily used for boxes.

SELECTION AND USES OF LUMBER

341. Lumber for cabinetwork and interior woodwork should have certain qualities, as beauty of grain and color, freedom from warping and shrinking, hardness, and strength.

The grain, more than the color of wood, is the important consideration in furniture construction. Woods that might otherwise be suitable, as for example "Philippine mahogany" (*indoako*), have no distinctive grain and are difficult to fill and polish. Cabinet woods having beautiful grain are mahogany, black-walnut burls, bird's-eye maple, cherry burls, quarter-sawed oak, birch, and red gum (Figs. 763, 764, 765, and 766).

Lumber that is free from undue warping and shrinkage is of most value to the woodworker. It certainly makes his work easier and better. Woods that warp and shrink but little are mahogany, black walnut, cherry, quarter-sawed oak, and chestnut. Woods that warp extensively are sycamore, elm, and beech, and to a less extent, birch, maple, and red gum.

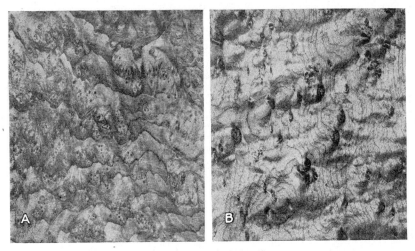

Fig. 763. Cabinet woods: A, cherry burl; B, bird's-eye maple

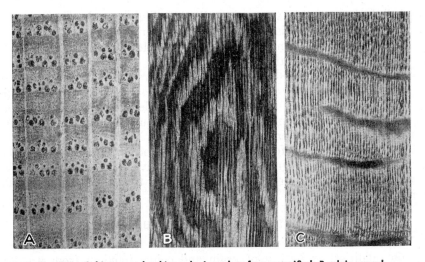

Fig. 764. Cabinet wood, white oak: A, end surface magnified; B, plain-sawed;
C, quarter-sawed surface

Hardness also is an important consideration. A medium grade of hardness is the most desirable as softwoods are too easily nicked and damaged, and extremely hardwoods are too difficult and costly to work. In this respect, mahogany, cherry, and walnut also are the most desirable. Elm and cypress are examples of woods that are respectively too hard and too soft.

Strength does not play as important a part in cabinet wood as it does in structural timbers. Yet, chestnut is too brittle to make it a desirable cabinet wood.

To most people, price is probably the decisive factor in the selection

Fig. 766. Cabinet woods; A, fiddle-back figure; B, raindrop figure in mahogany

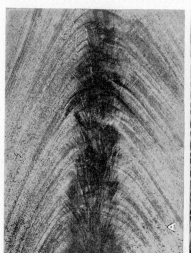

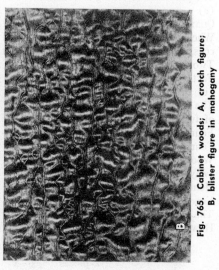

Fig. 765. Cabinet woods; A, croch figure; B, blister figure in mahogany

of cabinet wood. Were it not for the high cost of mahogany and walnut, most woodworkers would, no doubt, prefer to use these woods to the exclusion of most of the others.

342. Lumber for building purposes should have qualities that differ somewhat from those that are desirable for cabinetwork. Important considerations are durability or resistance to decay and attacks by insects and worms, strength, and hardness.

For use in patternmaking, white pine is unsurpassed.

REVIEW QUESTIONS

1. Trees are classified botanically in (a) ....; (b) ....; (c) ....
2. The green substance in the leaves is called ....
3. The food of a tree is ...., which is digested in ...., and forms ....
4. Of what importance is the evaporation of water from the leaves?
5. A tree uses starch for ....
6. A tree gives off .... and ...., and takes in ....
7. The cambium is located .... Its function is ....
8. Medullary rays are ....; they serve to ....
9. Spring wood has .... Summer wood has ....
10. Some of the commercial products obtained from the bark of trees are ....
    ....
11. Make a sketch of a cross section, a radial section, and a tangential section of a tree.
12. Why does wood float on water?
13. Trees reproduce themselves by .... or by ....
14. The processes of felling a tree are: (a) ....; (b) ....;
    (c) ....
15. Quartersawing a log means ....
16. When the fiber saturation point has been reached .... is out of the cells, but the .... is still in the ....
17. Two types of kilns are the .... and the ....
18. Factors necessary in kiln drying are: (a) ....; (b) ....;
    (c) ....
19. The moisture content of building lumber should be ....;
    of furniture lumber ....
20. Four desirable qualities in cabinet lumber are: ....
    Four desirable qualities in building lumber are: ....
21. Wood shrinks most along .... Boards therefore warp or bend away from ....
22. Honeycomb means ....
23. Veneers are cut by three methods: (a) ....; (b) ....; (c) ....
24. The most economical method of cutting veneers is by the ....
25. How many board feet does the following bill of lumber contain?

4 pieces	1¾″ x	1¾″ x	30″
2 pieces	⅞″ x	5″ x	1′–6″
6 pieces	⅞″ x	8″ x	2′–8″
1 piece	¾″ x	20″ x	34″

Chapter 20

APPLIED PROJECTS

347. Preliminary Steps in Construction. Before attempting the actual construction of an object, it is of utmost importance that the different steps or operations involved in its construction should be carefully analyzed and arranged in the most systematic and convenient order. A bill of material should be written, and full-size details should be laid out from the drawings, either on paper or on a wood surface such as a plywood panel. This is called "setting out," and is done in all furniture factories and by all professional cabinetmakers. Too much emphasis cannot be placed on this phase of the work, because any small error, which may have been made in the scale drawing, is thereby corrected. Furthermore, this procedure clarifies the whole problem of construction, and helps the student to organize and arrange his work in an orderly and systematic manner.

The ability to read drawings correctly is, of course, essential for this preliminary work. For the benefit of those who have had little experience with drawings, a few hints on blueprint reading are given in the following.

348. The Making of Drawings and Blueprints. The inventor or designer usually draws some rough sketches of the object he wishes to make. These are then worked out in detail with pencil and instruments. A piece of transparent cloth or paper, called tracing cloth or tracing paper, is fastened over the pencil drawing with thumbtacks. The pencil lines, which are visible through the transparent cloth or paper, are now traced on the latter with drawing ink. This ink drawing is called the "tracing." Any number of prints may be made from the tracing much in the same way that photographic prints are made from films or plates. The prints are made in sunlight or in artificial light on sensitized paper. This paper is then thoroughly rinsed in water and hung up to dry. The action of the sunlight causes these prints to turn a blue color when they are washed. The lines of the drawing, however, stand out white, because the light is not able to penetrate the black lines of the tracing. These prints are called "blueprints."

Blueprints are used by workmen in all parts of the world. They are not as easily soiled as a drawing made on white paper, and, moreover, they can always be replaced.

349. To Read Working Drawings. Persons who have not had a course in mechanical drawing, usually find it very difficult, if not impossible, to understand or interpret the kind of drawing used by the mechanic or artisan, because it does not represent an object as we are accustomed to seeing it. This type of drawing is called a "working drawing" because

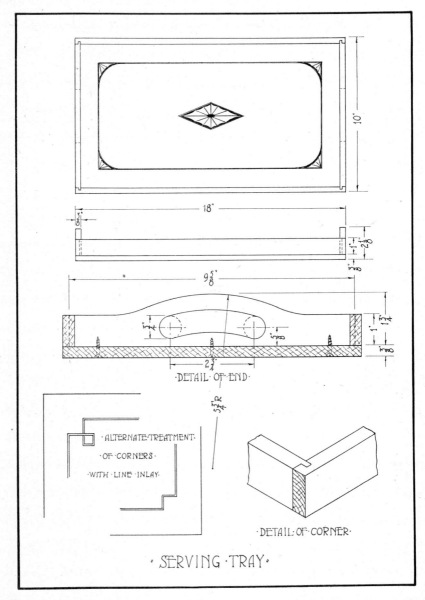

·ALTERNATE·TREATMENT·

·OF·CORNERS·

·WITH·LINE·INLAY·

·DETAIL·OF·END·

·DETAIL·OF·CORNER·

·SERVING·TRAY·

Fig. 769

work is produced according to the exact information about size, shape, material, and methods of construction which it contains.

Working drawings differ radically from pictorial drawings, which represent an object as it appears to the eye and not as it really is. Perspective drawings, such as are used by the architect, etchings, paintings, and photographs are all forms of pictorial drawings. These, however,

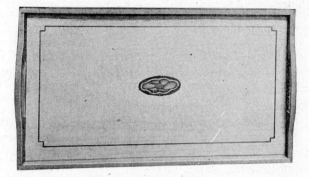

Fig. 770. Inlaid Serving Tray

cannot be used by the workman, because they give no exact information about size, shape, material, or methods of construction.

In order to interpret a working drawing correctly, it is necessary to be able to form a mental picture; i.e., a pictorial vision, of its final shape. The experienced workman or draftsman does this automatically and without conscious effort. The best way of acquiring this ability is by comparing a working drawing with a pictorial drawing, so that the relation of one set of lines to the other is seen and understood.

350. To Read the Drawing of the Serving Tray. Compare the drawing in Figure 769 with the illustration in Figure 770. In the illustration all parts of the tray — bottom, sides, and ends — are seen as they appear to the eye.

The upper view in the drawing, called the *plan view,* represents an object as it appears when looking directly down on it. It gives the exact length and width of the tray, and shows the inlay. The inlay in the drawing is not exactly like that in Figure 770. It merely shows that different designs may be chosen. Other treatments of the corner inlay are shown at the bottom of the drawing.

The plan view shows two parallel lines which run around the edge of the tray. They represent the sides and ends and show how they are joined in the corners. A pictorial view of a corner, drawn to a larger scale, is shown in the lower part of the drawing.

Directly below the plan view is a *side view* or *elevation* of the tray. This view, which shows it as it would appear at eye level, gives the thickness of the bottom and ends and the length and width of the sides. The width of the ends is found by subtracting the thickness of the bottom ($\frac{3}{8}$ in.) from the total height of the ends ($2\frac{1}{8}$ in.). The dotted lines indicate the joints in the corners.

A further view, called the *end view,* is necessary to give complete information about the shape and construction of the ends. The end view is also taken at eye level and is usually drawn to the same scale as the plan view and the elevation. In this case, however, a larger scale is used for the sake of clearness. The end view is usually drawn in line with the elevation and to the right of it as in Figure 771. On this drawing, however, it was necessary to place it below the elevation.

The end view shows the true width and length of the ends, the radius of the curves, and the shape of the hole cut for the hands that are to carry the tray. It also shows how the bottom is fastened to the frame with screws.

Suggested Order of Tool Operations

The tray may be made perfectly plain, but it may be made more attractive by the application of inlay or decalcomania transfers. If it is to be inlaid, the tray should be made of a close-grained cabinet wood as mahogany, walnut, gum, maple, birch, etc.

1. Square the pieces which form the frame, to dimensions, either by hand or by machinery (Art. 156). Make the ends about $1\frac{7}{8}$ in. wide throughout.

2. Smooth the inside surfaces with handscraper and sandpaper before making the joints.

3. The dado-and-rabbet joints are all laid out at the same time and cut either by hand or by machinery (Art. 171).

4. Lay out the shape of the ends on one of the pieces, and then nail the two pieces together on the waste side of the lines.

5. Bore a series of $\frac{3}{4}$-in. holes to form the handles. Bore from both sides to avoid splitting the wood, chisel away the triangular projections left by the bit, and smooth the edges with file and sandpaper. It is recommended to wrap the sandpaper around the file.

6. Saw the outside curves with a turning saw or on a band saw, and smooth the edges.

Glue the frame together, using a jig, as shown in Figure 481, to get it square.

8. The bottom may be made from solid wood or plywood. If plywood is used it need not be more than $\frac{1}{4}$ in. thick. Plywood is a great deal easier to use than solid wood. It is also stronger and does not shrink, but its edges are rather unsightly.

9. The bottom is inlaid according to the description given in Articles 262, 263, and 264, after which it is fastened to the frame with flathead screws as shown in the end view.

10. The outside edges of the bottom and frame are carefully planed and smoothed.

11. If made of mahogany, it is recommended to stain the tray with lime water, because this does not color the inlay (Art. 292). It may then be finished with two coats of alcohol-proof varnish (Art. 300).

Bill of Material

No. of Pieces	Description	Thickness in Inches	Width in Inches	Length in Inches
2	Sides	$\frac{3}{8}$	1	18
2	Ends	$\frac{3}{8}$	$1\frac{3}{4}$	$9\frac{5}{8}$
1	Bottom	$\frac{3}{8}$	10	18
	4 ft. Line Inlay, 4 Corner Insets, and 1 Center Inset			

351. To Read the Drawing of the Bookcase. In the drawing in Figure 771, the three customary views are arranged in the conventional manner. The plan view is divided in the middle by a center line (alternating dashes and dots). To the right of the center line the outline of the top is shown in full lines. The dotted lines indicate the front of the shelves, the back, the end of one side, and one cleat. One dotted line also shows the end of the shelf entering the dado in the side. To the left of the center line the top has been removed so that the shelf, side, back, and cleat can be shown in full lines. The cross hatching indicates end grain. The outline of the top is shown by a dotted line. Another dotted line which runs through the center of the side, shows how the end of the shelf enters into the side. The view of the shelf end shows its shape and width.

From the plan view we obtained the following information: the width, length, and shape of the top and shelves, as well as the width and thickness of the sides and back. Note that the total finished length of the shelves is 27¾ in.

The elevation shows the length of the sides, the thickness of the top and shelves, and how they are spaced. It also gives the thickness and width of the cleats, and shows how they are fastened to the sides and top. Their length is shown in the plan view.

The end view shows the length of the back and cleat and the width of the side and top. The dotted lines show the back, the shelves, and the baseboard screwed to the underside of the lower shelf, ½ in. from its front edge. The thickness of this board is given as ¾ in. Its width, 1¾ in., is shown on the elevation. Since no hidden lines are shown on the elevation, it is an indication that this board is 27 in. long, which is the width between the sides as shown on the plan view.

Suggested Order of Tool Operations

1. Square the sides, shelves, and top to dimensions either by hand or by machinery (Arts. 156 and 159).

2. Smooth the shelves with scrapers and sandpaper before making the joints.

3. Lay out and chisel the stopped dado joints (Art. 170), and cut the rabbets for the back in both sides and top (Art. 167).

4. When the joints fit, smooth the sides, and glue the shelves into them. Clamp and square them as shown in Figure 539, Article 217.

5. Square the baseboard to dimensions, and smooth its outside surface. Bore and countersink 3/16-in. holes for 2¼-in. by 10 screws, and glue and screw this board to the underside of the lower shelf as shown in the drawing.

6. Square the cleats to dimensions, and smooth; also bore 3/16-in. holes for 1½-in. by 9 screws. Glue and hand screw the cleats to the sides as shown. These joints may be reinforced by screws inserted from the inside surfaces of the sides.

7. The top is now smoothed and the corners are slightly rounded. The top is placed face down on the workbench, and should be protected from

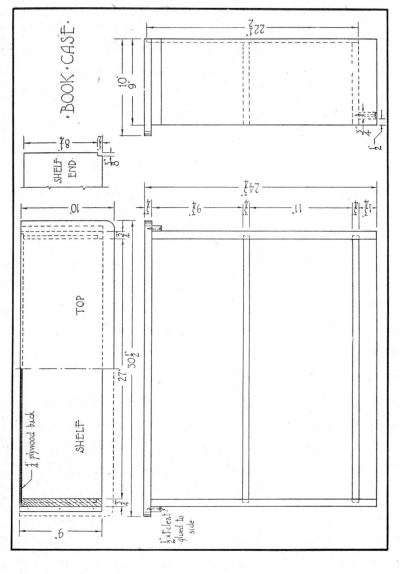

Fig. 771

Fig. 772. Bookcase with rounded top and shelves

being marred by placing cardboard or newspapers under it on the bench top. The sides are fastened to it by driving screws through the cleats.

8. The back may be either nailed or screwed to the shelves and to the rabbets cut in the sides and top.

9. The bookcase may be stained and finished with two or three coats of thin shellac (see Arts. 289 and 296).

Bill of Material

No. of Pieces	Description	Thickness in Inches	Width in Inches	Length in Inches
2	Sides	¾	9	24
2	Shelves	¾	8¾	27¾
1	Top	¾	10	30½
1	Back (plywood)	¼	28	22½
2	Cleats	½	1	9
1	Baseboard	¾	1¾	27

352. To Read the Drawing of the Lamp Standard. Only one view, the elevation, is necessary to show the shape of the lamp and give all the dimensions. A plan view would not be helpful as it would consist of a series of concentric circles and the hexagonal middle section. An end view would be exactly the same as the elevation.

The dimensions to the left give the diameters of the lamp at different heights shown at the right.

The dotted lines show the hole for the lamp cord through both base and upright. A tenon is also shown in dotted lines. It is turned on the end of the upright and is glued into a corresponding hole turned in the base. The section at the upper left shows that the lamp standard is glued up of two pieces into each of which a rectangular slot has previously been made. The sectional view to the right shows the hexagonal shape of the middle section. This is also shown by the two interior full lines on the elevation.

Note that, due to lack of space, these two sections have been drawn to a smaller scale.

A piece of ⅛-in. pipe is screwed into the upper end of the central hole. This pipe measures approximately ⅜ in. on the outside and is threaded all the way (running thread).

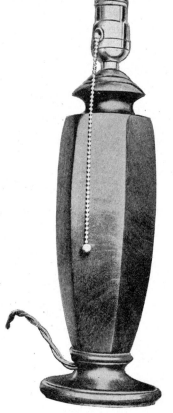

Fig. 774. Table-lamp standard

Suggested Order of Tool Operations

1. Saw and square the two pieces forming the upright to dimensions. It is important that the surfaces to be glued together are perfectly flat and smooth.

2. A groove ⅜ in. wide and 3/16 in. deep is cut along the center of both pieces on the circular saw. Make several parallel cuts or use the dado head (Art. 95).

3. Glue the pieces together, clamping them with three hand screws, so that a hole ⅜ in. square is formed through the upright.

4. When dry, plug up one end of the hole with a short piece of wood about 1 in. long and ⅜ in. square. Do not make the plug so big that it will open the glued joint when driven in place. Let the other end run on the dead (cone) center of the lathe. Turn according to directions given in Articles 246, 249, and 250.

5. Divide the turned upright into six equal parts by wrapping a strip of paper around it as shown in Figure 667. Place the lamp in a box, as in Figure 668, and mark the lines, but use the lead from a pencil in the marking gauge instead of the steel spur.

6. Clamp the upright end to end in a bench vise and plane the six sides.

7. Turn and chuck the base as explained in Article 256, making a shallow recess in the bottom (step 2). While in the lathe, bore a hole in its center, ¾ in. in diameter by 1 in. deep, for the tenon turned on the

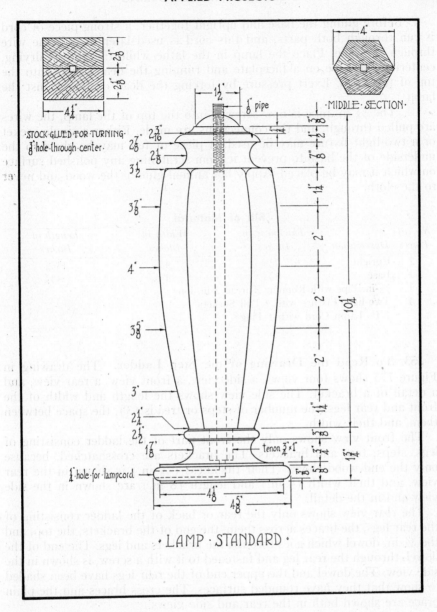

Fig. 773

upright. A ¼-in. hole is also bored for the electric wires from the edge
of the base to its center. This hole may be bored either before or after
turning.

8. It is best to finish the two parts of the lamp in the lathe as explained in Article 259. The hexagonal part is rubbed briskly lengthwise
while the lathe is turned slowly by hand.

9. Before gluing the base and upright together, a strong piece of cord is run through both parts, and this cord is used later to pull the wire through the hole. Place the lamp in the lathe while the glue is drying, centering the base on a faceplate and running the dead center into the top of the lamp. Exert pressure by forcing the dead center against the lamp.

10. The ⅛-in. pipe is now screwed into the top of the lamp, the wires are pulled through, and the connections are made. Either a single socket or a two-light fixture may be used. A piece of felt may be glued to the underside of the base to prevent it from scratching any polished surface on which it may be placed. Apply hot animal glue to the wood and never to the cloth.

Bill of Material

No. of Pieces	Description	Thickness in Inches	Width in Inches	Length in Inches
2	Upright	2⅛	4¼	11¼
1	Base	1¾	4⅝	4⅝
1	⅛-in. Pipe with Running Thread 2 in. long			
1	Two-light Fixture with 2 Pull Sockets			
	7 ft. Lamp Cord with 1 Plug			

353. To Read the Drawing of the Step Ladder. The drawing in Figure 775 shows four views, a side view, a front view, a rear view, and a detail of a bracket. The side view shows the length and width of the front and rear legs, the number of steps or treads (3), the space between them, and their width.

The front view shows only the front part of the ladder consisting of legs, steps, top, and brackets. The brackets are crosshatched, because only the end wood shows. Their thickness (⅞ in.) is shown in the rear view, and their width (4 in.) and length (8 in.) are shown in the side view and in the detail.

The rear view shows only the rear or back of the ladder consisting of the rear legs, the braces across them, the end of the brackets, the top, and the ¾-in. dowel which goes through the brackets and legs. The end of the dowel, through the rear leg and fastened to it with a screw, is shown in the side view. The dowel and the upper end of the rear legs have been shaded to show that they have rounded surfaces. The cross braces and the plain brace are shown both in the rear and side views.

Suggested Order of Tool Operations

1. Get out the stock for the front legs and steps first, square the parts to dimensions, and smooth them with scraper and sandpaper.

2. Lay out the angle as shown in the lower left-hand corner, set a sliding T bevel to this angle, and mark the dadoes to be cut in the legs for the steps. Place the legs with the inside faces together to make sure the dadoes are correctly marked.

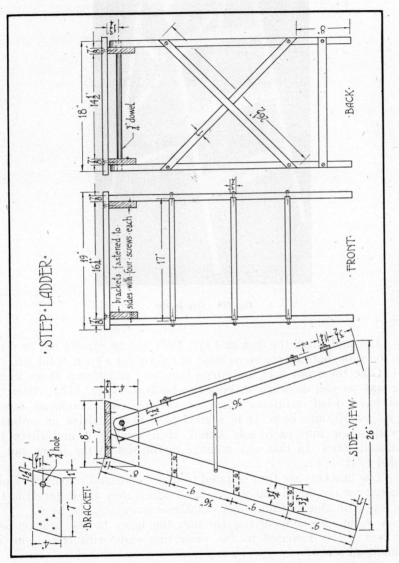

·STEP·LADDER·

·BACK·

·FRONT·

·SIDE·VIEW·

·BRACKET·

Fig. 775

Fig. 776. Step ladder

3. Saw and chisel the dadoes (Art. 169) and be careful not to make them too wide, because the steps must fit tightly for a good, solid job.

4. Glue the front legs and steps together, and clamp them in the same way as you do when making the bookcase (Art. 217). After the joints have dried, reinforce them by driving two roundhead screws 1¾ in. by 10, into each. It is a good plan first to drive an ordinary flathead screw into each hole bored, then remove it and drive the roundhead screw. In this way damage to the slot in the screw can be avoided (Art. 228).

5. The brackets are then squared to dimensions and smoothed. Holes are bored for the dowel and screws, after which they are fastened to the front legs with glue and four or five flathead screws 1¼ in. by 9.

6. A ¾-in. dowel is driven through the holes in the bracket and each rear leg is fastened to the projecting ends with one ¾-in. by 6 roundhead screw.

7. The braces which cross each other are made of ½-in. stock and are screwed to the rear legs, as shown, to stiffen them. The two are joined in the center with a cross-lap joint (Art. 182), and are fastened with 1-in. by 8 roundhead screws.

8. The top should now be made and fastened to the braces with four flathead screws 1½ in. by 10.

9. Finally the hinged iron braces are screwed or bolted to front and rear legs. Make any necessary adjustment in the beveled ends of the legs so that the ladder will stand firmly.

10. This project should preferably be made of hard or medium hard wood such as oak, birch, or whitewood. If it is given a finish, two or three light coats of shellac should be used. The ladder should not be painted.

Bill of Material

No. of Pieces	Description	Thickness in Inches	Width in Inches	Length in Inches
2	Sides	⅞	3¼	36
3	Steps	¾	3¾	17
2	Brackets	⅞	4	8
2	Rear Legs	⅞	1¾	36
2	Pieces for Cross-lap Joint	½	1	26½
1	Rear Brace	½	1¼	18
1	Dowel ¾ by 18 in.			
1	Top	¾	7	19
2	Metal Table-Leg Braces			

354. To Read the Drawing of the Cupboard. The view to the left in Figure 777 is a front view or elevation, which shows the edges of the top and sides as well as the baseboard and door with hinges and catch. The vertical section is what you would see if the cupboard were sawed through from top to bottom. It is like an end view, but with the side of the cupboard removed so that the ends of the shelves, back, and baseboard can be seen.

Note that four cleats are fastened to the sides and top. Those screwed to both sides and top hold the top firmly in place. The other two are fitted in between the sides and are glued and screwed to the top only. For the sake of clearness, the door is not shown in this section. Moreover, it would look practically the same as in the horizontal section.

To understand the horizontal section, imagine the cupboard sawed in two on a line parallel to the base. The sides, door, and back then show in section. The dotted lines indicate how deep the shelves are grooved into the sides. Two cleats are also shown glued to the sides. The rabbeted edges of the door fit against these cleats. The plywood back is fitted into a rabbet cut for it in the sides.

Suggested Order of Tool Operations

1. Square the sides and shelves to dimensions, noting that the bottom shelf is ¾ in. wider than the other three.

2. After smoothing and sanding these pieces, stopped dadoes are laid

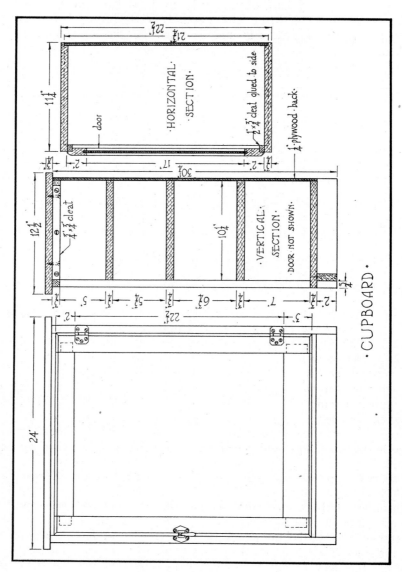

· CUPBOARD ·

Fig. 777

Fig. 778. Cupboard

out and chiseled on the sides (Art. 170). A rabbet for the back also is cut on the sides (Art. 172).

3. When the joints fit, the sides and shelves are glued together (Art. 217).

4. The baseboard is fitted in between the sides and is glued and screwed to the underside of the lower shelf (see the vertical section).

5. The two ¾ by ¾-in. cleats are then made, holes are bored and countersunk at right angles to each other, after which the top is made and is fastened to the sides as shown in A, Figure 590. The other two ¾ by ¾-in. cleats are fitted in between the sides and are glued and screwed to the underside of the top. One is flush with the front edges of the sides and the other is flush with the rabbet so that the back can be fastened to it.

6. Two more cleats, ½ by ¾ in., are glued to the inner surface of the sides flush with their front edges. As the door has rabbeted edges, called lips, it is necessary to add to the thickness of the sides to make room for the hinges and catch.

7. The rails and stiles of the door are mortised together and are grooved for the plywood panel (Art. 187). After gluing and smoothing, the rabbet is cut on the circular saw and the door is fitted in place.

8. The cupboard hinges and catch are simply screwed to the outside

surfaces. The back may be nailed or screwed to the rear edges of the shelves and to the rabbeted sides.

9. The cabinet, which is designed to hold various kitchen utensils and crockery, should be painted to harmonize with other kitchen cabinets (see Arts. 301 to 305).

Bill of Material

No. of Pieces	Description	Thickness in Inches	Width in Inches	Length in Inches
2	Sides	¾	11¼	30¼
3	Shelves	¾	10¼	21¾
1	Bottom Shelf	¾	11	21¾
1	Bottom Board	¾	2	21
2	Cleats Glued to Sides	½	¾	26¾
1	Top	¾	12½	24
2	Cleats Screwed to Top	¾	¾	21
1	Plywood Back	¼	21¾	28¼
2	Stiles for Door	¾	2	27½
1	Rail for Door	¾	2	18½
1	Rail for Door	¾	3	18½
1	Plywood Panel for Door	¼	17¾	23¼
2	Cupboard Hinges and 1 Latch			

355. To Read the Drawing of the Stool. The elevation or front view in Figure 779 shows two legs, one rail, one stretcher, and the upholstered top nailed to the upper part of the rail and legs. The upper ½ in. of the legs have been rabbeted to a depth of 3/16 in. shown on the section above the elevation. This view also shows that the rails are mortised into the legs so that their outside faces are in line with the rabbets. The two parallel dotted lines in the elevation indicate that a piece of plywood is nailed to the top of the stool to form a base on which to build up the upholstery. The meaning of the fine double lines on the rail and stretcher is explained in the sectional view of these members within the end view of the stool. The dotted lines within the square parts of the right front leg are a side view of the tenons.

The end view is the same as the elevation and merely serves to show that the stool is rectangular instead of square. The section above it shows

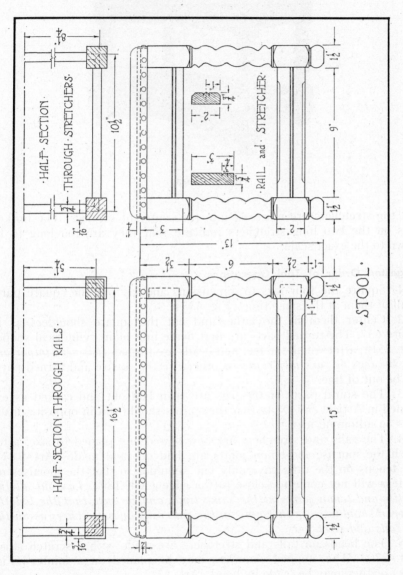

Fig. 779

Fig. 780. Stool

that the stretchers are mortised into the center of the legs. The broken lines on the two long stretchers indicate that they are too long to be shown to the exact scale.

Suggested Order of Tool Operations

1. Square the four legs to dimensions and lay out the square parts on all of them at the same time (Fig. 635).

2. Center them in the lathe, and cut the square shoulders as in Figure 637. The turned parts are first made into plain cylindrical shapes (Art. 251), after which the feet and beads are turned. *It is very important that the legs be carefully centered* otherwise the square and turned parts will be out of line.

3. The spiral parts of the legs are then laid out and carved as explained in Article 267. Note that the spirals should run in opposite directions on adjoining legs.

4. The rails and stretchers are now sawed and planed to size, after which the mortise-and-tenon joints are laid out and made (Art. 187). The tenons on the rails have only one shoulder so that the mortises on the legs will not come too close to the edge (Art. 189). *Lay out all the mortise-and-tenon joints at the same time, and be sure that the lengths between shoulders are the same on the side rails and stretchers as on the end rails and stretchers.*

5. The beads on rails and stretchers are made with a scratch stock (Art. 270). The stopped chamfers may be planed on a jointer (Fig. 684a) or they may be made by hand (Art. 271).

6. The rabbets on the upper end of the legs may be cut either before or after gluing.

7. Glue the legs as explained in Article 218 and shown in Figures 540 and 541.

8. It is best to stain and finish the stool before it is upholstered. A

shellac, varnish, or lacquer finish may be applied (see Arts. 296, 299, and 300).

9. Nail the plywood to the top, and upholster the stool according to directions given in Article 281.

Bill of Material

No. of Pieces	Description	Thickness in Inches	Width in Inches	Length in Inches
4	Legs	1½	1½	13
2	Rails	¾	3	16½
2	Rails	¾	3	10½
2	Stretchers	¾	2	16½
2	Stretchers	¾	2	10½
1	Plywood			
	Top	¼	11⅝	17⅝

Upholstery Materials (Hair, Muslin, Cover, Nails)

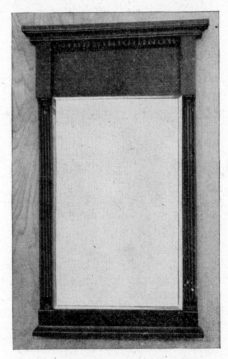

Fig. 781. Mirror frame

356. To Read the Drawing of the Mirror Frame. The two views to the left in Figure 782 show the front elevation and a vertical section of the mirror frame. Looking at the third view, we get a clearer understanding of how the frame is constructed. This view shows the sides of the frame joined to the upper and lower rails with dowel joints. The dotted line all around the opening shows the rabbet for the mirror. This

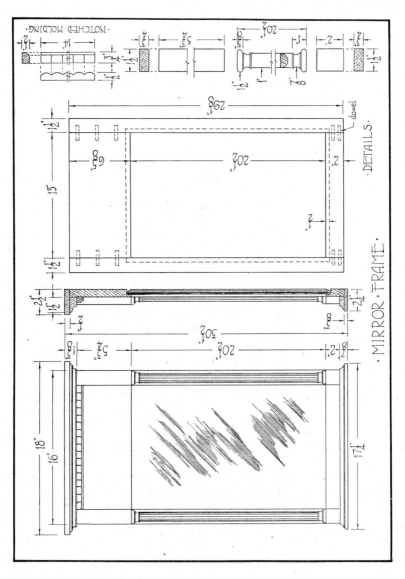

·MIRROR·FRAME·

Fig. 782

rabbet is cut before the joints are made. The decorative features, as moldings and columns, are built up on this frame (Fig. 781).

As shown in the section, a board is fastened to the top edge of the frame. Below that is a molding, and then come the two half columns glued to the sides. The bottom is finished with one board with a molded edge and one with a square edge. A notched molding is fitted in between the upper ends of the columns. This is also shown in the sectional view. Details of this molding and the parts of the column are shown at the right. From the sections it can be seen that the columns are half-columns and their upper and lower parts are rectangular in shape.

Bill of Material

No. of Pieces	Description	Thickness in Inches	Width in Inches	Length in Inches
2	Stiles	¾	1½	29⅛
1	Upper Rail	¾	6⅝	13
1	Lower Rail	¾	2	13
2	Half Columns	¾	1½	20½
2	Half Columns Tops	¾	1½	5¾
2	Half Columns Bases	¾	1½	2
1	Top Board	½	2½	18
1	Upper Molding	⅞	1½	17½
1	Notched Molding	½	¾	13
1	Lower Molding	½	1½	17
1	Baseboard	⅜	2¼	17¼
1	Back (plywood)	¼	15	21½
1	Plate-Glass Mirror	¼	14⅞	21⅜

Suggested Order of Tool Operations

1. Square the four pieces of the frame to dimensions and saw the rabbets on a circular saw (Art. 172). Note that the rabbets in the side pieces are stopped, that is, they do not extend from one end of the piece to the other.

2. Make the dowel joints as in Art. 175 and glue the frame together. When dry, smooth it with plane and sandpaper.

3. Fasten the top board to the upper edge of the frame with glue and screws.

4. Make the moldings on a portable shaper or with a scratch stock (Fig. 662). The moldings return around the sides and are, therefore, mitered in the corners.

5. The half columns are turned as explained in Article 253.

6. They may be reeded as shown in Figures 667, 668, and 670, or left plain.

7. The columns are then glued to the sides together with the rectangular blocks on top and bottom (see details).

8. The notched molding is carved with an ordinary chisel. Make the saw cuts first and then round the parts between them with the chisel. Smooth with sandpaper.

9. The mirror frame may be stained with water stain (Arts. 289 and 293) and finished with shellac, lacquer, or varnish (Arts. 296, 299, and 300).

10. Place a couple of sheets of paper between the mirror and the plywood back. The back may be held in place with a few brads driven diagonally into the frame. To keep out the dust, glue strips of paper over the joints.

357. To Read the Drawing of the Tilt-Top Table.   The plan view and the elevation are shown at the left in Figure 784. The plan view, which could not be drawn in full because of lack of space, shows a line of inlay near the edge of the top and an inset in its center. The dotted lines show that the table has three legs.

Two of the legs shown in the elevation are not true projections, but this is accepted drawing practice, because it is easier and gives the exact outline of the legs from which a pattern can be made. The 1-in. squares drawn across one leg are an aid in drawing a full-size pattern. The three heavy lines on the edge of the central leg indicate that the legs are decorated by reeding.

In this view the top is shown in a horizontal position. The dotted lines show it in a vertical or tilted position. The lines directly below the central portion of the top give an end view of the tilting mechanism. This is shown in plan on the underside of the top and in an isometric drawing, which is a form of pictorial drawing used to depict an object as it appears to the eye. The column is drawn to a larger scale, so that there will be room for all dimensions needed for turning it. It is made in three parts so that the ½-in. piece just above the legs may be more easily carved. The dotted lines through the two lower parts indicate a hole bored through them into which the 1-in. tenon of the upper part fits.

Suggested Order of Tool Operations

1. Turn the column according to directions given in Articles 249 and 250.

2. Before turning the lower part, bore a 1-in. hole through it, then slide it onto the lower tenon of the column, and turn it to size. It must fit so tightly on the tenon that it will not turn around when the tool is pressed against it.

Fig. 783. Tilt-top table

3. The ½-in. disk is turned on a faceplate and the hole is bored in the lathe with a skew chisel (Art. 255).

4. The carving is done as explained in Article 265, after which the three parts of the column are glued together.

5. Make a pattern of the leg by ruling off a piece of cardboard in 1-in. squares and trace the lines as shown in the drawing.

6. Cut the legs with a turning saw or on a band saw, and sand them smooth. Then bead them with a scratch stock (Figs. 681 and 682).

7. The legs are joined to the column with dowels (Figs. 402 and 403, Art. 178). Their ends are sanded to fit against the column, as shown in Figure 399. Test them for squareness, also after sanding them, as in Figure 400. They are glued as explained in Article 222. It is a good plan to strengthen the joint by driving a corrugated fastener into each leg and the end of the column.

8. The boards for the table top are jointed as explained in Article 157, after which they are glued as shown in Figure 535 (Art. 216).

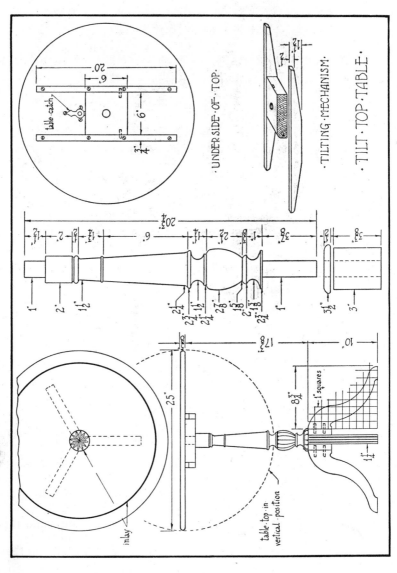

Fig. 784

9. The top is now planed on both sides (Arts. 158 and 159) and is smoothed with scraper and sandpaper. It is sawed to shape on a band saw, after which its edge is slightly rounded with a spokeshave and smoothed with file and sandpaper.

10. The lines and inset are inlaid as explained in Articles 263 and 264.

11. The tilting mechanism consists of a square block and two cleats. The cleats are planed to shape as shown in the isometric view.

12. Two ¼-in. dowels are glued into the block ¾ in. from one side and the same distance from the top. The block is centered between the cleats and corresponding holes are bored halfway through them. The upper edge of the block is rounded as shown so that it can move freely up and down when the cleats are screwed to the top.

13. A table catch (Fig. 581) is screwed to the underside of the top and the strike is fastened to the block so that it will lock against the top.

14. The block is glued to the column in such a way that when the top is in the vertical position it will be at right angles to one of the legs. This will prevent the table from toppling over (Fig. 784).

15. The table is now ready for the finish. If it is to be stained, the inlay should first be given a coat of thin white shellac so as not to darken it. The finishing coats may be either shellac, lacquer, or varnish (Arts. 296, 299, and 300).

Bill of Material

No. of Pieces	Description	Thickness in Inches	Width in Inches	Length in Inches
1	Column	2⅞	2⅞	20¾
1	Column Part	½	3½	3½
1	Column Part	3	3	3⅜
1	Three legs	1¼	3½	40
2	Tilting Mechanism	¾	1½	20
1	Tilting Mechanism	1½	6	6
1	Top	⅝	25	25
1	Table Catch			
1	Inset about 3 in. in diameter			
2	Yards Line Inlay about ⅛ in. wide			

358. To Read the Drawing of the Magazine Holder. The drawing in Figure 785 has the three conventional views: plan, elevation, and end views, besides two details. The four legs of the magazine holder are shown in section in the plan view. In the elevation and end views, it will be seen that the legs are turned and have two square parts into which the upper and lower rails are mortised. The detail of the leg is drawn to a larger scale, so that dimensions, both of length and thickness, can be shown.

Besides the rails, the plan view also shows two partitions doweled to the end rails. The detail gives a complete side view of the partitions. The

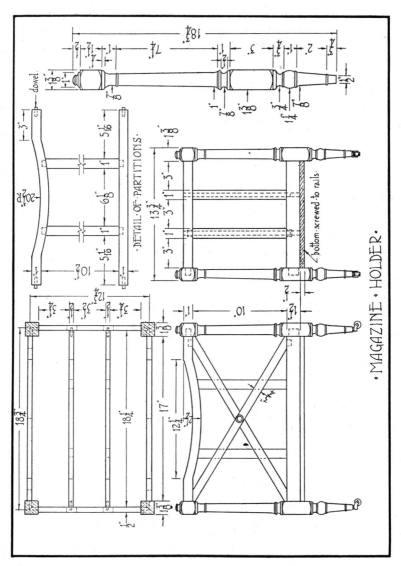

· MAGAZINE · HOLDER ·

· DETAIL · OF · PARTITIONS ·

bottom · screwed · to rails.

dowel.

Fig. 785

Fig. 786. Magazine holder

vertical lines on the elevation and the dotted lines on the end view show the vertical members of the partitions.

The elevation shows that the upper side rails are similar in shape to those of the partitions. A cross is mortised into the upper and lower side rails. The concentric circles indicate a turned rosette.

The end view shows that the top rail is straight and is joined to the bottom rail with two straight, vertical pieces. All the lower rails are straight. The bottom is screwed to their edges.

Suggested Order of Tool Operations

1. Square the four legs to dimensions, locating the centers carefully, and turn as explained in Articles 249 and 250.

2. Cut all the rails to shape, and make all the mortise-and-tenon joints (Art. 187).

3. It is recommended to lay out the side rails and cross, as well as the partitions, full size in order to cut and fit the various pieces accurately together. The cross may be either doweled or mortised to the rails.

4. The two sides should first be assembled and clamped as shown in Figure 540.

5. The partitions are then fitted to the end rails.

6. Finally, the end rails and partitions are glued at the same time between the sides.

7. The bottom is now made and fitted around the inside square parts

of the legs. It may be made flush with the lower rails or project slightly beyond them. It is screwed to the rails, and helps materially to strengthen the construction.

8. Staining and finishing may be done as explained in the previous project.

9. As a magazine holder such as this is likely to become quite heavy with accumulated publications, it is recommended to put casters on the legs to make it easier to move.

Bill of Material

No. of Pieces	Description	Thickness in Inches	Width in Inches	Length in Inches
4	Legs	1⅜	1⅜	18¾
2	Lower Side Rails	½	1½	18¾
2	Upper Side Rails	½	2½	18¾
2	Lower End Rails	½	1½	12¾
2	Upper End Rails	½	1	12¾
4	Vertical Pieces Between End Rails	½	1	11
4	Crosspieces Between Side Rails	½	¾	21
2	Top Partition Rails	½	2½	18¼
2	Bottom Partition Rails	½	1	18¼
4	Vertical Partition Pieces	½	1	11
1	Bottom	½	13¼	19¼
4	Casters			

359. To Read the Drawing of the Plain and Veneered Boxes. The plan view in Figure 787 is divided in two by a vertical center line. To the left is shown a design in veneers and inlay, which is later glued to the top of the box. To the right is shown the upper edge of the box without the lid. This view also shows the construction of the box and the placing of the hinges.

The elevation and end views give the dimensions of the box, and show the rounded corners and upper and lower molded edges.

The section to the right in the drawing shows how the top and bottom are joined to the sides and ends. It also gives the shape and dimensions of the lower molding. Notice that the height of the box is greater in

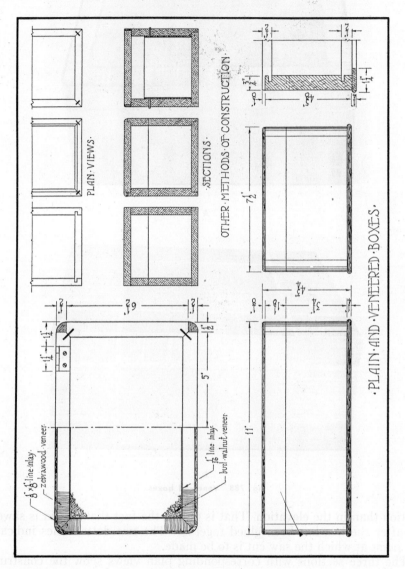

Fig. 787

A

B

Fig. 788. Veneered boxes

section than in the elevation. That is due to the fact that the lid is sawed off after the box has been glued together. The two dotted lines indicate the point at which the saw cut is to be made.

The three sections with corresponding plan views show the construction of simpler boxes.

Suggested Order of Tool Operations

1. When making a box, the sides, ends, top, and bottom are all glued together, after which the lid is separated by sawing through the sides and ends at the desired distance from the top.

C

D

Fig. 788a. Veneered boxes

2. The simplest kind of box is shown in the left section and plan view. The ends are joined to the sides with dado-and-rabbet joints (Art. 171). The top and bottom are simply glued to the edges of the sides and ends.

3. The middle section and plan view show a neater looking box. The sides and ends are joined with spline miter joints (Fig. 493), but first rabbets are cut on their edges for the top and bottom. The method of gluing sides and ends is shown in Figures 483 and 484.

4. After smoothing the surfaces of these boxes, they are cut through on the circular saw. The sawed edges are smoothed with a sharp plane and sandpaper, until they fit perfectly. The hinges are applied according to directions given in Article 231.

5. The box to the right has its bottom rabbeted into the sides and ends in the same way as the one in the center. Its top is glued to the sides and ends in the same way as the box at the left. A ⅛-in. strip is then cut off all around and a similar strip of contrasting wood is glued in its place and mitered in the corners.

6. After the top has been sawed off the box, a piece of ⅛-in. stock is glued to the inside surfaces as shown, and a similar piece may be glued to the sawed edge. No hinges are needed for this type of box because the projecting parts of the lining hold the lid in place.

7. The sides, ends, top, and bottom of the veneered box are first squared to dimensions and then are veneered across the grain on both surfaces (crossbands, Art. 275). Use dimensions given on the sectional view to allow for the saw cut.

8. The sides and ends are then joined with spline miter joints as explained above. Note that the spline is close to the inner edges in order to give room for the ½-in. square cut to be made after gluing.

9. The top and bottom are grooved into the sides and ends as shown in the section to the right. These cuts must be carefully made on a circular saw so that a good fit is obtained.

10. The cuts for the rounded corners are now made, after which the sides, ends, top, and bottom are all glued at the same time.

11. The sides and ends may be veneered with plain striped veneer with the grain running from side to side or vertically. Both sides are veneered at the same time and then both ends.

12. Four square strips of wood of a contrasting color are cut for the corners. They may be carefully rounded with plane and scraper, but a better way is to glue them all together to form a square, as explained in Article 253, and then turn this glued-up square. When split apart, each one will be a perfect quarter round, which is glued into one of the corners.

13. The veneer design for the top of the box is made up and taped together as explained in Article 275, after which it is glued in place. The grooves for the inlay and ⅛-in. border are then cut with a router machine (Fig. 664), and the lines are glued in place (Art. 263).

14. The box is finally cut open and the molding, shown in the section, is mitered and glued to the bottom.

15. Finish with two or three coats of thin shellac, lacquer, or varnish (Arts. 296, 299, and 300).

The box, A, Figure 788, is the one shown in Figure 787. B and C show other types of veneered boxes. Box D is made of solid wood.

Bill of Material

No. of Pieces	Description	Thickness in Inches	Width in Inches	Length in Inches
2	Sides	¾	4⅝	11
2	Ends	¾	4⅝	6½
2	Top and Bottom	½	7½	11
4	Corners	½	½	4⅝
1	Base Molding	¼	1¼	40
2	Brass Butt Hinges, 1½ in. wide, 1¼ in. long			
	Veneer and Inlay			

360. To Read the Drawings of the Early English Gate-Leg Table. The drawing in Figure 789 shows the plan view and elevation of the table, and Figure 790 shows various construction details which could not be incorporated in the plan and elevation.

The illustration in Figure 791 and the elevation look very much alike, although one is a pictorial and the other a mechanical representation of the object taken from the same viewpoint. The five legs connected by rails at the top and stretchers at the bottom can easily be recognized on the drawing when it is compared with the illustration.

The interrelation of these legs is seen in the plan view which shows the table in the open position. It will be seen that three of the legs are joined with rails and stretchers in the form of a right-angle triangle. The other two legs form the "gate" and are joined with other rails and stretchers. One of these legs turns on pivots between the rear rails and stretchers so that the other one can be swung out to support the leaf. To get a better understanding of this construction, however, we must turn to the detail drawing in Figure 790 which shows the rear assembly both in plan and elevation. The gate is shown between the two outer or rear legs, and it is also shown in a pictorial drawing to the right so that its construction may be thoroughly understood. The plan view of the rear assembly shows that the rail and stretcher are in two parts doweled into the rear legs and the pivot leg. Note the shape of the unturned portion of the rear legs. This is necessary in order to frame the rails and stretchers in the shape of a right triangle as shown on the plan view in Figure 789.

Returning to this view in Figure 789, we see four dotted lines connecting the front leg with the rear legs. The explanation of these lines is given in the detail of the front side. The vertical section shows that there is a double front rail; the upper one is rectangular and flush with the outside surfaces of the legs, the lower one has a concave lower edge and is set in ⅜ in. This view also shows a ¼-in. square molding and notched molding. A detail of the beveled pieces glued to the front and rear legs is shown in the upper right-hand corner. As can be seen in the elevation, the stretchers are mortised or doweled into the central part of the legs.

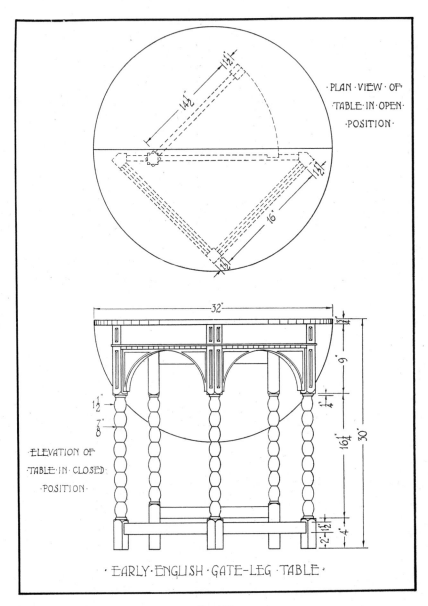

·PLAN · VIEW · OF·
·TABLE· IN ·OPEN·
·POSITION·

·ELEVATION OF·
·TABLE · IN · CLOSED·
·POSITION·

· EARLY· ENGLISH ·GATE-LEG · TABLE ·

Fig. 789

Suggested Order of Tool Operations

1. Turn the five legs according to the dimensions given in the drawing (Art. 251 and Fig. 636), but first square them and center them accurately in the lathe. Only the two rear legs are exactly alike. They are planed to the shape shown in the detail.

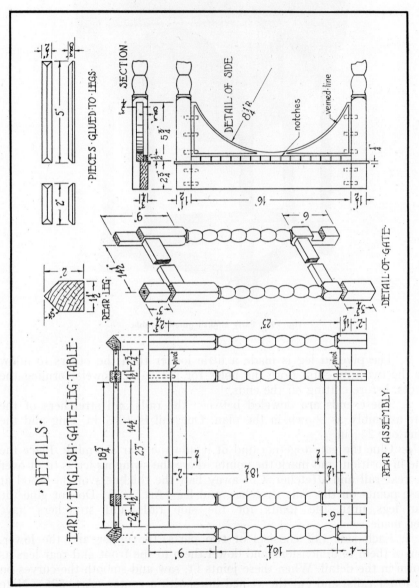

· DETAILS ·

· EARLY · ENGLISH · GATE-LEG · TABLE ·

· PIECES · GLUED · TO · LEGS ·

· SECTION ·

· DETAIL · OF · SIDE ·

notches

veined · line

· REAR · LEG ·

· DETAIL · OF · GATE ·

· REAR · ASSEMBLY ·

Fig. 790

Fig. 791. Early English gate-leg table

2. The pivoted leg is made a little longer than the others to allow for the two saw cuts. Bore the holes for the ⅜-in. dowels forming the pivots, before cutting off the ends.

3. These ends are doweled between the rails and stretchers of the rear assembly as shown in the plan. One rail is 18¾ in. long and the other one 2¾ in.

4. Glue the gate together and fit it into the rear assembly. Place the gate in position, and mark the points where the swinging leg is to fit over the rear rail and stretcher. Cut away half the thickness of the wood at these points on the rail, stretcher, and leg (Art. 182). Do not glue the rear legs until the joints for the side rails and stretchers have been made.

5. Each side rail consists of two parts, the upper and the lower. Square them to dimensions and dowel them to the front and rear legs as shown in the detail. When these joints fit, saw and smooth the curves on the lower rails, and cut the veined lines with a router (Art. 276). Note that the upper rail is flush with the face on the legs and the lower rail sets back ⅜ in.

6. The stretchers may be doweled or mortised into the lower square section of the legs. They should be joined to the legs in the center like the rear stretchers.

7. The rear legs may then be glued in place. When they are dry, the front leg, rails, and stretchers are glued to the rear assembly (Fig. 792).

8. The upper side rails are now smoothed flush with the legs, after which the notched moldings are made and glued along the upper edge of the lower rail. The notches are sawed to a depth of 3/16 in. A ¼-in. square molding is glued just above the notched molding.

9. Beveled strips of wood glued to the faces of front and rear legs complete the decorative features.

10. The top is glued up of enough boards to make the total finished width, 32 in. (Arts. 158, 159, and 216).

11. This top is then cut into halves, and is smoothed and jointed on two edges. The semicircle is laid out on one piece, after which the two pieces are nailed together on the waste side of the line and band sawed.

12. The two halves are hinged together with ordinary fast-joint butt hinges (Art. 230) unless a rule joint (Art. 210) is made. Fasten the top to the rails with cleats as shown in C, Figure 590.

13. If made of a light-colored wood, the table should be stained (Art. 289). If the wood is open grained, such as oak, a coat of wood filler is also necessary (Art. 294). Finish with linseed oil (Art. 298), as this type of finish is in keeping with the period of the table.

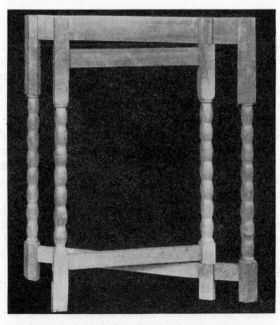

Fig. 792. Rear assembly of gate-leg table

Bill of Material

No. of Pieces	Description	Thickness in Inches	Width in Inches	Length in Inches
3	Legs	1½	1½	29¼
2	Legs	1½	2	29¼
2	Upper Side Rails	¾	2¾	16
2	Lower Side Rails	¾	5¾	16
2	Lower Stretchers	¾	1½	16
1	Rear Rail	¾	2¾	18¾
1	Rear Rail	¾	2¾	2¾
1	Gate Rail	¾	2	14½
1	Gate Stretcher	¾	1½	14½
1	Gate Stretcher	¾	1½	18¾
1	Gate Stretcher	¾	1½	2¾
1	Molding	¼	½	42
2	Molding	½	½	16
4	Leg Moldings	⅜	½	5
4	Leg Moldings	⅜	½	2
2	Tops	¾	16	32

361. To Read the Drawing of the End Table. The drawing in Figure 793 is quite simple and easy to understand. A glance at the plan, elevation, and end view shows that the table is rectangular, that it has four legs with carved spirals, and that the end frame of the table is wider at the bottom than at the top.

The dimensions in the plan view are those of the upper edges of the framework. Note also that the face of the rails is flush with the face of the legs. The stretchers, on the other hand, are mortised into the center of the legs. This is shown by the dotted lines on the elevation and end view. The double lines on the stretchers indicate that its outside edges are stop chamfered.

The width of rails and stretchers is given in the elevation. The supporting bracket for one leaf is shown both in full and dotted lines. As seen in full lines, it is folded against the rail when the leaf hangs down.

In the end view it is shown in its true dimensions, and it can be laid out according to the 1-in. squares drawn across it. The brackets are hinged to the side with a continuous hinge shown at the right.

The top of the table consists of three parts. The one in the center is fastened to the rails and the two leaves are joined to it with rule joints. The table is shown with one leaf extended and the other hanging down (Figs. 793 and 794).

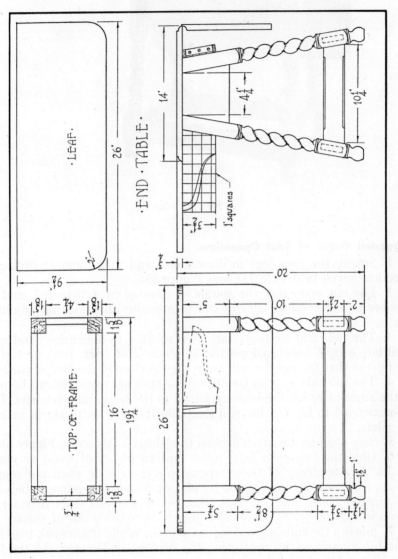

·LEAF·

·END·TABLE·

·TOP·OF·FRAME·

1 squares

Fig. 793

Fig. 794. End table

Suggested Order of Tool Operations

1. Square the four legs to dimensions, and turn them according to directions given in Article 251 and Figure 636.

2. Lay out and carve the spirals as directed in Article 267, and remember that the spirals should run in opposite directions on adjoining legs.

3. The rails and stretchers are then squared to dimensions and mortised into legs. A barefaced mortise-an-tenon joint (Art. 189) is used on the rails so that the mortise will not come too close to the face of the legs.

4. The sides are easy to frame, but the ends are more difficult because of the angle at which the legs are joined to the rails and stretchers. It is recommended to lay out the end assembly full size as an aid in making the joints.

5. Stop chamfer the stretchers on the jointer as shown in Figure 684a.

6. Glue the two ends first, using tapered pieces of wood as gluing blocks. Any tendency of these tapered pieces to slide when the clamps are applied may be counteracted by placing pieces of sandpaper between the tapered pieces and the legs. Handscrew the two ends together as shown in Figure 540 to prevent the legs from twisting out of shape.

7. Smooth the ends when dry, and glue the whole framework together. Test for squareness by measuring the diagonals. The ends of the legs may be beveled on a disk sander.

8. The top and leaves are now glued up of narrower boards, planed and squared to dimensions (Arts. 159 and 216).

9. The rule joints are made according to directions given in Article 210, after which the central part of the top is fastened to the rails with cleats (C, Fig. 590).

10. The brackets are laid out by drawing 1-in. squares on a piece of cardboard and tracing the outline. The edge is beveled as shown in

Figure 528. If it is desired to make a finger joint instead of using hinges, consult Article 211.

11. After staining, the table may be finished with shellac, lacquer, or varnish (Arts. 296, 299, and 300).

Bill of Material

No. of Pieces	Description	Thickness in Inches	Width in Inches	Length in Inches
4	Legs	1⅝	1⅝	19¼
2	Side Rails	¾	5	17½
2	End Rails	¾	5	7½
2	Side Stretchers	¾	2¼	17½
2	End Stretchers	¾	2¼	11¾
1	Top	¾	14	26
2	Leaves	¾	9½	26
2	Brackets	¾	3½	9
1	Continuous Hinge ¾ by 6 in.			

362. To Read the Drawing of the Sewing Table. At first glance we see from the elevation in Figure 795 that the table has two drawers and straight, grooved legs. The plan view or horizontal section shows that the front of the table is straight, the sides are grooved into the legs, and the rear legs are rabbeted for the plywood back. The dotted line all around the plan view indicates the top. The plan view is divided in two by a center line. To the right is shown half of one of the drawers. The dotted line shows the depth of the grooves cut for the bottom into the side and the front.

To the left is shown half of one of the frames which carry the drawers. The dotted lines show the depth of the dadoes, the dowels, and the screws. The dotted line in front indicates that the front rail is shaped, which is shown clearly in the detailed sectional view. The exterior full lines along the sides indicate the molding shown on the side view just above the triangular corners.

Plain, rectangular stretchers, joined to the front and rear legs, are shown on the elevation and side view. A third stretcher is joined to the side stretchers in the center.

Suggested Order of Tool Operations

1. Square the legs to dimensions, and shape them as shown in the detailed section. This is done quite easily with a scratch stock as shown in Figure 662. The grooves cut may be smoothed with sandpaper wrapped around a dowel. Note that the front legs are shaped on the two adjoining, outside edges, but the rear legs only on one edge.

2. Glue up stock for the sides, square the sides to dimensions, and make the groove-and-rabbet joint in them and in the legs (Art. 168). The grain in the sides should run up and down. The rabbets for the

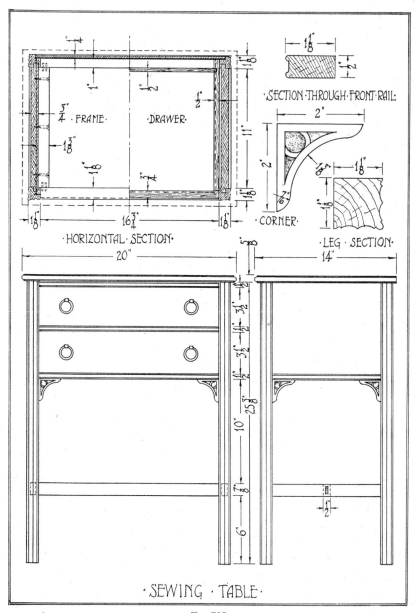

·SECTION·THROUGH·FRONT·RAIL·

·HORIZONTAL·SECTION·

·CORNER·

·LEG·SECTION·

·SEWING·TABLE·

Fig. 795

back also are cut at this time (Art. 172), and the side stretchers are mortised or doweled to the legs (Arts. 175 and 187).

3. The three frames, between which the drawers run, are doweled together as shown in the horizontal section (Art. 175). Cut all the pieces for the frames at the same time and clamp each frame to a flat surface while it is drying after gluing.

Fig. 796. Sewing table

4. Smooth both faces of the frames, and then hand screw them together while planing the edges so that they will all be square and of exactly the same size. The front rail on each frame is shaped with a scratch stock, as shown in the detail.

5. Before gluing the sides to the legs, they should be dadoed for the frames (Art. 172). The dadoes should be only ⅛ in. deep and are made mainly for locating the frames accurately. The mortise-and-tenon joints between the middle stretcher and the side stretchers also are made at this time.

6. Glue the sides together, using three bar clamps on each one and protecting the shaped edges of the legs with corrugated cardboard or cotton waste. Hand screw the inside flat edges of the legs together, as shown in Figure 540, to keep them straight and in line.

7. Notch the legs for the frames. Place one side of the table flat on the bench, and fasten the frames to it with glue and three flathead screws 1¾ in. by 10 each. Place the other side on the bench, glue the middle stretcher in place, and fasten the other end of the frames to it as described in the foregoing. Clamp the table together with four bar clamps, and test it for squareness (Figs. 539 and 541).

8. The drawers are made and fitted as explained in Articles 207 and 208. To obtain a more beautiful grain figure, the fronts may be veneered

Bill of Material

No. of Pieces	Description	Thickness in Inches	Width in Inches	Length in Inches
4	Legs	1⅛	1⅛	25⅜
2	Sides	¾	11¾	8½
2	Side Stretchers	½	⅞	12½
1	Middle Stretchers	½	⅞	18½
4	Corners	½	2	8½
1	Back (Plywood)	¼	8½	17¾
1	Molding for Sides	3/16	½	22
3	Pieces for Frame, Front	½	1⅛	17¼
3	Pieces for Frame, Back	½	1	17¼
6	Pieces for Frame, Sides	½	1⅜	11
2	Drawer Fronts	¾	3½	16¾
2	Drawer Backs	½	3	16¼
4	Drawer Sides	½	3½	12½
2	Drawer Bottoms (Plywood)	3/16	12	16¼
1	Top	⅝	14	20
4	Drawer Pulls			

(Art. 275) as shown in Figure 796. The veneering should be done before the joints are made.

9. The drawers may be fitted either with turned wooden knobs, metal knobs or rings, or pear-shaped metal pulls. Metal rods for spools of thread are placed in the front end of the top drawer as shown in Figure 797.

10. The back is made of ¼-in. plywood and is fastened to the frames and rabbets with ¾ in. by 6 flathead screws.

Fig. 797. Top drawer of sewing table

11. The corners are made from ½-in. stock. They may be recessed as shown, or pierced with a coping saw. They are glued and screwed in place together with the molding along the lower edge of the sides.

12. The top is made from two or three narrower boards glued together and smoothed with plane, scraper, and sandpaper. The edge is shaped on a machine or by hand with a scratch stock. The top is fastened to the upper frame with screws driven at a slight angle from below.

13. The sewing table should be made of a close-grained hardwood as mahogany, walnut, cherry, gum, birch, or maple. It may be stained as in Article 289 and finished with two or three coats of shellac, lacquer, or varnish (Arts. 296, 299, and 300).

363. To Read the Drawing of the Chest. The front and ends of the chest in Figure 798 are paneled as shown in the elevation and end view in Figure 799, while the back is made from a solid board shown in the vertical section. The frames for the front and ends are mortised together as shown at the upper right of the drawing. Blocks are also glued in the corners. The thickness of the members (¾ in.) is given in the vertical section.

The horizontal section shows the vertical members of the frames. It also shows that the front and ends are joined with a spline miter joint and the back and ends with a groove-and-rabbet joint. The front and ends are lined with ¼-in. plywood panels.

The elevation and end view show the moldings mitered and fitted around the blocks glued into the corners of the frame openings. These views also show the top and base moldings and the legs.

The view of the underside of the top shows that a frame is mortised together and screwed to the underside of the top. The lines drawn around

Fig. 798. Paneled chest

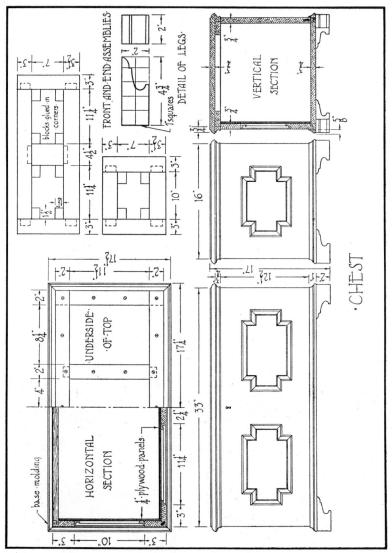

Fig. 799

the frame show the molding below the top. This molding, as well as the frame, are also shown in the vertical section. The bottom is grooved into the front and ends, but screwed to the underside of the back. A detail of the legs is drawn to a larger scale.

Suggested Tool Operations

1. Get out the stock for the front and end frames, make the mortise-and-tenon joints (Art. 193), and glue them together (Art. 218).

2. Glue the blocks into the corners of the frames and, when dry, square and smooth the frames with plane and scraper.

3. Also glue up the stock for the solid back and bottom, and square these parts to dimensions (Arts. 159 and 216).

4. Miter the corners between the front and ends, and reinforce them with splines (Art. 199).

5. Make the groove-and-rabbet joints on the back and ends as shown in the horizontal section (Art. 168). The bottom is joined in the same way to the front and ends, but is screwed to the back (see vertical section).

6. Clamp these parts together before applying the glue. When they fit, glue the front, back, and ends together (Fig. 483). The bottom is then pushed into the grooves cut for it and screwed to the back. Do not glue the bottom into the grooves (Art. 218).

7. Three plywood panels are now glued to the inside surfaces of the front and end frames. The grain should run from side to side.

8. The moldings are made on a shaper or with a scratch stock. They are mitered on a jig shown in Figure 477, and are fitted around the edges of the frame openings. They are glued to the edges of the frame and blocks and to the plywood backing. They may be held temporarily in place with fine brads driven part way into the edges of the frame, so that they can be easily withdrawn when the glue is dry.

9. The legs are cut to the shape shown in the detail, mitered in the corners, and glued and screwed to the bottom. The base molding is then mitered in the corners and glued in place.

10. The top is glued up of two or three boards (Arts. 159 and 216). It is then squared to dimensions, and the edge is shaped as explained in Article 274.

11. A frame of $\frac{3}{4}$-in. stock is then mortised together and screwed to the underside of the top to stiffen it. A molding, $\frac{3}{4}$ in. wide and $\frac{3}{4}$ in. thick, is mitered around this frame and glued to it as well as to the top.

12. Two chest hinges (Fig. 559) and a chest lock (Fig. 574) are applied according to directions given in Articles 230 and 233.

13. If the chest is made of white oak, it may be given a light- or weathered-oak stain. Wood filler of a contrasting color, for example white, may be used to accentuate the grain figure in the wood (Art. 294). The chest may be finished with a thin coat of white shellac or clear lacquer (Arts. 296 and 299), rubbed down with No. 3/0 steel wool.

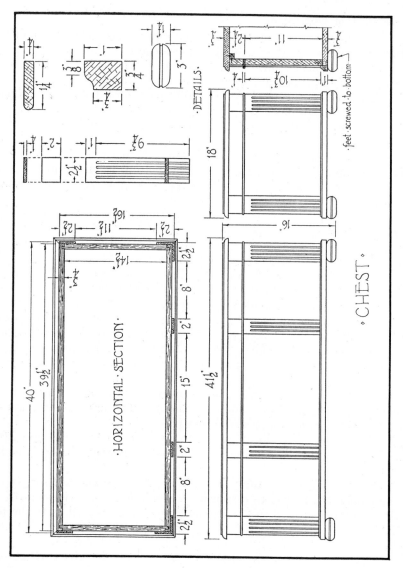

· CHEST ·

Fig. 800

Bill of Material

No. of Pieces	Description	Thickness in Inches	Width in Inches	Length in Inches
1	Upper Rail, Front Assembly	¾	3	29
1	Lower Rail, Front Assembly	¾	3½	29
1	Middle Rail, Front Assembly	¾	4½	9
6	Stiles, End and Front Assembly	¾	3	13½
2	Upper Rails, End Assembly	¾	3	12
2	Lower Rails, End Assembly	¾	3½	12
1	Back	¾	13½	32¼
1	Bottom	¾	15½	32¼
1	Top	¾	17½	34½
2	Sides, Top Frame	¾	2	32½
2	Ends, Top Frame	¾	2	15½
2	Middle, Top Frame	¾	2	13½
1	Top Molding	¾	¾	72
1	Base Molding	¾	1	72
1	Panel Molding	½	¾	160
8	Legs	2	2	4¾
1	Chest Lock			
2	Chest Hinges			
1	Escutcheon			
2	Table-Leg Braces			

For those who wish to make a chest of simpler construction, an alternate design is offered in Figure 800.

1. In this chest the sides and ends are made of solid wood joined together in the corners with dado-and-rabbet joints (Art. 171).

2. The bottom may be made as in the first chest, or simply screwed to the sides and ends. The joint is covered by a molding all around.

3. The top is made in the same way as the top for the first chest, and is fastened to the upper edges of the sides and ends with cleats.

4. The top of the chest is cut off in the same way as a box, after which the top is fastened to the upper part. A ¼-in. molding is glued to the edges of the lower part.

5. Fluted boards, glued to the sides and ends, give a paneled effect and conceal the joints in the corners. Four turned "bun" feet are screwed to the bottom.

Bill of Material

No. of Pieces	Description	Thickness in Inches	Width in Inches	Length in Inches
2	Front and Back	¾	13¼	39½
2	Ends	¾	13¼	15¼
1	Bottom	¾	16	39½
1	Top	¾	18	41½
6	Fluted Moldings	¼	2½	10¾
6	Plain Moldings	¼	2½	2
2	Fluted Moldings	¼	2	10¾
2	Plain Moldings	¼	2	2
1	Molding	¼	1¼	120
1	Molding, Base	¾	1	120
4	Turned Feet	1¼	3	3
2	Hinges, 1½ by 3 in., or one Continuous Hinge			
1	Chest Lock			
1	Escutcheon			
2	Table-Leg Braces			

INDEX

Abrasives, 96
Acanthus leaf, 323
Acid stain, 354
Adze, 33
Air-seasoning wood, 379
Animal glue, 230
Annual rings in wood, 370, 371
Auger bit, 27; sharpening, 115
Auger-bit gauge, 30
Automatic drills, 30
Automatic-stroke sander, 91
Ax, two-bitted, 33

Backsaw, 17, 18
Ball-bearing guide wheel, 52, 53
Ball catch, 255
Band saw, 50, 51; brazing, 124; filing, 126; first endless, 6; high-speed, 51; setting, 125
Band-saw blade, coiling, 54, 55
Band-saw brazer, electric, 125
Band-saw filing vise, 126
Band-saw fitting wheels, 125, 126
Band-saw guide, 52, 53
Band-saw setting machine, 125
Barefaced mortise-and-tenon joint, 191
Bark, 371
Beaded boards, 385
Beading tools, 271
Beads, cutting, 318
Belt-driven circular saw, 43
Belt sander, 90; bench, 93; portable, 91, 92, 93
Bench belt sander, 93
Bench dog, 8
Bench hook, 8
Bench jointer, 60, 61
Bench saw, 40
Bench shaper, 82, 83
Bench stop, 8
Bent-shank gouge, 26
Bits, auger, 27; car and ship augers, 27; dowel, 27; expansive, 27, 28; Foerstner, 28; gimlet, 28; router and veining, 86; twist, 28
Bit-brace extension, 29
Blades, jig-saw, 59
Blind mortise-and-tenon joint, 184
Block plane, 21, 22
Blood-albumen glue 231
Blueprints and drawings, 391
Board measure, 11, 383
Boards, matched, grooved, and beaded, 385
Bolts, 246
Bookcase, 395
Bookshelves, gluing, 234
Borders, carving, 319; simple carved, 322
Borer, single-spindle, 75, 76

Boring dowel holes with machine tools, 173
Boring tools, 27
Botanical division of trees, 368
Bow lathe, 261
Boxes, plain and veneered, 418
Brace measure, 10
Brace, plain, 29; ratchet, 29
Bradawl, 29
Brazing band saws, 124
Bronze tools, 2
Bullnose rabbet plane, 22
Butt chisel, 25
Butt gauge, 14
Butt hinge with loose pin, 247, 248
Butt joint, doweled, 166

Cabinet, gluing, 237
Cabinet locks, 252
Cabinet scraper, 23; sharpening and adjusting, 111, 112
Cabinet woods, 388, 389
Cabinetwork and interior woodwork, 387
Calipers, inside and outside, 15, 271
Cambium, 371
Cane seat, weaving, 346, 347
Cane webbing, applying, 348
Car bits and ship augers, 27
Card-table hinge, 249
Carpenter's pincers, 35
Carving, borders, 319; double spiral on turned cylinder, 315; simple, 317
Carving tools, 26, 318
Casein glue, 231
Casters, attaching, 256
Catches and door bolts, 254
C clamp, 34, 35
Cell formation in wood, 369
Centering and clamping stock in lathe, 272
Chair, gluing, 238
Chair tips, attaching, 256
Chamfers and hollows, cutting, 318
Chest, 435
Chest hinge, 247, 249
Chisels, 24, 270; butt, 25; diamond or spear-point, 270; firmer, socket, 24; framing, 25; hollow, 74; round-nose, 270; skew, 270; socket mortise, 25; square-nose, 270; tang paring, 24
Circular crosscut saw, filing, 123
Circular miter saws, filing, 124
Circular plane, 21, 22
Circular ripsaw, filing, 122; gumming, 120
Circular saw, 40; belt-driven, 43; jointing, 119; setting, 121
Chuck turning, 292
Clamps, 34; C, 34, 35; column, 34, 35; steel bar, 34

Clamping and gluing, 230
Claw hammer, 32
Coiling band-saw blade, 54, 55
Column clamp, 34, 35
Compasses or dividers, 14, 15
Compass saw, 18
Concave cuts, 282
Continuous hinge, 248, 249
Convex cuts, 283
Cope moldings, 210
Coping saw, 18
Countersink, rose, 29
Crosscut saw, 17
Cross-lap joint, 178
Cupboard, 403
Cupboard catch, 256
Cupboard hinge, 248, 250
Cutoff gauge, 44
Cutoff saw, self-contained, 69; swing, 68
Cutterheads, 83
Cutters, plug and washer, 29

Dado-and-rabbet joint, 159
Dado head, setting up, 47
Dado joint, 156; gain or stopped, 157
Dado plane, 22
Desk hinge, 247, 249
Diamond or spear-point chisels, 270; sharpening, 118
Disk sander, 93, 94
Disk turning, 290
Dividers, 271; or compasses, 14, 15
Door bolts and catches, 254
Door, hinging, 250
Double spiral carved on turned cylinder, 315
Dovetail joints, 213
Dovetail-lap joint, 180
Dovetail saw, 18
Dowel bit, 27
Doweled butt joint, 166
Doweled joints and segments, gluing, 238
Dowel holes, boring with machine tools, 173
Doweling boards edge to edge, 169
Dowel joints, 166
Draw-bolt joint, 168
Drawer, construction of, 217; gluing, 238
Drawer pulls, attaching, 256
Drawer rails and guides, 219
Drawings and blueprints, 391
Drawknife, 26
Drill press, 77, 78
Drill-press spindles, 78
Drills, automatic, 30; hand, 30; reciprocating, 30; twist, 28
Drum sanders, 96
Drying defects in wood, 383
Duplicate parts, turning, 287

Early English gate-leg table, 423
Egyptian furniture makers, 3
Egyptian tools, 4
Elbow catch, 255
Electric band-saw brazer, 125
Emery-wheel dressers, 134
Emery-wheel grinder, 109
End-lap joint, 175; with rabbet, 177

End table, 428
Expansive bit, 27, 28

Faceplate work, 289
Fast-joint butt hinge, 247, 248
Fiber seat, weaving, 343
Files, 33, 34; cleaning, 118, 119; jig-saw, 59
Filing, band saws, 126; circular crosscut saws, 123; circular miter saws, 124; circular ripsaw, 122
Filing machine, universal, 127
Filing saws, 107, 108
Finishing and polishing turned work, 299
Finishing coats, applying, 364
Firmer chisel, socket, 24
Fitting wheels, band-saw, 125, 126
Flooring, 384, 385
Flush bolt, 255
Foerstner bit, 28
Folding rule, 9
Fore plane, 21
Frame or panel, gluing, 236
Framing chisel, 25
Frets, 333

Gain or stopped dado-joint, 157
Gas pliers, 36
Gauge, auger-bit, 30; butt, 14; cutoff, 44; marking, 13; mortising, 14; panel, 13; plane, 23; slitting, 14; universal or miter, 45
Gimlet bit, 28
Glides, attaching, 256
Glue, properties and uses of, 230
Gluing, and clamping, 230; boards edge to edge, 233; bookshelves, 234; a cabinet, 237; a chair, 238; doweled joints and segments, 238; a drawer, 238; frame or panel, 238; mitered frames, 203
Gouges, 25, 269, 270; bent-shank, 26; sharpening, 111, 117
Great wheel lathe, 262, 264
Grinder, emery-wheel, 109
Grinding jointer and planer knives, 127
Grindstone, 101
Grooved boards, 385
Grooved joints, 153; cutting with machine tools, 160
Groove, making, 155
Gumming circular ripsaw, 120

Hack saw, 19
Half-lap, multiple, dovetail joint, 215
Hammer, claw, 32
Hand drill, 30
Hand planer or jointer, 60
Handsaw, power, 70
Hand scraper, 23; sharpening, 112, 113
Hand screws, 35
Hand tools, 7; sharpening, 106
Hatchet, 32
Haunched mortise-and-tenon joint, 190
Heartwood, 370
High-speed band saw, 51
Hinge hasp, 250
Hinges, 247

Hinging a door, 250
History, of upholstery, 335; of wood turning; 261; of woodworking tools, 1
Hold-down springs and guards, 85
Hollow-chisel mortiser, 72
Hollow chisels, 74; sharpening, 133
Horizontal mortiser, 75

Imperfections in surface, filling, 364
Inlaying, 303; lines or bands, 304
Inlay insets, 307
Inside and outside calipers, 271
Invisible hinge, 249
Iron spokeshave, 23

Jack plane, 19, 20
Jig saw, 57
Jig-saw blades, 59
Jig-saw files, 59
Joining legs to turned column with dowels, 170
Joint, barefaced mortise-and-tenon, 191; blind mortise-and-tenon, 184; cross-lap, 178; dado, 156; dado-and-rabbet, 159; dovetail, 213; dovetail-lap, 180; dowel, 166; doweled butt, 166; drawbolt, 168; end-lap, 175; end lap with rabbet, 177; gain or stopped dado, 157; grooved, 153; grooved, cutting with machine tools, 160; half-lap, multiple, dovetail, 215; haunched mortise-and-tenon, 190; keyed mortise-and-tenon, 193; lap, 182; lap or halving, 175; miter, 200; mortise-and-tenon, 184; rabbet, 153; rule, 223; slip, 192; through mortise-and-tenon, 192; through, multiple, dovetail, 213
Jointer, 21; and planer knives, grinding, 127; bench, 60, 61; or hand planer, 60
Jointing, boards for gluing, 141; circular saws, 119; a saw, 106

Keyed mortise-and-tenon joint, 193
Keyhole saw, 18,
Kiln-seasoning wood, 380
Kilns, types of, 381
Knife grinder, automatic, 101, 102
Knife-grinding attachment, 62
Knife-setting gauge, micrometer, 127, 128
Knives, shaper, 82
Knobs, attaching, 256

Lacquer, applying, 361
Lamp standard, 397
Lap joints made on circular saw, 182
Lap or halving joints, 175
Lathe, bow, 261; great wheel, 262, 264; pole, 261, 263; woodturning, 262, 265
Lathe holding tools, 268
Laying out tapered spirals, 316
Legs, for tables and cabinets, squaring, 147; joined to turned column with dowels, 170; with square parts, turning, 284
Lines or bands, inlaying, 304
Linseed oil, applying, 361
Locks, attaching, 254
Logging operations, 374

Logs, sawing, 376
Longer pieces, squaring, 52
Lumber, allowance for planing, 383; conservation of, 369; for building purposes, 390; manufactured, types of, 383, 384; selection and uses of, 387; standard lengths and thicknesses, 383

Machine boring bits, 76, 77
Machine tools, 39; sharpening, 119
Magazine holder, 415
Mallet, 32
Manufactured lumber, types of, 383, 384
Marking gauge, 13
Matched boards, 385
Matching plane, 22
Measuring tapes, 9
Measuring tools, 9
Medullary rays in wood, 371
Metal fastenings, 241
Micrometer knife-setting gauge, 127, 128
Mirror frame, 409
Miter and try square, 9
Miter box, 18, 19
Mitered frames, gluing, 203
Mitered joints, 200; reinforcing, 206
Miter saws, circular, filing, 124
Miter square, 9
Moisture content of wood, 380
Molding heads, 47, 48
Moldings, 323, 385
Monkey wrench, 35
Mortise-and-tenon joints, 184
Mortise chisel, socket, 25
Mortise made on mortising machine, 194
Mortiser, hollow-chisel, 72; horizontal, 75; oscillating-bit, 99, 100
Mortising gauge, 14
Mortising head, 73
Mortising machine, 70

Nails, 241; rules for driving, 243
Nail set, 32
Narrow stock, ripping, 50

Octagon measure, 10
Oil stain, 354
Oilstone grinder, 101
Oscillating-bit mortiser, 99, 100
Outfeed table, adjusting, 62, 63
Overlays, 332, 333

Pad seat with roll edge, 337
Painting furniture and interior woodwork, 363
Panel gauge, 13
Panel structure, 221
Paring chisel, tang, 24
Parting or cut-off tools, 270; sharpening, 118
Patternmaker's spokeshave, 23
Pitman mechanism, 58
Pivot or pin hinge, 249
Plain- and quarter-sawing, 376, 378
Plain and veneered boxes, 418
Plain brace, 29
Plain cylinder, turning, 274, 275

Plain pad seat, 335

Plane, 19; block, 21, 22; bullnose rabbet, 22; circular, 21, 22; dado, 22; fore, 21; jack, 19, 20; matching, 22; router, 22, 23; smooth, 21; universal, 22, 23; wooden, 19, 20

Plane gauge, 23

Plane iron, sharpening, 108, 109

Planer or surfacer, 64, 65

Planing and squaring to dimensions, 137

Plants, man's dependence on, 369

Pliers, gas, 36; side-cutting, 36

Plug cutter, 29

Plumb and level, 15

Plumb bob, 15

Plywood, 386; uses of, 387

Pneumatic sanding pad, 90

Pole lathe, 261, 263

Porous woods, 372, 373

Portable belt sander, 92, 93

Portable router, 88

Power handsaw, 70

Priming coat, applying, 363

Production router, 86

Projects, applied, 391

Pusher for jointer, 64

Push stick, 49

Quick-acting vise, 8

Rabbet and fillister plane, 22

Rabbet joint, 153

Rabbet plane, 22

Radial saw, 69, 70

Rafter run, rise, and pitch, 12

Rafter table, 12

Rasps, 33, 34; cleaning, 118, 119

Ratchet brace, 29

Reciprocating drills, 30

Resin glue, 231

Ripping fence, 43, 44

Ripping narrow stock, 50

Ripsaw, 16,

Roman tools, 5

Rose countersink, 29

Rotary planing, 79, 80

Round-nose chisel, 270; sharpening, 118

Router, 85; and veining bits, 86; portable, 88; production, 86

Router plane, 22, 23

Rule joint, 223

Rush seat, weaving, 344, 346

Rush woven slip seat, 344, 345

Sander, automatic-stroke, 91; belt, 90; belt, bench, 93; disk, 93, 94; drum, 96; portable belt, 92, 93; spindle, 94, 95; variety, 91, 92, 93

Sanding, in a lathe on a disk, 298; in a lathe on a spindle, 297

Sanding machines, 90

Sanding pad, pneumatic, 90

Sapwood, 370

Saw, 16; and splitter guard, 48; back, 17, 18; band, 50, 51; bench, 40; circular, 40; circular, belt-driven, 43; compass, 18;

coping, 18; crosscut, 17; cutoff, self-contained, 69; dovetail, 18; filing, 107, 108; hack, 19; jig, 47; jointing, 106; key-hole, 18; radial, 69, 70; setting, 106, 107; sharpening, 106; swing cutoff, 68; turning, 18; universal, 40, 41; variety, 40, 41

Saw arbor, 42

Sawing logs, 376

Saw set, trip-hammer, 121, 122

Saw table, two-section tilting, 42, 43

Scrapers, cabinet and hand, 23

Screen or double-acting hinge, 247, 249

Screw drivers, 31

Screws, for fastening wood, 243; rules for driving, 244

Seasoning wood, 378

Self-contained cutoff saw, 69

Serving tray, 392

Setting, band saws, 125; circular saws, 121; a saw, 106, 107

Sewing table, 431

Shaper, 80, 81; bench, 82, 83

Shaper attachments, 86, 87

Shaper collar, 83

Shaper head, 83, 84

Shaper knives, 82; and router bits, sharpening, 132

Sharpening, auger bit, 115; cabinet scraper, 111, 112; diamond-point or spear-point chisel, 118; gouges, 111, 117; hand scraper, 112, 113; hollow chisels, 133; machine tools, 119; parting or cut-off tool, 118; plane iron, 108, 109; round-nose chisel, 118; saw, 106; shaper knives and router bits, 132; skew-chisel, 117; skew or turning chisel, 118; square-nose chisel, 117; turning tools, 117

Sharpening machines, 100

Sharpening tools, 106

Sheathing, 384, 385

Shellac, applying, 357; production and manufacture of, 356

Shoulder cuts, 279

Shrinkage of wood, 381, 382

Side-cutting pliers, 36

Simple carved borders, 322

Simple carving, 317

Simple veneering, 326

Single-cut auger-bit file, 34

Single-spindle borer, 75, 76

Single spiral carved on turned cylinder, 313

Skew chisels, 270; sharpening, 117

Skew or turning chisel, sharpening, 118

Sliding T bevel, 9

Slip joint, 192

Slip seat, rush-woven, 344, 345; upholstering, 339

Slitting gauge, 14

Small boards, squaring, 137

Smooth plane, 21

Socket firmer chisel, 24

Socket mortise chisel, 25

Soss hinge, 249

Spindle sander, 94, 95

Spindle turning, 272

Spiral reeds, cutting, 313

Spirit stain, 354
Split turning, 288
Spokeshave, iron, 23; patternmaker's, 23
Spring hinge, 248, 250
Square legs, tapering, 149
Square-nose chisel, 270; sharpening, 117
Squaring, legs for tables and cabinets, 147; longer pieces, 52; small boards, 137; table legs, 148; table top, 143
Staining, general directions for, 355
Stains, 353
Steel bar clamp, 34
Steel square, 9
Steel tape, 9
Step ladder, 400
Stock, fastening to faceplate or screw chuck, 289
Stone tools, 1
Stool, 406
Straight reeds, cutting, 309
Strap hinge, 248, 250
Strapwork, carving, 320, 322
Supports for table leaves, 226
Surface decoration, 302
Surface hinge, 248, 249
Surface, preparing for painting, 363
Surfacer or planer, 64, 65
Swing cutoff saw, 68

Table catch, 255
Table, early English gate-leg, 423; end, 428; tilt-top, 412
Table leaves, supports for, 226
Table legs, squaring, 148; tapering on circular saw, 150; tapering on jointer, 150, 151
Table top, fastening to frame, 257; making and squaring, 146; shaping edges, 325; squaring, 143
Tail vise, 8
Tang paring chisel, 24
Taper cuts, 281
Tapered spirals, laying out, 316
Tapering, square legs, 149; table legs on circular saw, 150; table legs on jointer, 150, 151
T bevel, sliding, 9
Tenons cut on circular saw, 196
T hinge, 248, 250
Through mortise-and-tenon joint, 192
Through, multiple, dovetail joint, 213
Tilt-top table, 412
Tinner's snips, 36
Tools, boring, 27; carving, 26, 318; hand, 7; machine, 39; measuring, 9; wood-turning, 269

Trammel points, 14, 15
Tray, serving, 392
Trees, botanical division of, 368; life function of, 368; reproduction of, 374
Trimmer, wood, 98
Trip-hammer saw set, 121, 122
Try square, 9
Turned work, finishing and polishing, 299
Turning, duplicate parts, 287; legs with square parts, 284; method of, 272; a plain cylinder, 274, 275
Turning saw, 18
Turning tools, 116; sharpening, 117
Twist bit, 28
Twist drill, 28
Two-section tilting saw table, 42, 43

Undercoats, applying, 364
Universal filing machine, 127
Universal or miter gauge, 45
Universal plane, 22, 23
Universal saw, 40, 41
Upholstery, 335

Variety sander, 91, 92, 93
Variety saw, 40, 41
Varnish, applying, 362
Vegetable glue, 231
Veining, 333
Veneering, simple, 326
Veneers, 385
Vise, quick-acting, 8

Washer cutter, 29
Water stain, 354
Wax, applying, 360
Weaving a cane seat, 346, 347
Wood, 368; air-seasoning, 379; annual rings in, 370, 371; cell formation, 369, 370; drying defects in, 383; kiln-seasoning, 380; medullary rays, 371; moisture content of, 380; porous, 372, 373; seasoning, 378; shrinkage of, 381, 382; structure of, 369; weight of, 372, 373
Wooden plane, 19, 20
Wood filler, 355
Wood finishing, 351
Wood surface, preparing for finishing, 351, 353
Wood trimmer, 98
Wood turning, history of, 261
Wood-turning lathe, 262, 265
Wood-turning tools, 269
Woodworking tools, history of, 1
Workbench, 7
Working drawings, reading, 391